P9-ARP-203

UNIFORM SPACES AND TRANSFORMATION GROUPS

UNIFORM SPACES

TRANSFORMATION GROUPS

by Hidegoro Nakano WAYNE STATE UNIVERSITY

WAYNE STATE UNIVERSITY PRESS, DETROIT, 1968

Library of Congress Catalog Card Number 68-13935

CONTENTS

	Preface	ix
	Introduction	xi
	i. Spaces	xi
	ii. Sets	xii
	iii. Maximal Theorem	xiii
I.	*Uniformities*	1
	1. Connectors	1
	2. Uniformities	3
	3. Topologies	5
	4. Induced Topologies	7
	5. Relative Uniformities	9
	6. Totally Bounded Sets	12
	7. Convergent Systems	14
	8. Complete Sets	16
	9. Compact Sets	19
	10. Connected Sets	23
II.	*Uniformly Continuous Mappings*	27
	11. Inverse Images	27
	12. Uniformly Continuous Mappings	29
	13. Purifications	35
	14. Uniformly Open Mappings	37
	15. Equi-Continuous Systems	39
	16. Binary Mappings	43
	17. Convergence of Mappings	45
	18. Uniformly Continuous Functions	49
	19. Extension Theorems	54
	20. Comparison of Uniformities	57
III.	*Equi-Uniformities*	60
	21. Weakest Stronger Uniformities	60
	22. Local Unimorphisms	63
	23. Weak-Uniformities	65

Uniform Spaces

24. Products of Uniformities 69
25. Strong-Powers of Uniformities 72
26. Single Equi-Uniformities 76
27. Multiple Equi-Uniformities 79
28. Fundamental Theorems 82
29. Completions 84
30. Locally Compact Uniformities 88

IV. *Transformation Groups* 91

31. Transformation Groups 91
32. Invariant Uniformities 93
33. Point Mappings 96
34. Adjoint Uniformities 101
35. Sharp Uniformities 105
36. Invariant Sets 108

V. *Transitive Groups* 111

37. Regular Uniformities 111
38. Abstract Groups 115
39. Regular Neighbourhoods 119
40. Totally Bounded Neighbourhoods 124
41. Products of Elements 127
42. Adjusted Neighbourhoods 132
43. Strongly Adjusted Neighbourhoods 137
44. Reflexive Uniformities 140
45. Completions 145
46. Completion Closures 147
47. Transitive Closures 151
48. Equivalence 154

VI. *Integration Theory* 159

49. Measures 159
50. Regular Sets 161
51. Integrals 167
52. Binary Integrals 171
53. Products of Measures 173
54. Semi-Invariant Measures 177
55. Theorem of Existence 180
56. Theorem of Uniqueness 184
57. Measures on Groups 187
58. Steady Groups 193
59. Invariant Subgroups 195
60. Measure Characters 198
61. Double Integrals 199
62. Almost Uniformly Continuous Functions 204
63. Integration 209
64. Transformation Theorems 214

VII. *Almost Periodic Functions* 223

65. Definitions 223
66. Almost Periodic Parts 225
67. Periodic Functions 227
68. Means 230
69. Integration Theorems 233
70. Additive Characters 236
71. Complex Valued Functions 239
72. Normalized Systems 241
73. Approximation Theorems 243
74. Character Parts 248

Index 251

PREFACE

The concept of uniform spaces became familiar to mathematicians through the book: A. Weil, *Sur les espaces a structure uniforme,* Actual, Sci. et Industr. Paris (1938). As a method for constructing a uniformity, weak-uniformities were introduced in the book: H. Nakano, *Topology and linear topological spaces,* Tokyo (1951), reprinted by University Microfilms, Inc., Ann Arbor, Michigan. More generally, multiple equi-uniformities were considered in the papers: H. Nakano, "On completeness of uniform spaces," *Proc. Japan Acad.* Vol. 29 (1953) and H. Nakano, "A generalization of Ascoli's theorem," *Proc. Japan Acad.* Vol. 30 (1954). This method plays an important role in this book.

For a transformation group **G** on a uniform space *S,* we introduce a uniformity on **G** by a weak-uniformity and we consider relations between the uniformity on *S* and the uniformity on **G**. For an invariant measure on *S* by **G** we prove the existence and the uniqueness of a locally totally bounded uniformity on *S,* but we do not assume completeness. Thus this invariant measure is available for defining the mean for almost periodic functions.

Almost periodic functions were defined in abstract groups in the paper: J. von Neumann, "Almost periodic functions in a group I," *Trans. Amer. Math. Soc.* Vol. 36 (1934). In this book, almost periodic functions are defined more generally in a space with a transformation group.

The manuscript of this book was written for lectures given during three quarters in 1962-63 at Wayne State University. I have had the idea for a long time, but I did not get the opportunity to write the book before. I should like to thank the National Science Foundation for research funds. Also, I must thank the chairman, Dr. K. W. Folley, and staff members of the Department of Mathematics of Wayne State University who have urged publication of this book.

Hidegoro Nakano, March 3, 1964.

INTRODUCTION

i. **Spaces.** Concepts used in mathematics can be divided into two classes: intuitional concepts and explanatory concepts. We cannot explain intuitional concepts but we can understand them by examples. Everybody knows "one" but nobody can explain what "one" is. Explanatory concepts can be defined by some other concepts.

As the most basic concept in mathematics we have the concept of *space,* which is an intuitional concept. We can grasp objects in our thought by a *regulation.* For instance, by the regulation "persons in the world," we can grasp each person in the world. If by a regulation we can grasp each object *individually* and *independently* from other objects, then this regulation is called a *space.* For instance, by mathematical induction we can grasp each natural number, but mathematical induction is not a space as a regulation, because $n + 1$ depends on n.

For a space S, each object x, which is grasped by S, is called an *element* or a *point* of S, and we write $x \in S$ or $S \ni x$. A space which consists of a finite number of elements $a_1, a_2, \ldots, a_n$ is denoted by $\{a_1, a_2, \ldots, a_n\}$. We sometimes write $x = a_1, a_2, \ldots, a_n$ or $x = a_\nu$ $(\nu = 1, 2, \ldots, n)$ instead of $x \in \{a_1, a_2, \ldots, a_n\}$.

Let S and R be two spaces. A space M of pairs (x, y) for $x \in S$ and $y \in R$ is called a *mapping* from S to R, if 1) for any $x \in S$ there is $y \in R$ such that $(x, y) \in M$ and 2) $(x_1, y_1), (x_2, y_2) \in M$, $x_1 = x_2$ implies $y_1 = y_2$. Let M be a mapping from S to R. If $(x, y) \in M$, then y is called the *image* of x by M and denoted by xM, Mx or $M(x)$, according to the kind of mappings. A mapping from S to R is sometimes called a *system* $y_x \in R$ $(x \in S)$, representing the image of x by y_x. The term "system" will often be used instead of "space."

A mapping M from S to R is said to be *full,* if for any $y \in R$ we can find $x \in S$ such that y is the image of x by M, that is, $xM = y$. M is said to be *one-to-one,* if $(x_1, y_1), (x_2, y_2) \in M$, $x_1 \neq x_2$ imply $y_1 \neq y_2$. A mapping M from S to R is called a *transformation* from S to R, if M is full and one-to-one at the same time.

Let T be a transformation from S to R. The space T_1 of all pairs (y, x) such that $(x, y) \in T$ also is a mapping from R to S. Furthermore we see easily that T_1 is a transformation from R to S. This transformation T_1 is called the *inverse transformation* of T and is denoted by T^{-1}. About the inverse transformation T^{-1} of T we have obviously

$$(xT)T^{-1} = x \quad \text{for every } x \in S,$$
$$(yT^{-1})T = y \quad \text{for every } y \in R.$$

ii. Sets. Let S be a space. A mapping A from S to a space of two elements $\{\epsilon, \bar{\epsilon}\}$ is called a *set* of S. Let A be a set of S. For $x \in S$ we say x belongs to A and we write $x \in A$ or $A \ni x$ if the image of x by A is ϵ, and we say x does not belong to A and we write $x \bar{\in} A$ or $A \bar{\ni} x$ if the image of x by A is $\bar{\epsilon}$.

Setting $x \bar{\in} \emptyset$ for every $x \in S$, we obtain a set $\emptyset$ which is called the *empty* set of S. Setting $x \in I$ for every $x \in S$ we also obtain a set I of S, which is called the *whole* set of S. The whole set of S is usually denoted by S itself. We often write $A \subset S$ to mean that A is a set of S.

For two sets $A, B \subset S$ we say B includes A and we write $A \subset B$ or $B \supset A$, if $x \in A$ implies $x \in B$, and then A is called a subset of B. A set $A \subset S$ can itself be considered a space. In this sense A is called a *subspace* of S.

Let $\mathbf{A}(x)$ $(x \in S)$ be a condition about $x \in S$. We denote by

$$\{x\colon \mathbf{A}(x)\}$$

the set consisting of all elements $x \in S$ such that $\mathbf{A}(x)$ is satisfied, that is, $y \in \{x\colon \mathbf{A}(x)\}$ if and only if $\mathbf{A}(y)$ is satisfied.

For a system of sets $A_\lambda \subset S$ $(\lambda \in \Lambda)$, we define the union of them by

$$\bigcup_{\lambda \in \Lambda} A_\lambda = \{x\colon x \in A_\lambda \text{ for some } \lambda \in \Lambda\}$$

and the intersection of them by

$$\bigcap_{\lambda \epsilon \Lambda} A_\lambda = \{x: x \epsilon A_\lambda \text{ for every } \lambda \epsilon \Lambda\}.$$

For two sets $A_1, A_2 \subset S$ the union is denoted by $A_1 \cup A_2$ and the intersection is denoted by $A_1 \cap A_2$.

With this definition we can prove easily

$$(\bigcup_{\lambda \epsilon \Lambda} A_\lambda) \cap B = \bigcup_{\lambda \epsilon \Lambda} (A_\lambda \cap B)$$

$$(\bigcap_{\lambda \epsilon \Lambda} A_\lambda) \cup B = \bigcap_{\lambda \epsilon \Lambda} (A_\lambda \cup B).$$

For a double system $A_{\lambda,\gamma} \subset S$ $(\lambda \epsilon \Lambda, \gamma \epsilon \Gamma)$ we have

$$\bigcap_{\lambda \epsilon \Lambda} \bigcup_{\gamma \epsilon \Gamma} A_{\lambda,\gamma} = \bigcup_{\gamma_\lambda \epsilon \Gamma (\lambda \epsilon \Lambda)} \bigcap_{\lambda \epsilon \Lambda} A_{\lambda,\gamma_\lambda}.$$

Because if $x \epsilon \bigcap_{\lambda \epsilon \Lambda} \bigcup_{\gamma \epsilon \Gamma} A_{\lambda,\gamma}$, then $x \epsilon \bigcup_{\gamma \epsilon \Gamma} A_{\lambda,\gamma}$ for every $\lambda \epsilon \Lambda$, and hence there is a system $\gamma_\lambda \epsilon \Gamma$ $(\lambda \epsilon \Lambda)$ by Choice Axiom such that $x \epsilon A_{\lambda,\gamma_\lambda}$ for every $\lambda \epsilon \Lambda$. Thus

$$x \epsilon \bigcap_{\lambda \epsilon \Lambda} A_{\lambda,\gamma_\lambda} \subset \bigcup_{\gamma_\lambda \epsilon \Gamma (\lambda \epsilon \Lambda)} \bigcap_{\lambda \epsilon \Lambda} A_{\lambda,\gamma_\lambda}.$$

Conversely if $x \epsilon \bigcup_{\gamma_\lambda \epsilon \Gamma (\lambda \epsilon \Lambda)} \bigcap_{\lambda \epsilon \Lambda} A_{\lambda,\gamma_\lambda}$, then there is a system $\gamma_\lambda \epsilon \Gamma$ $(\lambda \epsilon \Lambda)$ such that $x \epsilon \bigcap_{\lambda \epsilon \Lambda} A_{\lambda,\gamma_\lambda}$, that is, $x \epsilon A_{\lambda,\gamma_\lambda}$ for every $\lambda \epsilon \Lambda$, and hence $x \epsilon \bigcup_{\gamma \epsilon \Gamma} A_{\lambda,\gamma}$ for every $\lambda \epsilon \Lambda$. Therefore $x \epsilon \bigcap_{\lambda \epsilon \Lambda} \bigcup_{\gamma \epsilon \Gamma} A_{\lambda,\gamma}$.

For a set $A \subset S$ we define the *complement* of A by

$$A' = \{x: x \epsilon A\}.$$

Then we see easily that $(A')' = A$, $\emptyset' = S$, $S' = \emptyset$,

$$(\bigcup_{\lambda \epsilon \Lambda} A_\lambda)' = \bigcap_{\lambda \epsilon \Lambda} A_\lambda', \quad (\bigcap_{\lambda \epsilon \Lambda} A_\lambda)' = \bigcup_{\lambda \epsilon \Lambda} A_\lambda'.$$

For two sets $A, B \subset S$ we define $A - B$ by

$$A - B = A \cap B',$$

that is, $A - B = \{x: x \epsilon A, x \epsilon B\}$.

iii. **Maximal Theorem.** We admit the following axiom due to Zermelo.

Choice Axiom. *For any space S there is a mapping C from the space* *of all sets of* S *to* S *such that* $AC \in A$ *for* $\emptyset \neq A \subset S$. Such a mapping C is called a mapping by Choice Axiom.

We can prove by Choice Axiom the so-called Zorn's lemma.

Maximal Theorem. *Let* $\mathbf{A}$ *be a condition for finite systems* $a_\nu \in S$ $(\nu = 1, 2, \ldots, n)$, $n = 1, 2, \ldots$. *We suppose there is a set* $A_0 \subset S$ *such that* $A_0 \neq \emptyset$ *and* A_0 *satisfies* $\mathbf{A}$, *that is,* $\mathbf{A}(x_1, x_2, \ldots, x_n)$ *is satisfied for every finite system* $x_\nu \in A_0$ $(\nu = 1, 2, \ldots, n)$. *Then there is a maximal set* $A \subset S$ *such that* $A_0 \subset A$ *and* A *satisfies* $\mathbf{A}$, *that is, if* $A \subset X$ *and* X *satisfies* $\mathbf{A}$, *then* $A = X$.

Proof. Let $\mathbf{K}_0$ be the system of all sets which include A_0 and satisfy $\mathbf{A}$. For $A \in \mathbf{K}_0$, if there is $x \bar{\in} A$ such that $\{A, x\} \in \mathbf{K}_0$, then setting

$$a_A = \{x: x \bar{\in} A, \{A, x\} \in \mathbf{K}_0\}C$$

for a mapping C by Choice axiom, we obtain $a_A \in S$ such that

$$a_A \bar{\in} A \text{ and } \{A, a_A\} \in \mathbf{K}_0.$$

If there is $A \in \mathbf{K}_0$ such that there is no such a_A for A, then A is maximal. Therefore we suppose that for every $A \in \mathbf{K}_0$ we have a_A.

We consider subsets $\mathbf{K} \subset \mathbf{K}_0$ which satisfy

1) $A_0 \in \mathbf{K}$,

2) $A \in \mathbf{K}$ implies $\{A, a_A\} \in \mathbf{K}$,

3) $A_\lambda \in \mathbf{K}$ $(\lambda \in \Lambda)$ implies $\bigcup_{\lambda \in \Lambda} A_\lambda \in \mathbf{K}$, if A_λ $(\lambda \in \Lambda)$ are mutually *comparable,* that is, if for any $\lambda_1, \lambda_2 \in \Lambda$ we have $A_{\lambda_1} \supset A_{\lambda_2}$ or $A_{\lambda_1} \subset A_{\lambda_2}$.

$\mathbf{K}_0$ obviously satisfies 1), 2) and 3). Let $\mathbf{K}_1$ be the intersection of all $\mathbf{K} \subset \mathbf{K}_0$ which satisfy 1), 2) and 3). Then we see easily that $\mathbf{K}_1$ also satisfies 1), 2) and 3). Therefore $\mathbf{K}_1$ is the least subset of $\mathbf{K}_0$ which satisfies 1), 2) and 3).

Let $\mathbf{K}_2$ be the system of all $A \in \mathbf{K}_1$ which are comparable with every $X \in \mathbf{K}_1$, that is, $A \subset X$ or $A \supset X$ for every $X \in \mathbf{K}_1$. Then we have obviously $A_0 \in \mathbf{K}_2$ and we see easily that $\mathbf{K}_2$ satisfies 2). For any $A_2 \in \mathbf{K}_2$ we set

$$\mathbf{K}_3 = \{A: A_2 \supset A \in \mathbf{K}_1\} \cup \{A: \{A_2, a_{A_2}\} \subset A \in \mathbf{K}_1\}.$$

Then we have obviously $A_0 \in \mathbf{K}_3$ and we see easily that $\mathbf{K}_3$ satisfies 3). Furthermore $\mathbf{K}_3$ satisfies 2). Because if $A \in \mathbf{K}_3$ but $\{A, a_A\} \bar{\in} \mathbf{K}_3$, then, since $A \in \mathbf{K}_1$ implies $\{A, a_A\} \in \mathbf{K}_1$ and since A_2 is comparable with every $X \in \mathbf{K}_1$, we have

$$A \subset A_2 \subset \{A, a_A\}$$

and hence $A = A_2$ or $A_2 = \{A, a_A\}$, contradicting the assumption $\{A, a_A\} \bar{\in} \mathbf{K}_3$. Therefore $\mathbf{K}_3$ satisfies 1), 2) and 3), and hence we obtain $\mathbf{K}_3 = \mathbf{K}_1$, because $\mathbf{K}_1$ is the least subset of $\mathbf{K}_0$ which satisfies 1), 2) and 3). Consequently $\{A_2, a_{A_2}\}$ is comparable with every $X \in \mathbf{K}_1$, that is, $\{A_2, a_{A_2}\} \in \mathbf{K}_2$. Thus $\mathbf{K}_2$ also satisfies 1), 2) and 3), and hence $\mathbf{K}_2 = \mathbf{K}_1$. Consequently for any $X, Y \in \mathbf{K}_1$ we have $X \subset Y$ or $X \supset Y$. Thus setting $A_1 = \bigcup_{X \in \mathbf{K}_1} X$, we obtain $A_1 \in \mathbf{K}_1$ by 3) and $A_1 \supset X$ for every $X \in \mathbf{K}_1$, contradicting $\{A_1, a_{A_1}\} \in \mathbf{K}_1$. Therefore there exists $A \in \mathbf{K}_0$ for which there is no $x \in S$ such that $\{A, x\} \in \mathbf{K}_0$. Such $A \in \mathbf{K}_0$ is obviously a maximal set which includes A_0 and satisfies **A**.

I. UNIFORMITIES

1. Connectors. Let S be a space. A mapping U from S to the space of all sets of S is called a *connector* on S, if $xU \ni x$ for every $x \in S$. Here xU denotes the image of x by the mapping U. Putting $xI = \{x\}$ for every $x \in S$, we obviously obtain a connector I on S, which will be called the *identical connector* on S and denoted by I.

For two connectors U, V we write $U \geqq V$ or $V \leqq U$, if $xU \supset xV$ for every $x \in S$. With this definition, we obviously have that $U \geqq V$, $V \geqq W$ implies $U \geqq W$; $U \geqq V$, $V \geqq U$ implies $U = V$; and $U \geqq I$ for any connector U.

For two connectors U, V, the *intersection* $U \cap V$ is defined by

$$x(U \cap V) = xU \cap xV \qquad \text{for every } x \in S.$$

Generally, for a system of connectors U_λ $(\lambda \in \Lambda)$ the *intersection* $\bigcap_{\lambda \in \Lambda} U_\lambda$ is defined by

$$x \bigcap_{\lambda \in \Lambda} U_\lambda = \bigcap_{\lambda \in \Lambda} xU_\lambda \qquad \text{for every } x \in S.$$

The intersection of connectors also is obviously a connector and

$$U \cap V = V \cap U \leqq V, \qquad I \cap U = U \cap I = I.$$

For an arbitrary set $A \subset S$ and for a connector U on S, we define AU by

$$AU = \bigcup_{x \in A} xU, \text{ if } A \neq \emptyset,$$

and $AU = \emptyset$ if $A = \emptyset$. With this definition, we have obviously

$A \subset AU$; $A = AI$; $A \subset B$ implies $AU \subset BU$; $U \leqq V$ implies $AU \subset AV$.

We also can prove easily

$$(\bigcup_{\lambda \in \Lambda} A_\lambda)U = \bigcup_{\lambda \in \Lambda} A_\lambda U, \qquad (\bigcap_{\lambda \in \Lambda} A_\lambda)U \subset \bigcap_{\lambda \in \Lambda} A_\lambda U.$$

We conclude immediately from the definition:

Theorem 1.1. *For a set A and for a connector U we have $x \in AU$ if and only if there is $y \in A$ such that $x \in yU$.*

For two connectors U, V, the *product* UV is defined by

$$x(UV) = (xU)V \qquad \text{for every } x \in S.$$

The product UV is obviously a connector on S, and we can show easily

$$(UV)W = U(VW), \qquad UI = IU = U, \qquad U \leqq UV, \qquad V \leqq UV,$$

and $U \leqq V$ implies $UW \leqq VW$ and $WU \leqq WV$. Thus we have

$$(\bigcap_{\lambda \in \Lambda} U_\lambda)U \leqq \bigcap_{\lambda \in \Lambda} U_\lambda U, \qquad U(\bigcap_{\lambda \in \Lambda} U_\lambda) \leqq \bigcap_{\lambda \in \Lambda} UU_\lambda.$$

For a set $A \subset S$, we also obviously have $(AU)V = A(UV)$.

For a connector U, its *inverse* U^{-1} is defined by

$$xU^{-1} = \{y\colon yU \ni x\} \qquad \text{for every } x \in S.$$

That is, we have $y \in xU^{-1}$ if and only if $x \in yU$. The inverse U^{-1} also is obviously a connector and we can show easily

$$I^{-1} = I, \; (U^{-1})^{-1} = U, \; (\bigcap_{\lambda \in \Lambda} U_\lambda)^{-1} = \bigcap_{\lambda \in \Lambda} U_\lambda^{-1}, \; (UV)^{-1} = V^{-1}U^{-1}, \text{ and}$$

$U \leqq V$ implies $U^{-1} \leqq V^{-1}$.

As $xU \ni y$ implies $x \in yU^{-1}$, we obtain by definition

Theorem 1.2. $xU \ni y$ implies $xU \subset yU^{-1}U$.

Theorem 1.3. *For two sets A, B, and for a connector U, we have $AU \cap B = \emptyset$ if and only if $A \cap BU^{-1} = \emptyset$.*

Proof. If $x \in AU \cap B$, then we have $x \in yU$ for some $y \in A$ by Theorem 1.1 and $y \in xU^{-1}$ by definition, and hence $y \in A \cap BU^{-1} \neq \emptyset$. Thus $AU \cap B \neq \emptyset$ implies $A \cap BU^{-1} \neq \emptyset$. Since $U = (U^{-1})^{-1}$, $A \cap BU^{-1} \neq \emptyset$ implies therefore $AU \cap B \neq \emptyset$.

A connector U is said to be *symmetric*, if $U^{-1} = U$. With this definition we obviously have

Theorem 1.4. *For any connector U, all of the connectors $U \cap U^{-1}$, UU^{-1} and $U^{-1}U$ are symmetric.*

For a connector U, we define U^ν ($\nu = 1, 2, \ldots$) by

$U^0 = I$, $U^\nu = U^{\nu-1}U$ for $\nu = 1, 2, \ldots$.

Then we have

Theorem 1.5. *For an arbitrary set $A \subset S$ and for a connector U, if $B = \bigcup_{\nu=1}^{\infty} AU^\nu$, then $V \leqq U$ implies $BV = B$ and $B'V^{-1} = B'$.*

Proof. We obtain by definition

$$B \subset BV = \bigcup_{\nu=1}^{\infty} AU^{\nu}V \subset \bigcup_{\nu=1}^{\infty} AU^{\nu+1} \subset B,$$

that is, $BV = B$. From $BV = B$ we conclude $BV \cap B' = \emptyset$ and $B \cap B'V^{-1} = \emptyset$ by Theorem 1.3. Therefore $B' \supset B'V^{-1} \supset B'$, that is, $B'V^{-1} = B'$.

For a connector U, we define $U^{-\nu}$ ($\nu = 1, 2, \ldots$) by

$$U^{-\nu} = (U^{-1})^{\nu} \quad (\nu = 1, 2, \ldots).$$

Theorem 1.6. $U^{-\mu}U^{-\nu} = U^{-(\mu+\nu)}$, $(U^{-\mu})^{\nu} = U^{-\mu\nu}$, $(U^{-\mu})^{-\nu} = U^{\mu\nu}$ *for* $\mu, \nu = 1, 2, \ldots$.

Proof. It is obvious by definition that

$U^{-\mu}U^{-\nu} = (U^{-1})^{\mu}(U^{-1})^{\nu} = (U^{-1})^{\mu+\nu} = U^{-(\mu+\nu)}$, $(U^{-\mu})^{\nu} = (U^{-1})^{\mu\nu} = U^{-\mu\nu}$

Since $(U^{-1})^{-1} = U$ by definition, if we assume $(U^{-\mu})^{-1} = U^{\mu}$, then

$$(U^{-(\mu+1)})^{-1} = (U^{-\mu}U^{-1})^{-1} = U(U^{-\mu})^{-1} = UU^{\mu} = U^{\mu+1}.$$

Thus we obtain $(U^{-\mu})^{-1} = U^{\mu}$ for all $\mu = 1, 2, \ldots$ by induction. In addition, we conclude then

$$(U^{-\mu})^{-\nu} = ((U^{-\mu})^{-1})^{\nu} = U^{\mu\nu}.$$

A connector U is said to be *discrete,* if $U^{-1}U = U$. Every discrete connector is symmetric, because $U^{-1}U$ is always symmetric. The identical connector is obviously discrete.

Theorem 1.7. *A connector U is discrete if and only if $xU \cap yU \neq \emptyset$ implies $xU = yU$.*

Proof. If U is discrete, then $xU \cap yU \neq \emptyset$ implies $xUU^{-1} \ni y$ by Theorem 1.3 and hence $yU \subset xUU^{-1}U = xU$. Thus $xU \cap yU \neq \emptyset$ implies $xU = yU$. Conversely, if $xU \cap yU = \emptyset$ implies $xU = yU$, then $xUU^{-1} \ni y$ implies $xU = yU \ni y$, that is, $UU^{-1} \leqq U$. Thus we obtain $UU^{-1} = U$, namely $(U^{-1})^{-1}U^{-1} = U^{-1}$. Therefore U^{-1} is discrete by definition. Consequently U is discrete, because any discrete connector is symmetric.

2. Uniformities. Let S be a space. A system of connectors $\mathbf{U}$ is called a *uniformity* on S, if $\mathbf{U}$ satisfies the *uniformity conditions:*

1) $\mathbf{U} \ni U \leqq V$ implies $\mathbf{U} \ni V$,
2) $\mathbf{U} \ni U, V$ implies $\mathbf{U} \ni U \cap V$,
3) for any $U \in \mathbf{U}$ we can find $V \in \mathbf{U}$ such that $V^{-1}V \leqq U$.

If $\mathbf{U}$ is a uniformity, then $\mathbf{U} \ni U$ implies $U^{-1} \in \mathbf{U}$. Because for any $U \in \mathbf{U}$ we can find $V \in \mathbf{U}$ by condition 3) such that $V^{-1}V \leqq U$. For such V we have $V^{-1} \leqq U$ and $V = (V^{-1})^{-1} \leqq U^{-1}$. Thus we obtain $U^{-1} \in \mathbf{U}$ by condition 1).

In condition 3), setting $W = V^{-1} \cap V$, we obtain a symmetric $W \in \mathbf{U}$ by condition 2), and we obviously have $WW \leqq V^{-1}V \leqq U$. Thus we can state

Theorem 2.1. *If* $\mathbf{U}$ *is a uniformity, then for any* $\nu = 1, 2, \ldots$ and for *any* $U \in \mathbf{U}$ *we can find a symmetric* $V \in \mathbf{U}$ *such that* $V^{\nu} \leqq U$.

For a uniformity $\mathbf{U}$, a subset $\mathbf{B} \subset \mathbf{U}$ is called a *basis* of $\mathbf{U}$, if for any $U \in \mathbf{U}$ we can find $V \in \mathbf{B}$ such that $V \leqq U$. We see easily by conditions 2) and 3) that every basis $\mathbf{B}$ of a uniformity satisfies the *basis conditions:*

1) for any $U, V \in \mathbf{B}$ there is $W \in \mathbf{B}$ such that $W \leqq U \cap V$,
2) for any $U \in \mathbf{B}$ there is $V \in \mathbf{B}$ such that $V^{-1}V \leqq U$.

Conversely we have:

Theorem 2.2. *If a system of connectors* $\mathbf{B}$ *satisfies the basis conditions* 1), 2), *then there exists uniquely a uniformity* $\mathbf{U}$ *such that* $\mathbf{B}$ *is a basis of* $\mathbf{U}$.

Proof. Let $\mathbf{U}$ be the system of all connectors U for which we can find $V \in \mathbf{B}$ such that $U \geqq V$. We see easily that $\mathbf{U}$ satisfies the uniformity conditions, and $\mathbf{B}$ is a basis of $\mathbf{U}$. The uniqueness of such a uniformity $\mathbf{U}$ is clear by the definition of basis.

A basis $\mathbf{B}$ of a uniformity $\mathbf{U}$ is said to be *symmetric,* if $\mathbf{B}$ consists of symmetric connectors. For any uniformity $\mathbf{U}$, the system $\{U^{-1} \cap U: U \in \mathbf{U}\}$ is obviously a symmetric basis of $\mathbf{U}$. Thus we have

Theorem 2.3. *Every uniformity has a symmetric basis.*

For a uniformity $\mathbf{U}$ on S, putting

$$I_{\mathbf{U}} = \bigcap_{U \in \mathbf{U}} U$$

we obtain a connector $I_{\mathbf{U}}$ on S, which will be called the *atom* of $\mathbf{U}$.

Theorem 2.4. *The atom* $I_{\mathbf{U}}$ *of a uniformity* $\mathbf{U}$ *is a discrete connector.*

Proof. For any $U \in \mathbf{U}$ we can find $V \in \mathbf{U}$ by definition such that $V^{-1}V \leqq U$. For such $U, V \in \mathbf{U}$ we have $I_{\mathbf{U}} \leqq V$ and $I_{\mathbf{U}}^{-1} V \leqq U$. Thus we obtain $I_{\mathbf{U}}^{-1} I_{\mathbf{U}} \leqq I_{\mathbf{U}}$ by definition.

A uniformity $\mathbf{U}$ is said to be *discrete,* if $\mathbf{U}$ contains its atom. A uniformity $\mathbf{U}$ is said to be *pure* at a point $x \in S$, if $xI_{\mathbf{U}} = \{x\}$. A uniformity $\mathbf{U}$ is said to be *pure* on a set $A \subset S$, if $\mathbf{U}$ is pure at every $x \in A$. A uniformity $\mathbf{U}$ is said to be *pure,* if $I_{\mathbf{U}} = I$. If a uniformity $\mathbf{U}$ contains I, then $\mathbf{U}$ contains all connectors on S by definition. Thus the pure discrete uniformity contains all connectors on S.

A uniformity $\mathbf{U}$ is said to be *sequential,* if $\mathbf{U}$ has a basis which consists of countably many connectors. A space S associated with a uniformity is called a *uniform space.*

3. Topologies. For a space S, a system of sets $\mathbf{T}$ is called a *topology,* on S, if $\mathbf{T}$ satisfies the *topology conditions:*

1) $\mathbf{T} \ni \emptyset, S$,
2) $\mathbf{T} \ni X, Y$ implies $\mathbf{T} \ni X \cap Y$,
3) $\mathbf{T} \ni X_\lambda$ $(\lambda \in \Lambda)$ implies $\mathbf{T} \ni \bigcup_{\lambda \in \Lambda} X_\lambda$

Let $\mathbf{T}$ be a topology on S. A set $X \subset S$ is said to be *open,* if $X \in \mathbf{T}$. For any set $A \subset S$, setting

$$A = \bigcup_{A \supset X \in \mathbf{T}} X$$

we obtain an open set A° by the topology condition 3). This open set A° is called the *interior* of A. The interior A° will be denoted by $A^{\mathbf{T}\circ}$, when we need to indicate the topology $\mathbf{T}$.

A set $A \subset S$ is said to be *closed* for $\mathbf{T}$, if the complement A' is open for $\mathbf{T}$. With this definition we see easily by the topology conditions that 1) $\emptyset$, S are closed, 2) if X and Y are closed, then $X \cup Y$ is closed, and 3) for a system of closed sets X_λ $(\lambda \in \Lambda)$, the intersection $\bigcap_{\lambda \in \Lambda} X_\lambda$ is closed. For any set $A \subset S$, setting

$$A^- = \bigcap_{A \subset X,\ X' \in \mathbf{T}} X.$$

we obtain a closed set A^- by 3). This closed set A^- is called the *closure* of A. The closure A^- will be denoted by $A^{\mathbf{T}-}$, when we need to indicate the topology $\mathbf{T}$.

About the interior and the closure, we see easily by definition

$$A^\circ \subset A \subset A^-,$$

$A = A^\circ$, if and only if A is open, and $A = A^-$ if and only if A is closed. Thus we obtain

$$A^{\circ\circ} = A^\circ, \quad A^{--} = A^-.$$

For the empty set $\emptyset$ and the whole set S, we obviously have

$$\emptyset^\circ = \emptyset^- = \emptyset, \quad S^\circ = S^- = S.$$

Since $A \supset X$ if and only if $A' \subset X'$, we obtain by definition

$$A^{\circ\prime} = \bigcap_{A \supset X \in \mathbf{T}} X' = \bigcap_{A' \subset X,\ X' \in \mathbf{T}} X = A'^-,$$

that is, $A^{\circ\prime} = A'^-$. We also obtain $A^{-\prime} = A'^\circ$ likewise.

Since $A \supset B$ obviously implies $A^\circ \supset B^\circ$, we have

$$A^\circ \cap B^\circ \supset (A \cap B)^\circ \supset (A^\circ \cap B^\circ)^\circ = A^\circ \cap B^\circ,$$

because $A^\circ \cap B^\circ$ is open. Therefore

$$(A \cap B)^\circ = A^\circ \cap B^\circ, \quad (A \cup B)^- = A^- \cup B^-$$

because $(A \cup B)^- = (A \cup B)'^{\circ\prime} = (A' \cap B')^{\circ\prime} = (A'^\circ \cap B'^\circ)' = A'^{\circ\prime} \cup B'^{\circ\prime} = A^- \cup B^-$.

As $A \subset B$ obviously implies $A^- \subset B^-$, we have $(A \cap B)^- \subset A^- \cap B^-$. On the other hand, since $A = (A \cap B) \cup (A \cap B') \subset (A \cap B) \cup B'$, we obtain

$$A^- \subset ((A \cap B) \cup B')^- = (A \cap B)^- \cup B'^- = (A \cap B)^- \cup B^{\circ\prime},$$

which implies $A^- \cap B^\circ \subset (A \cap B)^- \cap B^\circ \subset (A \cap B)^-$. Therefore

$$A^- \cap B^\circ \subset (A \cap B)^- \subset A^- \cap B^-.$$

We can prove similarly

$$A^- \cup B^\circ \supset (A \cup B)^\circ \supset A^\circ \cup B^\circ.$$

Thus we obtain

Theorem 3.1. *For any sets A, B*

$$(A \cap B)^\circ = A^\circ \cap B^\circ, \qquad (A \cup B)^- = A^- \cup B^-,$$
$$A^- \cap B^\circ \subset (A \cap B)^- \subset A^- \cap B^-, \qquad A^- \cup B^\circ \supset (A \cup B)^\circ \supset A^\circ \cup B^\circ.$$

Theorem 3.2. $A^{-\circ-\circ} = A^{-\circ}, \qquad A^{\circ-\circ-} = A^{\circ-}.$

Proof. Since $A^{-\circ-} \supset A^{-\circ}$, we obtain $A^{-\circ-\circ} \supset A^{-\circ\circ} = A^{-\circ}$. On the other hand, $A^{-\circ} \subset A$ implies $A^{-\circ-\circ} \subset A^{--\circ} = A^{-\circ}$. Thus $A^{-\circ-\circ} = A^{-\circ}$. We also obtain $A^{\circ-\circ-} = A'^{-\circ-\circ\prime} = A'^{-\circ\prime} = A^{\circ-}$.

Theorem 3.3. *If one of two sets A, B is open or closed, then*

$$(A \cap B)^{-\circ} = A^{-\circ} \cap B^{-\circ}, \qquad (A \cup B)^{\circ -} = A^{\circ -} \cup B^{\circ -}.$$

Proof. If A is open, then $A = A^{\circ}$ and we obtain by Theorem 3.1,

$$A^{-\circ} \cap B^{-\circ} = (A^{-} \cap B^{-})^{\circ} \supset (A \cap B)^{-\circ}$$
$$\supset (A^{\circ} \cap B^{-})^{-\circ} \supset (A^{-} \cap B^{-\circ})^{\circ} = A^{-\circ} \cap B^{-\circ}.$$

If A is closed, then $A = A^{-}$ and we obtain by Theorem 3.1,

$$A^{-\circ} \cap B^{-\circ} \supset (A \cap B)^{-\circ} \supset (A^{-\circ} \cap B^{-})^{\circ} = A^{-\circ} \cap B^{-\circ}.$$

The other equation is proved similarly.

For two sets A, B, we write $A \succ B$ or $B \prec A$, when $A^{\circ} \supset B^{-}$. With this definition we have obviously

(1) $A \succ B \supset C$ implies $A \succ C$,

(2) $C \supset A \succ B$ implies $C \succ B$.

$A_1^{\circ} \supset B_1^{-}$, $A_2^{\circ} \supset B_2^{-}$ implies by Theorem 3.1,

$$(A_1 \cap A_2)^{\circ} = A_1^{\circ} \cap A_2^{\circ} \supset B_1^{-} \cap B_2^{-} \supset (B_1 \cap B_2)^{-},$$
$$(A_1 \cup A_2)^{\circ} \supset A_1^{\circ} \cup A_2^{\circ} \supset B_1^{-} \cup B_2^{-} = (B_1 \cup B_2)^{-}.$$

Thus we obtain

(3) $A_1 \succ B_1$, $A_2 \succ B_2$ implies $A_1 \cap A_2 \succ B_1 \cap B_2$ and $A_1 \cup A_2 \succ B_1 \cup B_2$.

4. **Induced Topologies.** Let $\mathbf{U}$ be a uniformity on a space S. Setting

$$\mathbf{T}(\mathbf{U}) = \{X: X \ni x \text{ implies } X \supset xU \text{ for some } U \in \mathbf{U}\}$$

we can show easily that $\mathbf{T}(\mathbf{U})$ satisfies the topology conditions, that is, $\mathbf{T}(\mathbf{U})$ is a topology on S. This topology $\mathbf{T}(\mathbf{U})$ is called the *induced topology* of $\mathbf{U}$.

For the induced topology $\mathbf{T}(\mathbf{U})$ we have

(1) $A^{\circ} = \{x: A \supset xU \text{ for some } U \in \mathbf{U}\}$

for any set $A \subset S$. Because, denoting the right side by B, we have obviously $A^{\circ} \subset B \subset A$. For any $a \in B$, there is $U \in \mathbf{U}$ such that $aU \subset A$. For such U, we can find a symmetric $V \in \mathbf{U}$ by Theorem 2.1 such that $V^2 \leqq U$. Then we have $A \supset aU \supset aVV$, which implies $B \supset aV$. Therefore $B \in \mathbf{T}(\mathbf{U})$ by definition. Thus we conclude $A^{\circ} = B$. The interior A° of A for $\mathbf{T}(\mathbf{U})$ will be denoted by $A^{\mathbf{U}\circ}$, when we need to indicate $\mathbf{T}(\mathbf{U})$.

For any $U \in \mathbf{U}$ there is a symmetric $V \in \mathbf{U}$ such that $V^2 \leqq U$. For such U, V it is obvious that $y \in xV$ implies $yV \subset xV^2 \subset xU$. Therefore $xV \subset (xU)^\circ$ for every $x \in S$ by (1). Thus setting

(2) $xU^\circ = (xU)^\circ$ for every $x \in S$,

we obtain a connector U° on S and $U^\circ \in \mathbf{U}$, because $U^\circ \geqq V$. This connector $U^\circ \in \mathbf{U}$ is called the *interior* of $U \in \mathbf{U}$ and denoted by $U^{\mathbf{U}\circ}$, when we need to indicate $\mathbf{U}$. It is obvious that $U^\circ \leqq U$ for every $U \in \mathbf{U}$ by definition.

A connector $U \in \mathbf{U}$ is said to be *open,* if xU is open by $\mathbf{T}(\mathbf{U})$ for every $x \in S$. Then we can state by (2) that $U \in \mathbf{U}$ is open if and only if $U = U^\circ$.

Since $A^- = A'^{\circ}{}'$, we obtain by (1)

$A^- = \{x\colon A \cap xU \neq \emptyset$ for every $U \in \mathbf{U}\}$.

Thus we conclude by Theorem 1.3

$A^- = \{x\colon AU^{-1} \ni x$ for every $U \in \mathbf{U}\}$.

As $U^{-1} \in \mathbf{U}$ for every $U \in \mathbf{U}$, we obtain therefore

(3) $A^- = \bigcap_{U \in \mathbf{U}} AU$.

Since $AU = \bigcup_{x \in A} xU$ for $S \supset A \neq \emptyset$, AU is open for any open $U \in \mathbf{U}$.

Thus we obtain by (3)

(4) $A^- \subset AU^\circ \subset (AU)^\circ$ for every $U \in \mathbf{U}$.

The closure A^- will be denoted by $A^{\mathbf{U}-}$, when we need to indicate $\mathbf{U}$. For the atom $I_{\mathbf{U}}$ of $\mathbf{U}$, it is obvious by (1), (2)

(5) $A^\circ I_{\mathbf{U}} = A^\circ$, $A^- I_{\mathbf{U}} = A^-$.

Theorem 4.1. $\bigcup_{\nu=1}^{\infty} AU^\nu$ is open and closed for every $U \in \mathbf{U}$.

Proof. Setting $B = \bigcup_{\nu=1}^{\infty} AU^\nu$, we obtain $B = BU$ by Theorem 1.5 and $B^- \subset (BU)^\circ = B^\circ$ by (4). As $B^\circ \subset B \subset B^-$, we hence conclude that $B = B^- = B^\circ$.

Let $\mathbf{T}$ be an arbitrary topology on S. We consider now relations between $\mathbf{T}$ and the induced topology $\mathbf{T}(\mathbf{U})$.

Theorem 4.2. $\mathbf{T} \subset \mathbf{T}(\mathbf{U})$ *if and only if* $x \in (xU)^{\mathbf{T}\circ}$ *for every* $x \in S$ *and* $U \in \mathbf{U}$.

Proof. If $\mathbf{T} \supset \mathbf{T}(\mathbf{U})$, then $A^{\mathbf{T}\circ} \supset A^{\mathbf{U}\circ}$ for any set A by definition. Thus $x \in xU^{\circ} = (xU)^{\mathbf{U}\circ} \subset (xU)^{\mathbf{T}\circ}$ for every $x \in S$ and $U \in \mathbf{U}$.

Conversely we suppose that $x \in (xU)^{\mathbf{T}\circ}$ for every $x \in S$ and $U \in \mathbf{U}$. Let A be an arbitrary open set for $\mathbf{T}(\mathbf{U})$. For any $x \in A$ we can find $U_x \in \mathbf{U}$ by definition such that $xU_x \subset A$. For such $U_x \in \mathbf{U}$ $(x \in A)$, we obtain $x \in (xU_x)^{\mathbf{T}\circ} \subset xU_x \subset A$ by assumption. Thus

$$A = \bigcup_{x \in A} (xU_x)^{\mathbf{T}\circ} \in \mathbf{T}.$$

Therefore $\mathbf{T}(\mathbf{U}) \subset \mathbf{T}$.

Theorem 4.3. $\mathbf{T} \subset \mathbf{T}(\mathbf{U})$ *if and only if* $x \in A \in \mathbf{T}$ *implies* $xU \subset A$ *for some* $U \in \mathbf{U}$.

Proof. If $\mathbf{T} \subset \mathbf{T}(\mathbf{U})$, then $x \in A \in \mathbf{T}$ implies $xU \subset A$ for some $U \in \mathbf{U}$ by the definition of $\mathbf{T}(\mathbf{U})$. Conversely, if $x \in A \in \mathbf{T}$ implies $xU \subset A$ for some $U \in \mathbf{U}$, then $A \in \mathbf{T}$ implies $A \in \mathbf{T}(\mathbf{U})$ by definition.

For two uniformities $\mathbf{U}$, $\mathbf{V}$ on S, $\mathbf{U}$ is said to be *homeomorphic* to $\mathbf{V}$, if $\mathbf{T}(\mathbf{U}) = \mathbf{T}(\mathbf{V})$. As a criterion of homeomorphism, we have

Theorem 4.4. $\mathbf{T}(\mathbf{U}) \subset \mathbf{T}(\mathbf{V})$ *if and only if for any* $x \in S$ *and* $U \in \mathbf{U}$ *we can find* $V \in \mathbf{V}$ *such that* $xU \supset xV$.

Proof. If $\mathbf{T}(\mathbf{U}) \subset \mathbf{T}(\mathbf{V})$, then for any $U \in \mathbf{U}$ we have $U^{\circ} \in \mathbf{U}$ and $xU^{\circ} \in \mathbf{T}(\mathbf{U})$ by (2). Thus there is $V \in \mathbf{V}$ by Theorem 4.3 such that $xV \subset xU^{\circ} \subset xU$. Conversely, we suppose that for any $x \in S$ and $U \in \mathbf{U}$ we can find $V \in \mathbf{V}$ such that $xU \supset xV$. Then $x \in A \in \mathbf{T}(\mathbf{U})$ implies $xU \subset A$ for some $U \in \mathbf{U}$ by definition. Hence $xV \subset A$ for some $V \in \mathbf{V}$ by assumption. Thus we obtain $\mathbf{T}(\mathbf{U}) \subset \mathbf{T}(\mathbf{V})$ by Theorem 4.3.

5. Relative Uniformities. Let S be a space and let R be a subspace of S. For a connector U on S, setting

$$xU^{R} = xU \cap R \qquad \text{for } x \in R,$$

we obviously obtain a connector U^{R} on R, which will be called the *relative connector* of U on R.

Concerning relative connectors, we obviously have by definition

(1) $U \leqq V$ implies $U^{R} \leqq V^{R}$,

(2) $\left(\bigcap_{\lambda \in \Lambda} U_{\lambda}\right)^{R} = \bigcap_{\lambda \in \Lambda} U_{\lambda}^{R}$.

For any $x, y \in R$, we have $x \in yU^R$ if and only if $x \in yU$. Thus

(3) $(U^{-1})^R = (U^R)^{-1}$.

For a set $A \subset S$, when we consider $A \cap R$ a set of the subspace R, the set $A \cap R$ of R is called the *relative set* of A on R and denoted by A^R, that is,

$$A^R = A \cap R \qquad \text{for every } A \subset S.$$

With this definition, we have

(4) $(AU)^R \supset A^R U^R$. for $A \subset S$ and a connector U.

Because $(AU)^R = \bigcup_{x \in A} xU \cap R \supset \bigcup_{x \in A \cap R} xU \cap R = A^R U^R$.

As an immediate consequence of (4), we obtain for connectors U, V

(5) $(UV)^R \geqq U^R V^R$,

(6) $(U^\nu)^R \geqq (U^R)^\nu$ for $\nu = \pm 1, \pm 2, \ldots$.

Let $\mathbf{U}$ be a uniformity on S. We can show easily by (1), (2), (3), (5) that the system of connectors $\{U^R: U \in \mathbf{U}\}$ on R satisfies the uniformity conditions 2) and 3) on R. If $U^R \leqq W$ for $U \in \mathbf{U}$ and for a connector W on R, then, setting

$$xV = \begin{cases} xU \cup xW & \text{for } x \in R, \\ xU & \text{for } x \bar{\in} R, \end{cases}$$

we obtain a connector V on S such that $V \geqq U$. Thus $V \in \mathbf{U}$, and

$$xV^R = (xU \cup xW) \cap R = xU^R \cup xW = xW$$

for every $x \in R$, because $U^R \leqq W$ by assumption. Therefore $\{U^R: U \in \mathbf{U}\}$ satisfies the uniformity condition 1) on R too. This uniformity on R is called the *relative uniformity* of $\mathbf{U}$ on R and denoted by $\mathbf{U}^R$, that is,

(7) $\mathbf{U}^R = \{U^R: U \in \mathbf{U}\}$.

For $S \supset R \supset A \neq \emptyset$, it is obvious that $U^A = (U^R)^A$ for every connector U on S. Thus

(8) $\mathbf{U}^A = (\mathbf{U}^R)^A$ for $S \supset R \supset A \neq \emptyset$.

Between the atoms of $\mathbf{U}$ and $\mathbf{U}^R$, we have by (2) the relation

(9) $(I_{\mathbf{U}})^R = I_{\mathbf{U}^R}$.

For a set $A \subset S$, the interior and the closure of the relative set A^R for the induced topology $\mathbf{T}(\mathbf{U}^R)$ of the relative uniformity $\mathbf{U}^R$ will be denoted by $A^{R\circ}$ and A^{R-} respectively, while A° and A^- denote respectively the interior and the closure of A for $\mathbf{T}(\mathbf{U})$. With this notation, we have

(10) $A^{R\circ} = (A \cup R')^{\circ R}, \quad A^{R-} = (A \cap R)^{-R}.$

Because we obtain by (3) in (4)

$$A^{R-} = \bigcap_{U \in \mathbf{U}} A^R U^R = \bigcap_{U \in \mathbf{U}} ((A \cap R)U)^R = (A \cap R)^{-R}$$

and this relation implies

$$A^{R\circ} = A^{R'-'} = A'^{R-'} = (A' \cap R)^{-R'} = (A \cup R')'^{-'R} = (A \cup R')^{\circ R},$$

since $A^{R'} = R \cap A' = A'^R$

We conclude immediately from (10)

(11) $A^{\circ R} \subset A^{R\circ} \subset A^{R-} \subset A^{-R}.$

Theorem 5.1. *A set $A \subset R$ is open for $\mathbf{T}(\mathbf{U}^R)$ if and only if there is an open set B for $\mathbf{T}(\mathbf{U})$ such that $A = B \cap R$. A set $A \subset R$ is closed for $\mathbf{T}(\mathbf{U}^R)$ if and only if there is a closed set B for $\mathbf{T}(\mathbf{U})$ such that $A = B \cap R$.*

Proof. If $A \subset R$ is open for $\mathbf{T}(\mathbf{U}^R)$, then we obtain by (10)

$$A = A^{R\circ} = (A \cup R')^{\circ R} = (A \cup R')^{\circ} \cap R,$$

and $(A \cup R')^{\circ}$ is open for $\mathbf{T}(\mathbf{U})$. Conversely, for any open set B we have by (11) $B^R = B^{\circ R} \subset B^{R\circ} \subset B^R$; that is, $B^R = B^{R\circ}$.

If $A \subset R$ is closed for $\mathbf{T}(\mathbf{U}^R)$, then we obtain by (10)

$$A = A^{R-} = (A \cap R)^{-R} = (A \cap R)^{-} \cap R$$

and $(A \cap R)^{-}$ is closed for $\mathbf{T}(\mathbf{U})$. Conversely, for any closed set B we have by (11) $B^R = B^{-R} \supset B^{R-} \supset B^R$, that is, $B^R = B^{R-}$.

Theorem 5.2. *If $R^{-} = S$, then $G^{R-} = G^{-R}$ for any open set G and $F^{R\circ} = F^{\circ R}$ for any closed set F.*

Proof. If $R^{-} = S$, then for any open set G we obtain by Theorem 3.1

$$G^{-R} = (G^{\circ} \cap R^{-})^{-R} \subset (G \cap R)^{-R} \subset G^{-R} \cap R^{-R} = G^{-R}$$

We hence conclude that $G^{R-} = G^{-R}$ for an open set G by (10). Thus we have $F^{R\circ'} = F'^{R-} = F'^{-R} = F^{\circ R'}$, for a closed set F, since F' is open. Therefore $F^{R\circ} = F^{\circ R}$ for a closed set F.

6. **Totally Bounded Sets.** Let S be a space with a uniformity **U**. A set $A \subset S$ is said to be *bounded,* if for any $U \in \mathbf{U}$ we can find $\sigma = 1, 2, \ldots$ and a finite system $a_\nu \in S$ $(\nu = 1, 2, \ldots, n)$ such that

$$A \subset \bigcup_{\nu=1}^{n} a_\nu U^\sigma.$$

Here we can find $a_\nu \in S$ $(\nu = 1, 2, \ldots, n)$ in A, if $A \neq \emptyset$. Because, if $A \subset \bigcup_{\nu=1}^{n} a_\nu U^\sigma$ for a symmetric $U \in \mathbf{U}$, then we have by Theorems 1.2 and 1.6

$$A \subset \bigcup_{\nu=1}^{n} x_\nu U^{2\sigma} \text{ for } x_\nu \in A \cap a_\nu U^\sigma \ (\nu = 1, 2, \ldots, n).$$

With this definition, it is obvious that every subset of a bounded set is bounded too, and for any finite system of bounded sets A_ν $(\nu = 1, 2, \ldots, n)$, $\bigcup_{\nu=1}^{n} A_\nu$ also is bounded.

Theorem 6.1. *If A is bounded, then its closure $A^{\mathbf{U}-}$ also is bounded.*

Proof. If $A \subset \bigcup_{\nu=1}^{n} a_\nu U^\sigma$, then we have by (3) in 4

$$A^- \subset AU \subset \bigcup_{\nu=1}^{n} a_\nu U^{\sigma+1}.$$

A set $A \subset S$ is said to be *totally bounded,* if for any $U \in \mathbf{U}$ we can find a finite system $a_\nu \in S$ $(\nu = 1, 2, \ldots, n)$ such that

$$A \subset \bigcup_{\nu=1}^{n} a_\nu U.$$

Here we can find $a_\nu \in S$ $(\nu = 1, 2, \ldots, n)$ in A, if $A \neq \emptyset$. Because, for any $U \in \mathbf{U}$ there is a symmetric $V \in \mathbf{U}$ such that $V^2 \leqq U$, and for such V we can find by definition a finite system $a_\nu \in S$ $(\nu = 1, 2, \ldots, n)$ such that $A \subset \bigcup_{\nu=1}^{n} a_\nu V$. Then

$$A \subset \bigcup_{\nu=1}^{n} x_\nu V^2 \subset \bigcup_{\nu=1}^{n} x_\nu U \quad \text{for } x_\nu \in A \cap a_\nu V \ (\nu = 1, 2, \ldots, n).$$

With this definition, it is obvious that every subset of a totally bounded set is totally bounded too, and for any finite system of totally bounded sets A_ν $(\nu = 1, 2, \dots, n)$, $\bigcup_{\nu=1}^{n} A_\nu$ also is totally bounded.

Theorem 6.2. *If A is totally bounded, then its closure $A^{\mathbf{U}-}$ also is totally bounded.*

Proof. If $A \subset \bigcup_{\nu=1}^{n} a_\nu V$ and $V^2 \leqq U$ for a symmetric $V \in \mathbf{U}$, then we have by (3) in 4

$$A^{\mathbf{U}-} \subset AV \subset \bigcup_{\nu=1}^{n} a_\nu V^2 \subset \bigcup_{\nu=1}^{n} a_\nu U.$$

Theorem 6.3. *A set $A \neq \emptyset$ is totally bounded if and only if A is totally bounded for the relative uniformity $\mathbf{U}^A$.*

Proof. $\emptyset \neq A \subset \bigcup_{\nu=1}^{n} a_\nu U$ implies

$$A = \bigcup_{\nu=1}^{n} a_\nu U \cap A = \bigcup_{\nu=1}^{n} a_\nu U^A.$$

Conversely, $A = \bigcup_{\nu=1}^{n} a_\nu U^A$ implies $A \subset \bigcup_{\nu=1}^{n} a_\nu U$, because $a_\nu U^A = a_\nu U \cap A \subset a_\nu U$.

A property about a set A for a uniformity $\mathbf{U}$ is said to be *absolute*, if A has this property if and only if A has the same property for the relative uniformity $\mathbf{U}^A$. According to Theorem 6.3, it is absolute that a set is totally bounded. But it is not absolute that a set is bounded.

Theorem 6.4. *A set A is totally bounded for $\mathbf{U}$ if and only if every subset $B \subset A$ is bounded for the relative uniformity $\mathbf{U}^B$.*

Proof. If A is totally bounded, then every subset $B \subset A$ also is totally bounded. Thus Theorem 6.3 shows us that B is totally bounded and consequently bounded for the relative uniformity $\mathbf{U}^B$. If A is not totally bounded, then there is $U \in \mathbf{U}$ by definition such that $\bigcup_{\nu=1}^{n} a_\nu U$ does not include A for any finite system $a_\nu \in A$ $(\nu = 1, 2, \dots, n)$. Thus we can find a sequence $a_\nu \in A$ $(\nu = 1, 2, \dots)$ such that $a_\nu U \not\ni a_\mu$ for $\nu \neq \mu$. For such $U \in \mathbf{U}$ there is a symmetric $V \in \mathbf{U}$ such that $V^2 \leqq U$. Then

$$a_\nu V \cap a_\mu V = \emptyset \quad \text{for } \nu \neq \mu.$$

Therefore, putting $B = \{a_\nu: \nu = 1, 2, \dots\}$, we have $B \subset A$, but B is not bounded for $\mathbf{U}^B$, because $a_\nu (V^B)^\sigma = \{a_\nu\}$ for all $\nu, \sigma = 1, 2, \dots$.

A uniformity $\mathbf{U}$ on S is said to be *bounded* or *totally bounded,* if the whole set S is bounded or totally bounded for $\mathbf{U}$. A connector U on S is said to be *totally bounded* for a uniformity $\mathbf{U}$, if AU is totally bounded for every totally bounded set A. With this definition, it is obvious that if a connector U is totally bounded, then every connector $V \leqq U$ also is totally bounded, and all of the connectors U^ν ($\nu = 1, 2, \dots$) are totally bounded too.

A uniformity $\mathbf{U}$ on S is said to be *locally totally bounded,* if there is $U \in \mathbf{U}$ such that xU is totally bounded for every $x \in S$. With this definition we have

Theorem 6.5. *A uniformity* $\mathbf{U}$ *on* S *is locally totally bounded if and only if there is a totally bounded* $U \in \mathbf{U}$.

Proof. If $\mathbf{U}$ is locally totally bounded, then there is $U \in \mathbf{U}$ by definition such that xU is totally bounded for every $x \in S$. For such $U \in \mathbf{U}$ we can find a symmetric $V \in \mathbf{U}$ such that $V^2 \leqq U$. Then, for any totally bounded set $A \neq \emptyset$ we can find a finite system $a_\nu \in A$ ($\nu = 1, 2, \dots, n$) $A \subset \bigcup_{\nu=1}^{n} a_\nu V$. Thus we have

$$AV \subset \bigcup_{\nu=1}^{n} a_\nu V^2 \subset \bigcup_{\nu=1}^{n} a_\nu U.$$

Since $a_\nu U$ is totally bounded for every $\nu = 1, 2, \dots, n$, AV also is totally bounded. Conversely, if there is a totally bounded $U \in \mathbf{U}$, then $\mathbf{U}$ is obviously locally totally bounded by definition.

7. **Convergent Systems.** A space Δ is said to be *directed,* if an order $\geqq$ is defined on Δ, such that

1) $\delta_1 \geqq \delta_2$, $\delta_2 \geqq \delta_3$ implies $\delta_1 \geqq \delta_3$,
2) for any two δ_1, $\delta_2 \in \Delta$ there is $\delta \in \Delta$ such that $\delta_1 \geqq \delta$ and $\delta_2 \geqq \delta$.

We write $\delta_1 \leqq \delta_2$ sometime instead of $\delta_2 \geqq \delta_1$.

Let S be a space and let Δ be a directed space. A mapping from Δ to S is called a *directed system* of S and denoted by $x_\delta \in S$ ($\delta \in \Delta$) for the image x_δ of δ.

For a directed space Δ, a directed system $\delta_\gamma \in \Delta$ $(\gamma \in \Gamma)$ is called a *partial system* of Δ, if for any $\delta_0 \in \Delta$ we can find $\gamma_0 \in \Gamma$ such that $\delta_0 \geqq \delta_\gamma$ for $\gamma_0 \geqq \gamma \in \Gamma$. We see easily that for a partial system $\delta_\gamma \in \Delta$ $(\gamma \in \Gamma)$ and for a partial system $\gamma_\lambda \in \Gamma$ $(\lambda \in \Lambda)$, $\delta_{\gamma_\lambda} \in \Delta$ $(\lambda \in \Lambda)$ also is a partial system of Δ.

Let $\mathbf{U}$ be a uniformity on S. A directed system $x_\delta \in S$ $(\delta \in \Delta)$ is said to be *convergent* to $a \in S$ and we write $x_\delta \underset{\delta\in\Delta}{\longrightarrow} a$, if for any $U \in \mathbf{U}$ we can find $\delta_0 \in \Delta$ such that $x_\delta \in aU$ for $\delta_0 \geqq \delta \in \Delta$.

For a directed system $x_\delta \in S$ $(\delta \in \Delta)$, we obtain another directed system $x_\delta \in S$ $(\delta_0 \geqq \delta \in \Delta)$ for any $\delta_0 \in \Delta$, and we have obviously by definition that $x_\delta \underset{\delta\in\Delta}{\longrightarrow} a$ if and only if $x_\delta \underset{\delta_0 \geqq \delta\in\Delta}{\longrightarrow} a$.

Theorem 7.1. *For a convergent system $x_\delta \underset{\delta\in\Delta}{\longrightarrow} a$, we have $x_\delta \underset{\delta\in\Delta}{\longrightarrow} b$ if and only if $a \in bI_{\mathbf{U}}$ for the atom $I_{\mathbf{U}}$ of* $\mathbf{U}$. *$x_\delta \underset{\delta\in\Delta}{\longrightarrow} a$ implies $y_\delta \underset{\delta\in\Delta}{\longrightarrow} a$ for $y_\delta \in x_\delta I_{\mathbf{U}}$ $(\delta \in \Delta)$.*

Proof. If $x_\delta \underset{\delta\in\Delta}{\longrightarrow} a$ and $x_\delta \underset{\delta\in\Delta}{\longrightarrow} b$, then for any $U \in \mathbf{U}$ we can find δ_1, $\delta_2 \in \Delta$ such that $x_\delta \in aU$ for $\delta \leqq \delta_1$ and $x_\delta \in bU$ for $\delta \leqq \delta_2$. Since there is $\delta \in \Delta$ such that $\delta \leqq \delta_1$ and $\delta \leqq \delta_2$, we hence have $aU \cap bU \neq \emptyset$. Thus we obtain $a \in bUU^{-1}$ by Theorem 1.3. Therefore we conclude $a \in bI_{\mathbf{U}}$ by Theorem 2.1. Conversely, if $a \in bI_{\mathbf{U}}$, then $x_\delta \underset{\delta\in\Delta}{\longrightarrow} a$ implies $x_\delta \underset{\delta\in\Delta}{\longrightarrow} b$, because $a \in bI_{\mathbf{U}}$ implies $a \in bU$ and $aU \subset bU^2$ for every $U \in \mathbf{U}$.

For any $U \in \mathbf{U}$ we can find a symmetric $V \in \mathbf{U}$ such that $V^2 \leqq U$, and we have $VI_{\mathbf{U}} \subset V^2 \subset U$. Thus $x_\delta \in aV$ for $\delta \leqq \delta_0$ implies

$$y_\delta \in x_\delta I_{\mathbf{U}} \subset aVI_{\mathbf{U}} \subset aU \quad \text{for} \quad \delta \leqq \delta_0.$$

We conclude immediately from the definition

Theorem 7.2. *$x_\delta \underset{\delta\in\Delta}{\longrightarrow} a$ implies $x_\gamma \underset{\gamma\in\Gamma}{\longrightarrow} a$ for any partial system $\delta_\gamma \in \Delta$ $(\gamma \in \Gamma)$.*

Theorem 7.3. *For a set $A \neq \emptyset$ we have $a \in A^{\mathbf{U}-}$ if and only if we can find a convergent system $x_\delta \in A$ $(\delta \in \Delta)$ such that $x_\delta \underset{\delta\in\Delta}{\longrightarrow} a$.*

Proof. If $a \in A^{\mathbf{U}-}$, then $a \in AU^{-1}$ for every $U \in \mathbf{U}$ by (3) in 4. Thus $A \cap aU \neq \emptyset$ for every $U \in \mathbf{U}$ by Theorem 1.3. Therefore we can find a system $x_U \in A$ $(U \in \mathbf{U})$ such that $x_U \in A \cap aU$ for every $U \in \mathbf{U}$. Since $\mathbf{U}$

is a directed space for the order of connectors, $x_U \in A$ $(U \in \mathbf{U})$ is a directed system, and $x_V \in aV \subset aU$ for $V \leqq U$, that is, $x_U \xrightarrow[U \in \mathbf{U}]{} a$.

Conversely, if $A \ni x_\delta \xrightarrow[\delta \in \Delta]{} a$, then $A \cap aU \neq \emptyset$ for every $U \in \mathbf{U}$ by definition. Thus $a \in AU^{-1}$ for every $U \in \mathbf{U}$ by Theorem 1.3. Therefore $a \in A^{\mathbf{U}-}$ by (3) in 4.

It is obvious by definition that convergence is an absolute property, that is, we have $x_\delta \xrightarrow[\delta \in \Delta]{} a$ for $\mathbf{U}$ if and only if $x_\delta \xrightarrow[\delta \in \Delta]{} a$ for the relative uniformity $\mathbf{U}^A$ where $A = \{a, x_\delta: \delta \in \Delta\}$. Since for any open set $X \ni a$ we can find $U \in \mathbf{U}$ such that $X \supset aU$ by definition, we have $x_\delta \xrightarrow[\delta \in \Delta]{} a$ if and only if for any open set $X \ni a$ we can find $\delta_0 \in \Delta$ such that $x_\delta \in X$ for $\delta \leqq \delta_0$. Therefore the convergence depends just on the induced topology $\mathbf{T}(\mathbf{U})$. Such a property is called a *topological property*. Thus we can state that convergence is a topological property.

8. **Complete Sets.** Let $\mathbf{U}$ be a uniformity on a space S. A directed system $x_\delta \in S$ $(\delta \in \Delta)$ is called a *Cauchy system*, if for any $U \in \mathbf{U}$ we can find $\delta_0 \in \Delta$ such that $x_\delta \in x_{\delta_0} U$ for $\delta \leqq \delta_0$. If $x_\delta \in S$ $(\delta \in \Delta)$ is a Cauchy system, then for any $U \in \mathbf{U}$ we can find $\delta_0 \in \Delta$ such that $x_{\delta_1} \in x_{\delta_2} U$ for $\delta_1, \delta_2 \leqq \delta_0$. Because, for any $U \in \mathbf{U}$ there is $V \in \mathbf{U}$ such that $V^{-1}V \leqq U$, and for such $V \in \mathbf{U}$ we can find $\delta_0 \in \Delta$ such that $x_\delta \in x_{\delta_0} V$ for $\delta \leqq \delta_0$. Then for $\delta_1, \delta_2 \leqq \delta_0$ we have $x_{\delta_1} \in x_{\delta_0} V$, $x_{\delta_2} \in x_{\delta_0} V$. Consequently $x_{\delta_1} \in x_{\delta_2} V^{-1} V \subset x_{\delta_2} U$ for $\delta_1, \delta_2 \leqq \delta_0$.

Every convergent system is a Cauchy system. Because, if $x_\delta \xrightarrow[\delta \in \Delta]{} a$, then for any $U \in \mathbf{U}$ we can find δ_0 such that $x_\delta \in aU$ for $\delta \leqq \delta$, and we hence have $x_\delta \in x_{\delta_0} U^{-1} U$ for $\delta \leqq \delta_0$. However, a Cauchy system is not always convergent. We see easily by definition that if $x_\delta \in S$ $(\delta \in \Delta)$ is a Cauchy system, then x_{δ_γ} $(\gamma \in \Gamma)$ also is a Cauchy system for any partial system $\delta_\gamma \in \Delta$ $(\gamma \in \Gamma)$.

Theorem 8.1. *Let $x_\delta \in S$ $(\delta \in \Delta)$ be a Cauchy system. For a point $a \in S$, if for any $U \in \mathbf{U}$ and for any $\delta_0 \in \Delta$ we can find $\delta \leqq \delta_0$ such that $x_\delta \in aU$, then $x_\delta \xrightarrow[\delta \in \Delta]{} a$.*

Proof. For any $U \in \mathbf{U}$ we can find a symmetric $V \in \mathbf{U}$ such that $V^3 \leqq U$, and there is $\delta_0 \in \Delta$ such that $x_\delta \in x_{\delta_0}V$ for $\delta \leqq \delta_0$, since x_δ $(\delta \in \Delta)$ is a Cauchy system by assumption. Then $x_{\delta_0} V \cap aV \neq \emptyset$ by assumption, and $x_{\delta_0} \in aV^2$ by Theorem 1.3. Thus $x_\delta \in x_{\delta_0} V \subset aV^3 \subset aU$ for $\delta \leqq \delta_0$, that is, $x_\delta \xrightarrow[\delta \in \Delta]{} a$.

A set $A \subset S$ is said to be *complete* for $\mathbf{U}$, if every Cauchy system $x_\delta \in A$ $(\delta \in \Delta)$ is convergent to a point of A.

Theorem 8.2. *If A is complete, then $A \cap B$ also is complete for any closed set B.*

Proof. For any Cauchy system $x_\delta \in A \cap B$ $(\delta \in \Delta)$ there is $a \in A$ by assumption such that $x_\delta \xrightarrow[\delta \in \Delta]{} a$. Then $a \in B^- = B$ by Theorem 7.3.

Theorem 8.3. *A set $A \subset S$ is complete if and only if $AI_{\mathbf{U}}$ is complete, and then $A^{\mathbf{U}-} = AI_{\mathbf{U}}$ for the atom $I_{\mathbf{U}}$ of* $\mathbf{U}$.

Proof. For a directed system $x_\delta \in AI_{\mathbf{U}}$ $(\delta \in \Delta)$, we can find $a_\delta \in A$ $(\delta \in \Delta)$ such that $x_\delta \in a_\delta I_{\mathbf{U}}$ $(\delta \in \Delta)$. Then x_δ $(\delta \in \Delta)$ is a Cauchy system if and only if a_δ $(\delta \in \Delta)$ is a Cauchy system. Because for any $U \in \mathbf{U}$ there is a symmetric $V \in \mathbf{U}$ such that $V^3 \leqq U$. For such $V \in \mathbf{U}$, we have $I_{\mathbf{U}} V I_{\mathbf{U}} \leqq V^3 \leqq U$, and $x_\delta \in x_{\delta_0} V$f for $\delta \leqq \delta_0$ implies $a_\delta \in x_\delta I_{\mathbf{U}} \subset x_{\delta_0} V I_{\mathbf{U}} \subset a_{\delta_0} I_{\mathbf{U}} V I_{\mathbf{U}} \subset a_{\delta_0} U$ for $\delta \leqq \delta_0$, and $a_\delta \in a_{\delta_0} V$ for $\delta \leqq \delta_0$ implies $x_\delta \in x_{\delta_0} U$ for $\delta \leqq \delta_0$. If A is complete and $x_\delta \in AI_{\mathbf{U}}$ $(\delta \in \Delta)$ is a Cauchy system, then $a_\delta \in A$ $(\delta \in \Delta)$ also is a Cauchy system and there is $a \in A$ such that $a_\delta \xrightarrow[\delta \in \Delta]{} a$ which implies $x_\delta \xrightarrow[\delta \in \Delta]{} a$ by Theorem 7.1. Consequently $AI_{\mathbf{U}}$ is complete by definition. Thus $AI_{\mathbf{U}} \ni x_\delta \xrightarrow[\delta \in \Delta]{} x$ implies $x_\delta \xrightarrow[\delta \in \Delta]{} a$ for some $a \in AI_{\mathbf{U}}$, and $x \in aI_{\mathbf{U}} \subset AI_{\mathbf{U}}$ by Theorem 7.1. Therefore $AI_{\mathbf{U}}$ is closed and we obtain $A^{\mathbf{U}-} = AI_{\mathbf{U}}$ by (3) in 4. Conversely if $AI_{\mathbf{U}}$ is complete, then for a Cauchy system $a_\delta \in A$ $(\delta \in \Delta)$ we can find $a \in A$ and $x \in aI_{\mathbf{U}}$ such that $c_\delta \xrightarrow[\delta \in \Delta]{} x$, and we hence obtain $a_\delta \xrightarrow[\delta \in \Delta]{} a$ by Theorem 7.1. Thus A is complete by definition.

Every basis $\mathbf{B}$ of $\mathbf{U}$ is a directed space for the order of connectors.

Theorem 8.4. *Let $\mathbf{B}$ be a basis of* $\mathbf{U}$. *For a directed system $x_U \in S$ $(U \in \mathbf{B})$, if there is $\sigma = 1, 2, \ldots$ such that*

$$x_U U^\sigma \cap x_V V^\sigma \neq \emptyset \quad \text{for } U, V \in \mathbf{B},$$

then x_U $(U \in \mathbf{B})$ *is a Cauchy system.*

Proof. For any $U \in \mathbf{U}$ there is a symmetric $W \in \mathbf{U}$ such that $W^{2\sigma} \leqq U$. For such $W \in \mathbf{U}$ we can find $U_0 \in \mathbf{B}$ such that $U_0 \leqq W$. Then

$$x_V V^\sigma \cap x_{U_0} U_0^\sigma \neq \emptyset \quad \text{for } U_0 \geqq V \in \mathbf{B}$$

by assumption. Thus we obtain by Theorem 1.3

$$x_V \in x_{U_0} U_0^\sigma (V^\sigma)^{-1} \subset x_{U_0} W^{2\sigma} \subset x_{U_0} U \quad \text{for } U_0 \geqq V \in \mathbf{B}.$$

Theorem 8.5. *Let* $\mathbf{B}$ *be a basis of* $\mathbf{U}$. *For a set* $A \neq \emptyset$, *if every Cauchy system* $x_U \in A$ $(U \in \mathbf{B})$ *is convergent to a point of* A, *then* A *is complete.*

Proof. Let $x_\delta \in A$ $(\delta \in \Delta)$ be a Cauchy system. For any $U \in \mathbf{B}$ we can find $\delta_U \in \Delta$ such that $x_\delta \in x_{\delta_U} U$ for $\delta \leqq \delta_U$. Then, setting $x_U = x_{\delta_U}$, we obviously have $x_U U \cap x_V V \neq \emptyset$ for $U, V \in \mathbf{B}$. Thus $x_U \in A$ $(U \in \mathbf{B})$ is a Cauchy system by Theorem 8.4, and $x_U \xrightarrow[U \in \mathbf{B}]{} a$ for some $a \in A$ by assumption. Therefore for any $U_0 \in \mathbf{U}$ we can find $U, V \in \mathbf{B}$ such that $U_0 \geqq U^2$, $U \geqq V$, $x_V \in aU$, and we hence obtain

$$x_\delta \in x_V V \subset aUV \subset aU_0 \quad \text{for } \delta \leqq \delta_V,$$

that is, $x_\delta \xrightarrow[\delta \in \Delta]{} a$.

It is obviously an absolute property for a directed system $x_\delta \in S$ $(\delta \in \Delta)$ to be a Cauchy system. Since convergence is an absolute property, it is also an absolute property for a set $A \subset S$ to be complete, that is, a set $A \neq \emptyset$ is complete for $\mathbf{U}$ if and only if A is complete for the relative uniformity $\mathbf{U}^A$.

A uniformity $\mathbf{U}$ on a space S is said to be *complete,* if the whole set S is complete for $\mathbf{U}$. With this definition we have

Theorem 8.6. *For a uniformity* $\mathbf{U}$ *on* S, *if we can find* $U \in \mathbf{U}$, *such that* $(xU)^{\mathbf{U}-}$ *is complete for every* $x \in S$, *then* $\mathbf{U}$ *is complete.*

Proof. Let $x_\delta \in S$ $(\delta \in \Delta)$ be a Cauchy system. For $U \in \mathbf{U}$ indicated in Theorem 8.6, we can find $\delta_0 \in \Delta$ such that $x_\delta \in x_{\delta_0} U$ for $\delta \leqq \delta_0$ Then x_δ $(\delta_0 \geqq \delta \in \Delta)$ also is a Cauchy system. Since $(x_{\delta_0} U)^{\mathbf{U}-}$ is complete by assumption, we can hence find $a \in (x_{\delta_0} U)^{\mathbf{U}-}$ such that

$x_\delta \xrightarrow[\delta_0 \geqq \delta \in \Delta]{} a$, which implies $x_\delta \xrightarrow[\delta \in \Delta]{} a$. Therefore **U** is complete by definition.

Theorem 8.7. *For a uniformity* **U** *on S, if there is a set* $A \subset S$ *such that* $A^{\mathbf{U}-} = S$ *and every Cauchy system* $a_\delta \in A$ $(\delta \in \Delta)$ *is convergent, then* **U** *is complete.*

Proof. For a Cauchy system $x_\delta \in S$ $(\delta \in \Delta)$ we can find a system $a_{U,\delta} \in A$ $(\delta \in \Delta,\ U \in \mathbf{U})$ such that $a_{U,\delta} \in x_\delta U$ for $U \in \mathbf{U}$, $\delta \in \Delta$, since $A^{\mathbf{U}-} = S$ by assumption. The pairs (U, δ) for $U \in \mathbf{U}$, $\delta \in \Delta$, constitute a directed space with the order: $(U_1, \delta_1) \geqq (U_2, \delta_2)$ if and only if $U_1 \geqq U_2$ and $\delta_1 \geqq \delta_2$. Then $a_{U,\delta}$ $(U \in \mathbf{U},\ \delta \in \Delta)$ is a Cauchy system. Because for any symmetric $U \in \mathbf{U}$ there is $\delta_0 \in \Delta$ such that $x_\delta \in x_{\delta_0} U$ for $\delta \leqq \delta_0$. Since $a_{U,\delta_0} \in X_{\delta_0} U$, we hence obtain

$$a_{V,\delta} \in x_\delta V \subset x_{\delta_0} UV \subset a_{U,\delta_0} U^3 \quad \text{for } V \leqq U,\ \delta \leqq \delta_0.$$

Thus there is $x \in S$ by assumption such that $a_{U,\delta} \xrightarrow[(U,\delta)]{} x$. For any $U \in \mathbf{U}$ there is $\delta_0 \in \Delta$ and a symmetric $U_0 \in \mathbf{U}$ such that $U_0 \leqq U$ and $a_{V,\delta} \notin xU$ for $V \leqq U_0$, $\delta \leqq \delta_0$. Therefore

$$x_\delta \in a_{V,\delta} V^{-1} \subset xUV^{-1} \subset xU^2 \quad \text{for } V \leqq U_0,\ \delta \leqq \delta_0.$$

Thus we conclude $x_\delta \xrightarrow[\delta \in \Delta]{} x$.

9. Compact Sets. Let **U** be a uniformity on a Space S. A set $A \subset S$ is said to be *compact,* if for any system $U_x \in \mathbf{U}$ $(x \in A)$ we can find a finite system $x_\nu \in A$ $(\nu = 1, 2, \ldots, n)$ such that $A \subset \bigcup_{\nu=1}^{n} x_\nu U_{x_\nu}$. The empty set $\emptyset$ is considered a compact set.

With this definition we have

Theorem 9.1. *A set* $A \subset S$ *is compact if and only if A is totally bounded and complete.*

Proof. If $A \neq \emptyset$ is compact, then for any $U \in \mathbf{U}$, considering $U_x = U$ for every $x \in A$, we can find a finite system $x_\nu \in A$ $(\nu = 1, 2, \ldots, n)$ by definition such that $A \subset \bigcup_{\nu=1}^{n} x_\nu U$. Thus A is totally bounded. For a

Cauchy system $a_\delta \in A$ $(\delta \in \Delta)$, if there is no point $a \in A$ such that $a_\delta \xrightarrow[\delta\in\Delta]{} a$, then for any $x \in A$ we can find $U_x \in \mathbf{U}$ by Theorem 8.1 such that there is $\delta_x \in \Delta$ for which $xU_x \bar{\ni} a$ for every $\delta \leqq \delta_x$. For such $U_x \in \mathbf{U}$ $(x \in A)$ we can find symmetric $V_x \in \mathbf{U}$ $(x \in A)$ such that $V_x{}^2 \leqq U_x$ for $x \in A$. There is a finite system $x_\nu \in A$ $(\nu = 1, 2, ..., n)$ such that $A \subset \bigcup_{\nu=1}^{n} x_\nu V_{x_\nu}$, since A is compact by assumption. For such $x_\nu \in A$ $(\nu = 1, 2, ..., n)$, setting $U = \bigcap_{\nu=1}^{n} V_{x_\nu}$, we have $U \in \mathbf{U}$, and there is $\delta_0 \in \Delta$ such that $a_\delta \in a_{\delta_0} U$ for $\delta \leqq \delta_0$, because $a_\delta \in A$ $(\delta \in \Delta)$ is a Cauchy system by assumption. Then, since $a_{\delta_0} \in A$, we have $a_{\delta_0} \in x_\nu V_{x_\nu}$ for some $\nu = 1, 2, ..., n$, and

$$a_\delta \in a_{\delta_0} U \subset x_\nu V_{x_\nu} U \subset x_\nu V_{x_\nu}{}^2 \subset x_\nu U_{x_\nu} \quad \text{for } \delta \leqq \delta_0,$$

contradicting $a_\delta \bar{\in} xU_x$ for $\delta \leqq \delta_x$. Thus there is a point $a \in A$ such that $a_\delta \xrightarrow[\delta\in\Delta]{} a$, that is, A is complete by definition.

Conversely we suppose that $A \neq \emptyset$ is totally bounded and complete. For a system $U_x \in \mathbf{U}$ $(x \in A)$, if $\bigcup_{\nu=1}^{n} x_\nu U_{x_\nu}$ does not include A for any finite system $x_\nu \in A$ $(\nu = 1, 2, ..., n)$, then, setting

$$\mathbf{P} = \{A \cap (\bigcup_{\nu=1}^{n} x_\nu U_{x_\nu})' : x_\nu \in A \ (\nu = 1, 2, ..., n), n = 1, 2, ...\},$$

we have

(1) for any $x \in A$ there is $X \in \mathbf{P}$ such that $xU_x \cap X = \emptyset$,

(2) $\bigcap_{\nu=1}^{n} X_\nu \neq \emptyset$ for any finite system $X_\nu \in \mathbf{P}$ $(\nu = 1, 2, ..., n)$.

Applying Maximal Theorem, we can find a maximal system of sets $\mathbf{P}_0$ such that $\mathbf{P}_0 \supset \mathbf{P}$ and $\bigcap_{\nu=1}^{n} X_\nu \neq \emptyset$ for any finite system $X_\nu \in \mathbf{P}_0$ $(\nu = 1, 2, ..., n)$. For such $\mathbf{P}_0$ we obviously have by the maximality of $\mathbf{P}_0$

(3) $Y \cap X \neq \emptyset$ for every $X \in \mathbf{P}_0$ implies $Y \in \mathbf{P}_0$.

We conclude immediately from (3)

(4) $\mathbf{P}_0 \ni X \subset Y$ implies $\mathbf{P}_0 \ni Y$,

(5) $\mathbf{P}_0 \ni A$,

(6) $\mathbf{P}_0 \ni X, Y$ implies $\mathbf{P}_0 \ni X \cap Y$.

If $Y_\nu \bar{\in} \mathbf{P}_0 ((\nu = 1, 2, ..., n)$, then we can find $X_\nu \in \mathbf{P}_0$ $(\nu = 1, 2, ..., n)$ by (3) such that $Y_\nu \cap X_\nu = \emptyset$ $(\nu = 1, 2, ..., n)$. Thus

$$\bigcup_{\nu=1}^{n} Y_\nu \cap \bigcap_{\nu=1}^{n} X_\nu = \emptyset \text{ but } \bigcap_{\nu=1}^{n} X_\nu \in \mathbf{P}_0$$

by (6). Therefore

(7) $\bigcup_{\nu=1}^{n} Y_\nu \in \mathbf{P}_0$ implies $Y_\nu \in \mathbf{P}_0$ for some $\nu = 1, 2, ..., n$.

For any $U \in \mathbf{U}$ we can find a finite system $a_\nu \in A$ $(\nu = 1, 2, ..., n)$ such that $A \subset \bigcup_{\nu=1}^{n} a_\nu U$, because A is totally bounded by assumption. Then $a_\nu U \in \mathbf{P}_0$ for some $\nu = 1, 2, ..., n$ by (4), (5), (7). Thus we can find a directed system $a_U \in A$ $(U \in \mathbf{U})$ such that $a\ U \in \mathbf{P}_0$, and we have

$$a_U U \cap a_V V \neq \emptyset \text{ for } U, Y \in \mathbf{U}$$

by (6). Therefore $a_U \in A$ $(U \in \mathbf{U})$ is a Cauchy system by Theorem 8.4, and there is $a \in A$ such that $a_U \xrightarrow[U \in \mathbf{U}]{} a$, because A is complete by assumption. For such $a \in A$ we can find $V_0 \in \mathbf{U}$ such that $V_0^{-1} V_0 \leqq U_a$, and $U_0 \in \mathbf{U}$ such that $a_U \in a V_0^{-1}$ for $U_0 \geqq U \in \mathbf{U}$. Then, for any $U \in \mathbf{U}$ such that $U \leqq U_0 \cap V_0$ we have

$$a_U U \subset a V_0^{-1} U \subset a V_0^{-1} V_0 \subset a U_a.$$

As $a_U U \in \mathbf{P}_0$, we obtain $a U_a \in \mathbf{P}_0$ by (4). Thus $a U_a \cap X \neq \emptyset$ for every $X \in \mathbf{P}_0$, contradicting (1). Therefore there is a finite system $x_\nu \in A$ $(\nu = 1, 2, ..., n)$ such that $\bigcup_{\nu=1}^{n} x_\nu U_{x_\nu} \supset A$.

Referring to Theorem 8.2, we conclude from Theorem 9.1

Theorem 9.2. *If A is compact, then $A \cap B$ also is compact for any closed set B.*

Referring to Theorem 8.3, we obtain

Theorem 9.3. *A set $A \subset S$ is compact if and only if $A I_{\mathbf{U}}$ is compact, and then $A^{\mathbf{U}-} = A I_{\mathbf{U}}$ for the atom $I_{\mathbf{U}}$ of $\mathbf{U}$.*

Theorem 9.4. *If A is compact and $A \subset B$ for an open set B, then there is $U \in \mathbf{U}$ such that $AU \subset B$.*

Proof. Since B is open by assumption, for any $x \in A$ we can find $U_x \in \mathbf{U}$ such that $xU_x{}^2 \subset B$. Since A is compact by assumption, there is a finite system $x_\nu \in A$ $(\nu = 1, 2, \ldots, n)$ such that $A \subset \bigcup_{\nu=1}^{n} x_\nu U_{x_\nu}$. Then, setting $U = \bigcap_{\nu=1}^{n} U_{x_\nu}$, we have $U \in \mathbf{U}$ and

$$AU \subset \bigcup_{\nu=1}^{n} x_\nu U_{x_\nu} U \subset \bigcup_{\nu=1}^{n} x_\nu U_{x_\nu}{}^2 \subset B.$$

It is obviously an absolute property for a set to be compact. It also is a topological property, that is, we have

Theorem 9.5. *A set A is compact, if and only if $A \subset \bigcup_{\lambda\in\Lambda} X$ for a system of open sets $X_\lambda \in \mathbf{T}(\mathbf{U})$ $(\lambda \in \Lambda)$ implies $A \subset \bigcup_{\nu=1}^{n} X_{\lambda_\nu}$ for some finite system $\lambda_\nu \in \Lambda$ $(\nu = 1, 2, \ldots, n)$.*

Proof. If $A \neq \emptyset$ is compact and $A \subset \bigcup_{\lambda\in\Lambda} X_\lambda$, $X_\lambda \in \mathbf{T}(\mathbf{U})$ $(\lambda \in \Lambda)$, then for any $x \in A$ we can find $\lambda_x \in \Lambda$ and $U_x \in \mathbf{U}$ such that $xU_x \subset X_{\lambda_x}$, and we hence obtain $A \subset \bigcup_{\nu=1}^{n} x_\nu U_{x_\nu} \subset \bigcup_{\nu=1}^{n} X_{\lambda_{x_\nu}}$ for some finite system $x_\nu \in A$ $(\nu = 1, 2, \ldots, n)$. Conversely, for any system $U_x \in \mathbf{U}$ $(x \in A)$ we have $A \subset \bigcup_{x\in A} xU_x^{\circ} = \bigcup_{x\in A} (xU_x)^\circ$. Thus, if A satisfies the condition indicated in Theorem 9.5, then we can find a finite system $x_\nu \in A$ $(\nu = 1, 2, \ldots, n)$ such that $A \subset \bigcup_{\nu=1}^{n} (x_\nu U_{x_\nu})^\circ \subset \bigcup_{\nu=1}^{n} x_\nu U_{x_\nu}$.

As an immediate consequence of Theorem 9.5 we obtain

Theorem 9.6. *A set A is compact if and only if $A \cap \bigcap_{\lambda\in\Lambda} X_\lambda = \emptyset$ for a system of closed sets X_λ $(\lambda \in \Lambda)$ implies $A \cap \bigcap_{\nu=1}^{n} X_{\lambda_\nu} = \emptyset$ for some finite system $\lambda_\nu \in \Lambda$ $(\nu = 1, 2, \ldots, n)$.*

A uniformity $\mathbf{U}$ on a space S is said to be *compact,* if the whole set S is compact for $\mathbf{U}$. Since it is a topological property for a set to be compact, if a uniformity $\mathbf{U}$ is compact, then every uniformity homeomorphic to $\mathbf{U}$ is also compact. Furthermore we have

Theorem 9.7. *For two uniformities* **U** *and* **V** *on a space S, if* **T(U)** = **T(V)** *and if* **U** *is compact, then* **U** = **V**.

Proof. If **T(U)** = **T(V)**, then for any $V \epsilon$ **V** we can find a system $U_x \epsilon$ **U** $(x \epsilon S)$ by Theorem 4.4 such that $xU_x \subset xV$, and for such U_x we also can find symmetric $W_x \epsilon$ **U** $(x \epsilon S)$ such that $W_x{}^2 \leqq U_x$ for every $x \epsilon S$. If **U** is compact, then there is a finite system $x_\nu \epsilon S$ $(\nu = 1, 2, \ldots, n)$ such that $S = \bigcup_{\nu=1}^{n} x_\nu W_{x_\nu}$, and putting $W = \bigcap_{\nu=1}^{n} W_{x_\nu}$, we have $W \epsilon$ **U**. For any $x \epsilon S$ we can find $\nu = 1, 2, \ldots, n$ such that $x \epsilon x_\nu W_{x_\nu}$ and

$$xW \subset x_\nu W_{x_\nu} W \subset x_\nu W_{x_\nu}{}^2 \subset x_\nu U_{x_\nu} \subset x_\nu V.$$

As $x \epsilon xW$, we hence obtain $x_\nu V \subset xV^{-1}V$ by Theorem 1.2. Therefore $W \leqq V^{-1}V$. As $V \epsilon$ **V** is arbitrary, we conclude that **V** $\subset$ **U**. If **U** is compact, then **V** also is compact, because **T(U)** = **T(V)** by assumption. Thus we conclude **U** $\subset$ **V** too, in the same way.

10. **Connected Sets.** Let S be a space. For a connector U on S, a set $A \neq \emptyset$ is said to be *U-connected,* if for any $a, b \epsilon A$ we can find a finite system $x_\nu \epsilon A$ $(\nu = 1, 2, \ldots, n)$ such that putting $a = x_0$, $b = x_{n+1}$ we have $x_\nu U \ni x_{\nu+1}$ for $\nu = 0, 1, 2, \ldots, n$. The empty set $\emptyset$ is not considered to be U-connected. With this definition, we see easily that a set A is U-connected if and only if $A = \bigcup_{\nu=1}^{\infty} x(U^A)^\nu$ for every $x \epsilon A$. Here U^A is the relative connector of U on A. If U is symmetric, then U^A also is symmetric by (3) in 5, and $x(U^A)^\nu \ni y$ implies $y(U^A)^\nu \ni x$. Thus, for a symmetric connector U, a set A is U-connected if and only if $A = \bigcup_{\nu=1}^{\infty} x(U^A)^\nu$ for some $x \epsilon A$. It is obvious by definition that if A is U-connected, then A also is V-connected for any connector $V \geqq U$.

For a uniformity **U** on S, a set A is said to be **U**-*connected,* if A is *U-connected* for every $U \epsilon$ **U**. With this definition, it is obviously an absolute property for a set to be **U**-connected. Referring to (3) in 4, we see easily by definition

Theorem 10.1. *If A is* **U**-*connected, then* $A^{\mathbf{U}-}$ *also is* **U**-*connected.*

Theorem 10.2. *For a system of* **U**-*connected sets* A_λ $(\lambda \in \Lambda)$, *if* $\bigcap_{\lambda\in\Lambda} A_\lambda \neq \emptyset$, *then* $\bigcup_{\lambda\in\Lambda} A_\lambda$ *also is* **U**-*connected.*

Proof. Let $a \in \bigcap_{\delta\in\Delta} A_\lambda$. For any $x \in \bigcup_{\delta\in\Delta} A_\lambda$ we can find $\lambda \in \Lambda$ such that $x \in A_\lambda$, and for any $U \in \mathbf{U}$ there is a finite system $x_\nu \in A_\lambda$ $(\nu = 1, 2, \ldots, n)$ such that $x_\nu U \ni x_{\nu+1}$ for $\nu = 0, 1, 2, \ldots, n$, $a = x_0$, $x = x_{n+1}$, because A is **U**-connected by assumption. Then $x_\nu \in \bigcup_{\delta\in\Delta} A_\lambda$ $(\nu = 1, 2, \ldots, n)$. Therefore $\bigcup_{\lambda\in\Lambda} A_\lambda$ is **U**-connected by definition.

For any $x \in S$ the set $xI_{\mathbf{U}}$ is **U**-connected, because $xI_{\mathbf{U}} \subset xU$ for every $U \in \mathbf{U}$. The union of all **U**-connected sets containing x also is **U**-connected by Theorem 10.2. This **U**-connected set is called the **U**-*component* of x and denoted by $C_x^{\mathbf{U}}$, that is,

$$C_x^{\mathbf{U}} = \bigcup\{X\colon x \in X \ \mathbf{U}\text{-connected}\}.$$

$C_x^{\mathbf{U}}$ is the largest **U**-connected set containing x. Thus $C_x^{\mathbf{U}}$ is closed by Theorem 10.1.

Theorem 10.3. *The system of all* **U**-*components gives a partition of* S, *that is,* $C_x^{\mathbf{U}} \cap C_y^{\mathbf{U}} = \emptyset$ *or* $C_x^{\mathbf{U}} = C_y^{\mathbf{U}}$.

Proof. If $C_x^{\mathbf{U}} \cap C_y^{\mathbf{U}} \neq \emptyset$, then $C_x^{\mathbf{U}} \cup C_y^{\mathbf{U}}$ also is **U**-connected by Theorem 10.2, and $C_x^{\mathbf{U}} = C_x^{\mathbf{U}} \cup C_y^{\mathbf{U}} = C_y^{\mathbf{U}}$ by definition.

Let **T** be a topology on S. A set $A \subset S$ is said to be *connected* for **T**, if $A \cap X \cap Y = \emptyset$ $A \subset X \cup Y$ for $X, Y \in \mathbf{T}$ implies $A \cap X = \emptyset$ or $A \cap Y = \emptyset$. The empty set $\emptyset$ is not considered to be connected for **T**.

Theorem 10.4. *If A is connected for* **T**, *then* A^- *also is connected.*

Proof. If $A^- \cap X \cap Y = \emptyset$, $A^- \subset X \cup Y$ for $X, Y \in \mathbf{T}$, then $A \cap X = \emptyset$ or $A \cap Y = \emptyset$, because $A \subset A^-$ and A is connected by assumption. Since $A^- \cap X \subset (A \cap X)^-$ by Theorem 3.1, $A \cap X = \emptyset$ implies $A^- \cap X = \emptyset$, and $A \cap Y = \emptyset$ implies $A^- \cap Y = \emptyset$ by the same reason. Therefore A^- also is connected for **T**.

Theorem 10.5. *For a system of connected sets* A_λ $(\lambda \in \Lambda)$, *if* $\bigcap_{\lambda\in\Lambda} A_\lambda \neq \emptyset$, *then* $\bigcup_{\lambda\in\Lambda} A_\lambda$ *also is connected.*

Proof. If $\bigcup_{\lambda \epsilon \Lambda} A_\lambda \cap X \cap Y = \emptyset$, $\bigcup_{\lambda \epsilon \Lambda} A_\lambda \subset X \cup Y$ for $X, Y \epsilon \mathbf{T}$, then $A_\lambda \cap X \cap Y = \emptyset$, $A_\lambda \subset X \cup Y$ for every $\lambda \epsilon \Lambda$. Thus $A_\lambda \cap X = \emptyset$ or $A_\lambda \cap Y = \emptyset$ for every $\lambda \epsilon \Lambda$, because every A_λ is connected. If $A_\lambda \cap X = \emptyset$ and $A_\rho \cap Y = \emptyset$ for $\lambda, \rho \epsilon \Lambda$, then

$$A_\lambda \cap A_\rho = (A_\lambda \cap A_\rho) \cap (X \cup Y) = (A_\lambda \cap A_\rho \cap X) \cup (A_\lambda \cap A_\rho \cap Y) = \emptyset,$$

contradicting the assumption $\bigcap_{\lambda \epsilon \Lambda} A_\lambda \neq \emptyset$. Thus we have $A_\lambda \cap X \neq \emptyset$ for every $\lambda \epsilon \Lambda$ or $A_\lambda \cap Y = \emptyset$ for every $\lambda \epsilon \Lambda$, that is, $\bigcup_{\lambda \epsilon \Lambda} A_\lambda \cap X = \emptyset$ or $\bigcup_{\lambda \epsilon \Lambda} A_\lambda \cap Y = \emptyset$.

By means of Theorem 10.5, we can define *component* C_x $(x \epsilon S)$ by

$$C_x = \bigcup \{X: x \epsilon X \text{ connected for } \mathbf{T}\}.$$

With this definition, one can prove easily

Theorem 10.6. *The system of all components* C_x $(x \epsilon S)$ *for* $\mathbf{T}$ *gives a partition of* S, *that is,* $C_x \cap C_y = \emptyset$ or $C_x = C_y$.

For a uniformity $\mathbf{U}$ on S, a set $A \subset S$ is said to be *connected* for $\mathbf{U}$, if A is connected for the induced topology $\mathbf{T}(\mathbf{U})$. With this definition we have

Theorem 10.7. *If a set A is connected for* $\mathbf{U}$, *then A is* $\mathbf{U}$-*connected.*

Proof. If a set $A \neq \emptyset$ is not $\mathbf{U}$-connected, then we can find $a \epsilon A$ and $U \epsilon \mathbf{U}$ such that $A \neq \bigcup_{\nu=1}^{\infty} a(U^A)^\nu$. Setting $B = \bigcup_{\nu=1}^{\infty} a(U^A)^\nu$ and $C = A \cap B'$, we have $B \neq \emptyset$, $C \neq \emptyset$ and $BU^A \cap C = \emptyset$ by Theorem 1.5. Since $A = B \cup C$, we hence obtain $BU \cap C = \emptyset$. For a symmetric $V \epsilon \mathbf{U}$ such that $V^2 \leqq U$, we conclude $BV \cap CV = \emptyset$ by Theorem 1.3. Setting $X = BV^\circ$ and $Y = CV^\circ$, we then have $X, Y \epsilon \mathbf{T}(\mathbf{U})$, $X \cap Y = \emptyset$, $A \subset X \cup Y$, but $A \cap X = B \neq \emptyset$, $A \cap Y = C \neq \emptyset$. Therefore A is not connected for $\mathbf{T}(\mathbf{U})$.

A uniformity $\mathbf{U}$ on S is said to be *connected* if S is $\mathbf{U}$-connected. $\mathbf{U}$ is said to be *topologically connected* if S is connected for $\mathbf{U}$. Then we can state by Theorem 10.7: every topologically connected uniformity is connected.

Theorem 10.8. $\mathbf{U}$ *is connected and bounded if and only if for any* $U \epsilon \mathbf{U}$ *we can find* $\sigma = 1, 2, \ldots$ *such that* $xU^\sigma = S$ *for every* $x \epsilon S$.

Proof. If for any $U \in \mathbf{U}$ there is $\sigma = 1, 2, \ldots$ such that $xU^{\sigma} = S$, then $\mathbf{U}$ is obviously bounded and connected by definition. Conversely if $\mathbf{U}$ is bounded, then for a symmetric $V \in \mathbf{U}$ such that $V^2 \leqq U \in \mathbf{U}$, we can find a finite system $a_{\nu} \in S$ $(\nu = 1, 2, \ldots, n)$ and $\sigma = 1, 2, \ldots$ such that $S = \bigcup_{\nu=1}^{n} a_{\nu}V^{\sigma}$. If $\mathbf{U}$ is connected in addition, then we can find $\mu = 1, 2, \ldots$ such that $a_{\nu} \in a_1 V^{\mu}$ for every $\nu = 1, 2, \ldots, n$, and we have $S = a_1 V^{\sigma+\mu}$. Since V is symmetric, we hence obtain

$$S = xV^{2(\sigma+\mu)} = xU^{\sigma+\mu} \quad \text{for every } x \in S.$$

II. UNIFORMLY CONTINUOUS MAPPINGS

11. Inverse Images. Let M be a mapping from S to R. For a set $A \subset R$, the set

$$AM^{-1} = \{x: xM \in A\}$$

is called the *inverse image* of A by M and denoted by AM^{-1}. Thus we have $x \in AM^{-1}$ if and only if $xM \in A$.

Concerning inverse images, we have clearly by definition

(1) $\emptyset M^{-1} = \emptyset,\ \ RM^{-1} = S,$

(2) $A'M^{-1} = (AM^{-1})'$

(3) $(\bigcup_{\lambda \in \Lambda} A_\lambda)M^{-1} = \bigcup_{\lambda \in \Lambda} (A_\lambda M^{-1}).$

These three relations are characteristic of mappings, that is, for any M^{-1} satisfying (1), (2), (3) there exists uniquely a mapping from S to R for which M^{-1} gives the inverse image. Therefore all of the other properties about mappings can be obtained from (1), (2), (3).

As an immediate consequence of (2) and (3) we have

(4) $(\bigcap_{\lambda \in \Lambda} A_\lambda)M^{-1} = \bigcap_{\lambda \in \Lambda} (A_\lambda M^{-1}).$

From (3) we conclude that $A \subset B$ implies $AM^{-1} \subset BM^{-1}$, and from (4) we obtain that $A \cap B = \emptyset$ implies $AM^{-1} \cap BM^{-1} = \emptyset$

For a set $X \subset S$, the *image* of X by M is defined by

$$XM = \{xM: x \in X\} \quad \text{for } X \neq \emptyset$$

and $\emptyset M = \emptyset$. With this definition we have obviously that $XM \subset A$ if and only if $X \subset AM^{-1}$, and

(5) $XM = \bigcap_{X \subset AM^{-1}} A.$

Thus we see easily that $X \subset Y$ implies $XM \subset YM$.

(6) $(\bigcup_{\lambda\in\Lambda} X_\lambda)M = \bigcup_{\lambda\in\Lambda} (X_\lambda M)$.

Because we obviously have $(\bigcup_{\lambda\in\Lambda} X_\lambda)M \supset \bigcup_{\lambda\in\Lambda} (X_\lambda M)$, and on the other hand we obtain by (5)

$$\bigcup_{\lambda\in\Lambda} (X_\lambda M) = \bigcup_{\lambda\in\Lambda} \bigcap_{X_\lambda \subset AM^{-1}} A = \bigcap_{X_\lambda \subset A_\lambda M^{-1}} \bigcup_{\lambda\in\Lambda} A_\lambda \supset (\bigcup_{\lambda\in\Lambda} X_\lambda)M,$$

since $X_\lambda \subset A_\lambda M^{-1}$ $(\lambda \in \Lambda)$ implies $\bigcup_{\lambda\in\Lambda} X_\lambda \subset \bigcup_{\lambda\in\Lambda} (A_\lambda M^{-1}) = (\bigcup_{\lambda\in\Lambda} A_\lambda)M^{-1}$ by (3).

Referring to (4), we conclude from (5)

(7) $XMM^{-1} \supset X$.

For $X \subset S$, $A \subset R$ we obtain by (5)

$$(AM^{-1} \cap X)M = \bigcap \{B: AM^{-1} \cap X \subset BM^{-1}\}$$
$$= \bigcap \{A \cap B: AM^{-1} \cap X \subset BM^{-1}\}$$

because $AM^{-1} \cap X \subset BM^{-1}$ implies by (4)

$$AM^{-1} \cap X \subset AM^{-1} \cap BM^{-1} = (A \cap B)M^{-1}.$$

Since $AM^{-1} \cap X \subset BM^{-1}$ if and only if $X \subset (AM^{-1})' \cup BM^{-1}$;

$$(AM^{-1})' \cup BM^{-1} = (A' \cup B)M^{-1} \text{ by (2), (3);}$$

and $A \cap B = A \cap (A' \cup B)$, we obtain by (5)

$$(AM^{-1} \cap X)M = \bigcap \{A \cap C: X \subset CM^{-1}\}$$
$$= A \cap \bigcap \{C: X \subset CM^{-1}\} = A \cap (XM).$$

Thus we have

(8) $(AM^{-1} \cap X)M = A \cap XM$ for $X \subset S$, $A \subset R$.

Setting $X = S$ in (8) we obtain

(9) $AM^{-1}M = A \cap SM$.

Since $(XM)'M^{-1} = (XMM^{-1})' \subset X'$ by (2), (7), we obtain by (9)

(10) $(XM)' \cap SM \subset X'M$.

As an immediate consequence of (9) we have

Theorem 11.1. *If a mapping M is full: $SM = R$, then*

$$AM^{-1}M = A \quad \textit{for every } A \subset S.$$

For a connector U on R, setting

$$x(MUM^{-1}) = xMUM^{-1} \quad \text{for } x \in S,$$

we obtain a connector MUM^{-1} on S, because $xM \in xMU$ implies $x \in xMUM^{-1}$ by the definition of the inverse image. This connector MUM^{-1} on S is called the *inverse image* of U by M. With this definition we obviously have

(11) $X(MUM^{-1}) = XMUM^{-1}$ for $X \subset S$.

Concerning inverse images of connectors, we see easily by definition that $U \leqq V$ implies $MUM^{-1} \leqq MVM^{-1}$. For a system of connectors U_λ $(\lambda \in \Lambda)$

(12) $M \bigcap_{\lambda\in\Lambda} U_\lambda M^{-1} = \bigcap_{\lambda\in\Lambda} MU_\lambda M^{-1}$.

Because $x(M \bigcap_{\lambda\in\Lambda} U_\lambda M^{-1}) = (\bigcap_{\lambda\in\Lambda} xMU_\lambda)M^{-1} = \bigcap_{\lambda\in\Lambda} x(MU_\lambda M^{-1})$. It is obvious by definition that $x \in yMUM^{-1}$ is equivalent to $xM \in yMU$, which is equivalent to $xMU^{-1} \ni yM$, that is, $xMU^{-1}M^{-1} \ni y$. Thus we have

(13) $MU^{-1}M^{-1} = (MUM^{-1})^{-1}$.

Since $x(MUM^{-1})(MVM^{-1}) = xMUM^{-1}MVM^{-1}$, we obtain by (3)

(14) $(MUM^{-1})(MVM^{-1}) \leqq MUVM^{-1}$

and by Theorem 11.1

Theorem 11.2. *If a mapping M is full, then*

$$(MUM^{-1})(MVM^{-1}) = MUVM^{-1}.$$

For $\emptyset \neq X \subset S$, every mapping M from S to R can be considered a mapping from X to R. This mapping is called the *relative mapping* of M on X and denoted by M^X. With this definition we have obviously

(15) $xM^X = xM$ for $x \in X$,

(16) $A(M^X)^{-1} = (AM^{-1})^X$ for $A \subset R$.

Thus, for a connector U on R and for $x \in X$, we have

$$xM^XU(M^X)^{-1} = (xMUM^{-1})^X = x(MUM^{-1})^X,$$

that is,

(17) $M^XU(M^X)^{-1} = (MUM^{-1})^X$.

12. **Uniformly Continuous Mappings.** Let M be a mapping from a space S with a uniformity $\mathbf{U}$ to a space R with a uniformity $\mathbf{V}$. M is said to be *continuous at* a point $a \in S$, if for any $V \in \mathbf{V}$ we can find $U \in \mathbf{U}$ such that $aUM \subset aMV$. With this definition we have

Theorem 12.1. *M is continuous at $a \in S$ if and only if $S \ni a_\delta \xrightarrow[\delta\in\Delta]{} a$ implies $a_\delta M \xrightarrow[\delta\in\Delta]{} aM$ in R.*

Proof. If M is continuous at $a \in S$, then for any $V \in \mathbf{V}$ we can find $U \in \mathbf{U}$ such that $aUM \subset aMV$. If $a_\delta \xrightarrow[\delta\in\Delta]{} a$, then for such $U \in \mathbf{U}$ there is $\delta_0 \in \Delta$ such that $a_\delta \in aU$ for $\delta \leqq \delta_0$, and we have

$$a_\delta M \in aUM \subset aMV \quad \text{for } \delta \leqq \delta_0.$$

Thus we obtain $a_\delta M \xrightarrow[\delta\in\Delta]{} aM$.

If M is not continuous at $a \in S$, then there is $V \in \mathbf{V}$ such that we can find a system $x_U \in aU$ ($U \in \mathbf{U}$) for which $x_U M \bar{\in} aMV$ for every $U \in \mathbf{U}$. Then we obviously have $x_U \xrightarrow[U\in\mathbf{U}]{} a$, but not $x_U M \xrightarrow[U\in\mathbf{U}]{} aM$.

A mapping M is said to be *continuous*, if M is continuous at every point of S. We have then

Theorem 12.2. *M is continuous if and only if $AM^{-1} \in \mathbf{T}(\mathbf{U})$ for every $A \in \mathbf{T}(\mathbf{V})$, and if and only if $X^- M \subset (XM)^-$ for every $X \subset S$.*

Proof. If M is continuous on S and if $A \in \mathbf{T}(\mathbf{V})$, then for any $x \in AM^{-1}$, as $xM \in A$, we can find $V \in \mathbf{V}$ such that $xMV \subset A$, and for such $V \in \mathbf{V}$ there is $U \in \mathbf{U}$ such that $xUM \subset xMV$. Thus we obtain by (7)

$$xU \subset xUMM^{-1} \subset xMVM^{-1} \subset AM^{-1}.$$

Therefore $AM^{-1} \in \mathbf{T}(\mathbf{U})$ by definition.

Conversely if $AM^{-1} \in \mathbf{T}(\mathbf{U})$ for every $A \in \mathbf{T}(\mathbf{V})$, then for any $V \in \mathbf{V}$ and for any $a \in S$ we have $aMV^{\mathbf{V}\circ}M^{-1} \in \mathbf{T}(\mathbf{U})$. Thus there is $U \in \mathbf{U}$ such that $aU \subset aMV^{\mathbf{V}\circ}M^{-1}$, and we obtain by (9)

$$aUM \subset aMV^{\mathbf{V}\circ}M^{-1}M \subset aMV^{\mathbf{V}\circ} \subset aMV.$$

Therefore M is continuous at every point $a \in S$.

For any $x \in X^-$ we can find a directed system $X \ni x_\delta \xrightarrow[\delta\in\Delta]{} x$ by Theorem 7.3. Thus, if M is continuous, then $x_\delta M \xrightarrow[\delta\in\Delta]{} xM$ by Theorem 12.1. Consequently $X^- M \subset (XM)^-$ by Theorem 7.3. If $S \ni x_\delta \xrightarrow[\delta\in\Delta]{} x$ but not $x_\delta M \xrightarrow[\delta\in\Delta]{} xM$, then there is $V \in \mathbf{V}$ such that $\Delta_0 = \{\delta\colon x_\delta M \bar{\in} xMV\}$ is also a directed system and $x_\delta \xrightarrow[\delta \in \Delta_0]{} x$. Setting $X = \{x_\delta : \delta \in \Delta_0\}$, we hence have $x \in X^-$ but $xM \bar{\in} (XM)^-$. Therefore, if $X^-M \subset (XM)^-$ for every $X \subset S$, then M is continuous by Theorem 12.1.

Theorem 12.2 shows that it is a topological property for a mapping to be continuous.

Theorem 12.3. *For a continuous mapping M, if a set $X \subset S$ is compact, then XM also is compact, and if X is connected, then XM also is connected.*

Proof. For a compact set $X \subset S$, if $XM \subset \bigcup_{\lambda \in \Lambda} A_\lambda$ for a system of open sets $A_\lambda \in \mathbf{T}(\mathbf{V})$ $(\lambda \in \Lambda)$, then we have by Theorem 12.2

$$X \subset \bigcup_{\lambda \in \Lambda} A_\lambda M^{-1}, \quad A_\lambda M^{-1} \in \mathbf{T}(\mathbf{U}) \ (\lambda \in \Lambda),$$

and hence we can find a finite system $\lambda_\nu \in \Lambda$ $(\nu = 1, 2, \ldots, n)$ such that $X \subset \bigcup_{\nu=1}^{n} A_{\lambda_\nu} M^{-1}$, that is, $XM \subset \bigcup_{\nu=1}^{n} A_{\lambda_\nu}$. Therefore XM is compact.

For a connected set $X \subset S$, if $XM \cap A \cap B = \emptyset$, $XM \subset A \cup B$ for A, $B \in \mathbf{T}(\mathbf{V})$, then we have

$$X \cap AM^{-1} \cap BM^{-1} = \emptyset; \quad X \subset AM^{-1} \cup BM^{-1}; \quad AM^{-1}, BM^{-1} \in \mathbf{T}(\mathbf{U}),$$

and hence $X \cap AM^{-1} = \emptyset$ or $X \cap BM^{-1} = \emptyset$. Since $X \cap AM^{-1} = \emptyset$ implies $XM \cap A = \emptyset$ by (8) in 11, we conclude that XM is connected.

A mapping M is said to be *uniformly continuous,* if for any $V \in \mathbf{V}$ we can find $U \in \mathbf{U}$ such that $xUM \subset xMV$ for every $x \in S$. With this definition, it is obvious that every uniformly continuous mapping is continuous. Since $xUM \subset xMV$ if and only if $xU \subset xMVM^{-1}$, we have by definition

Theorem 12.4. *A mapping M is uniformly continuous if and only if $MVM^{-1} \in \mathbf{U}$ for every $V \in \mathbf{V}$.*

Theorem 12.5. *For a uniformly continuous mapping M, if a set $X \subset S$ is bounded, then XM also is bounded; if X is totally bounded, then XM also is totally bounded; if X is* **U**-*connected then XM is* **V**-*connected; and if $x_\delta \in S$ $(\delta \in \Delta)$ is a Cauchy system, then $x_\delta M$ $(\delta \in \Delta)$ also is a Cauchy system.*

Proof. For a uniformly continuous mapping M we have $MVM^{-1} \in \mathbf{U}$

for every $V \in \mathbf{V}$ by Theorem 12.4. Thus, if X is bounded, then for any $V \in \mathbf{V}$ we can find a finite system $x_\nu \in X$ $(\nu = 1, 2, \ldots, n)$ and $\sigma = 1, 2, \ldots$ such that $X \subset \bigcup_{\nu=1}^{n} x_\nu (MVM^{-1})^\sigma$, and hence $XM \subset \bigcup_{\nu=1}^{n} x_\nu MV^\sigma$ by (9), (14) in 11. If X is totally bounded, then for any $V \in \mathbf{V}$ we can find a finite system $x_\nu \in X$ $(\nu = 1, 2, \ldots, n)$ such that $X \subset \bigcup_{\nu=1}^{n} x_\nu MVM^{-1}$, and hence $xM \subset \bigcup_{\nu=1}^{n} x_\nu MV$. If X is $\mathbf{U}$-connected, then for any $V \in \mathbf{V}$ and $a, b \in X$ we can find a finite system $x_\nu \in X$ $(\nu = 1, 2, \ldots, n)$ such that $x_\nu MVM^{-1} \ni x_{\nu+1}$ $(\nu = 0, 1, \ldots, n)$ for $x_0 = a$, $x_{n+1} = b$, and hence $x_\nu MV \ni x_{\nu+1} M$ $(\nu = 0, 1, \ldots, n)$. Therefore XM is $\mathbf{V}$-connected. If $x_\delta \in S$ $(\delta \in \Delta)$ is a Cauchy system, then for any $V \in \mathbf{V}$ there is $\delta_0 \in \Delta$ such that $x_\delta \in x_{\delta_0} MVM^{-1}$ for $\delta \leqq \delta_0$, that is, $x_\delta M \in x_{\delta_0} MV$ for $\delta \leqq \delta_0$.

For a set $\emptyset \neq X \subset S$, a mapping M is said to be *uniformly continuous* on X, if the relative mapping M^X is uniformly continuous for the relative uniformity $\mathbf{U}^X$, that is, for any $V \in \mathbf{V}$ we can find $U \in \mathbf{U}$ such that

$$(xU \cap X)M \subset xMV \quad \text{for every } x \in X,$$

because $YM^X = YM$ for $Y \subset X$.

Referring to (17) in 11, we conclude from Theorem 12.4

Theorem 12.6. *A mapping M is uniformly continuous on $X \subset S$ if and only if $(MVM^{-1})^X \in \mathbf{U}^X$ for every $V \in \mathbf{V}$.*

Therefore, if M is uniformly continuous, then M^X also is uniformly continuous for any set $\emptyset \neq X \subset S$.

Theorem 12.7. *If a mapping M is uniformly continuous on a set $X \subset S$ and if for any $x \in S$ we can find a convergent system $X \ni x_\delta \xrightarrow[\delta \in \Delta]{} x$ such that $x_\delta M \xrightarrow[\delta \in \Delta]{} xM$, then M is uniformly continuous.*

Proof. For any $V \in \mathbf{V}$ there is a symmetric $W \in \mathbf{V}$ by Theorem 2.1 such that $W^3 \leqq V$. As M is uniformly continuous on X, we can find $U_0 \in \mathbf{U}$ by Theorem 12.4 such that $U_0{}^X \leqq M^X W (M^X)^{-1}$. For such $U_0 \in \mathbf{U}$ there is a symmetric $U \in \mathbf{U}$ such that $U^3 \leqq U_0$. For any $x \in S$ we can find $x_0 \in X$ such that $x_0 \in xU$, $x_0 M \in xMW$, because there is a convergent system $X \ni x_\delta \xrightarrow[\delta \in \Delta]{} x$ with $x_\delta M \xrightarrow[\delta \in \Delta]{} xM$. If $x \in yU$, then for $x_0, y_0 \in X$

with $x_0 \in xU$, $y_0 \in yU$, $x_0M \in xMW$, $y_0M \in yMW$, we have

$$x_0 \in xU \subset yU^2 \subset y_0U^3 \subset y_0U_0,$$

and hence $x_0 \in y_0M^XW(M^X)^{-1}$, that is, $x_0M = x_0M^X \in y_0M^XW = y_0MW$. Thus

$$xM \in x_0MW \subset y_0MW^2 \subset yMW^3 \subset yMV.$$

Consequently $x \in yU$ implies $xM \in yMV$, that is, $yUM \subset yMV$ for every $y \in S$. Therefore M is uniformly continuous by definition.

Referring to Theorem 7.3 and 12.1, we conclude immediately from Theorem 12.7

Theorem 12.8. *If a continuous mapping M from S to R is uniformly continuous on a set $X \subset S$ such that $X^{\mathbf{U}-} = S$, then M is uniformly continuous.*

Theorem 12.9. *Every continuous mapping M is uniformly continuous on any compact set $X \neq \emptyset$.*

Proof. If M is continuous, then for any $V \in \mathbf{V}$ we can find a system $U_x \in \mathbf{U}$ $(x \in S)$ such that $xU_xM \subset xMV$ for every $x \in S$. For such U_x $(x \in S)$ we can find symmetric $W_x \in \mathbf{U}$ such that $W_x{}^2 \leqq U_x$ for every $x \in S$. If X is compact, then there is a finite system $x_\nu \in X$ $(\nu = 1, 2, \ldots, n)$ such that $X \subset \bigcup_{\nu=1}^{n} x_\nu W_{x_\nu}$. Setting $U = \bigcap_{\nu=1}^{n} W_{x_\nu}$, we have $U \in \mathbf{U}$ and for any $x \in X$ we can find x_ν such that $x \in x_\nu W_{x_\nu}$. Thus we have

$$xU \subset x_\nu W_{x_\nu} U \subset x_\nu W_{x_\nu}{}^2 \subset x_\nu U_{x_\nu}$$

and hence $xUM \subset x_\nu U_{x_\nu} M \subset x_\nu MV$. Since $xM \in xUM$, we thus obtain $x_\nu MV \subset xMV^{-1}V$, and consequently $xUM \subset xMV^{-1}V$ for every $x \in X$. Therefore M is uniformly continuous on X by definition.

If M is uniformly continuous on X, then M also is obviously uniformly continuous on every set $Y \subset X$.

Theorem 12.10. *For a finite system $X_\nu \subset S$ $(\nu = 1, 2, \ldots, n)$ and $U_\nu \in \mathbf{U}$ $(\nu = 1, 2, \ldots, n)$, if M is uniformly continuous on $X_\nu U_\nu$ for every $\nu = 1, 2, \ldots, n$, then M is uniformly continuous on $\bigcup_{\nu=1}^{n} X_\nu$.*

Proof. For any $V \in \mathbf{V}$ there is a system $V_\nu \in \mathbf{U}$ $(\nu = 1, 2, \ldots, n)$ by assumption such that $(xV_\nu \cap X_\nu U_\nu)M \subset xMV$ for $x \in X_\nu U_\nu$ $(\nu = 1, 2, \ldots,$

n). Putting $W = \bigcap_{\mu,\nu=1}^{n} (V_\nu \cap U_\mu)$, we have then

$$xWM \subset (xV_\nu \cap X_\nu U_\nu)M \subset xMV \quad \text{for } x \in X_\nu,$$

and hence $xWM \subset xMV$ for any $x \in \bigcup_{\nu=1}^{n} X_\nu$. Therefore M is uniformly continuous on $\bigcup_{\nu=1}^{n} X_\nu$.

A mapping M is said to be *locally uniformly continuous,* if there is $U \in \mathbf{U}$ such that M is uniformly continuous on xU for every $x \in S$.

Theorem 12.11. *If M is locally uniformly continuous, then there is $U \in \mathbf{U}$ such that for any totally bounded set A, M is uniformly continuous on AU.*

Proof. If M is uniformly continuous on xU_0 for every $x \in S$ and $U_0 \in \mathbf{U}$, then for any totally bounded set $A \neq \emptyset$ and for $U \in \mathbf{U}$ such that $U^3 \leqq U_0$ we can find a finite system $a_\nu \in A$ ($\nu = 1, 2, \ldots, n$) such that $A \subset \bigcup_{\nu=1}^{n} a_\nu U$. Since M is uniformly continuous on $a_\nu U^3 \subset a_\nu U_0$ for every $\nu = 1, 2, \ldots, n$, M is uniformly continuous on $\bigcup_{\nu=1}^{n} a_\nu U^2 \supset AU$ by Theorem 12.10.

Theorem 12.12. *If M is locally uniformly continuous, then for any Cauchy system $x_\delta \in S$ ($\delta \in \Delta$), the images $x_\delta M$ ($\delta \in \Delta$) also is a Cauchy system; and for a totally bounded set X, the image XM also is totally bounded.*

Proof. Let $U_0 \in \mathbf{U}$ and let M be uniformly continuous on xU_0 for every $x \in S$. For any Cauchy system $x_\delta \in S$ ($\delta \in \Delta$) we can find $\delta_0 \in \Delta$ such that $x_\delta \in x_{\delta_0} U_0$ for $\delta \leqq \delta_0$. Then $x_\delta M$ ($\delta \leqq \delta_0$) is a Cauchy system by Theorem 12.5, and hence $x_\delta M$ ($\delta \in \Delta$) also is a Cauchy system by definition. For a totally bounded set $X \subset S$, we can find $U \in \mathbf{U}$ by Theorem 12.11 such that M is uniformly continuous on XU. Thus XM also is totally bounded by Theorem 12.5.

Theorem 12.13. *For a locally uniformly continuous mapping M from $X \subset S$ to a space R with a complete uniformity $\mathbf{V}$, if $X^{\mathbf{U}-} = S$, then there is a locally uniformly continuous mapping $\widetilde{M}$ from S to R such that*

$x\widetilde{M} = xM$ *for every* $x \in X$. *If* M *is uniformly continuous, then* $\widetilde{M}$ *also is uniformly continuous.*

Proof. For each $y \in X'$, we can find $x_\delta \in X$ $(\delta \in \Delta)$ by Theorem 7.3 such that $x_\delta \xrightarrow[\delta\in\Delta]{} y$. Then x_δ $(\delta \in \Delta)$ is a Cauchy system, and hence $x_\delta M$ $(\delta \in \Delta)$ also is a Cauchy system by Theorem 12.12. Since **V** is complete by assumption, we can find $z \in R$ such that $x_\delta M \xrightarrow[\delta\in\Delta]{} z$. Setting $y\widetilde{M} = z$, and $x\widetilde{M} = xM$ for $x \in X$, we obtain a mapping $\widetilde{M}$ from S to R. If M is uniformly continuous, then $\widetilde{M}$ also is uniformly continuous by Theorem 12.7. Furthermore we see easily by Theorem 12.7 that if M is uniformly continuous on a set $A \subset X$, then $\widetilde{M}$ is uniformly continuous on $A^{\mathbf{U}-}$. Since M is locally uniformly continuous by assumption, there is $U \in \mathbf{U}$ such that M is uniformly continuous on xU^X for every $x \in X$. For such $U \in \mathbf{U}$ we can find $V \in \mathbf{U}$ such that $V^{-1}V \leqq U$. Then for any $y \in S$ there is $x \in X$ such that $x \in yV^\circ$, and we have

$$yV^\circ \subset x(V^\circ)^{-1}V^\circ \subset xV^{-1}V \subset xU.$$

Thus $\widetilde{M}$ is uniformly continuous on $(yV^\circ \cap X)^-$. Since $(yV^\circ \cap X)^- \supset (yV^\circ)^\circ \cap X^- = yV^\circ$, $\widetilde{M}$ is uniformly continuous on yV° for every $y \in S$. Therefore $\widetilde{M}$ is locally uniformly continuous.

13. **Purifications.** Let **U** be a uniformity on a space S. A set $X \subset S$ is said to be *topological,* if $x \in X$ implies $xI_{\mathbf{U}} \subset X$ for the atom $I_{\mathbf{U}}$ of **U**, that is, if $XI_{\mathbf{U}} = X$. Since $I_{\mathbf{U}}^2 = I_{\mathbf{U}}$, we can state that $XI_{\mathbf{U}}$ is topological for every set $X \subset S$. All of the open sets and closed sets for the induced topology **T(U)** are topological by (5).

A connector V on S is said to be *topological* for **U**, if xV is topological for every $x \in S$ and $x \in yI_{\mathbf{U}}$ implies $xV = yV$, that is, if $VI_{\mathbf{U}} = I_{\mathbf{U}}V = V$. Therefore V is topological for **U** if and only if $I_{\mathbf{U}}VI_{\mathbf{U}} = V$. Furthermore $I_{\mathbf{U}}VI_{\mathbf{U}}$ is always topological for **U** for any connector V on S.

Theorem 13.1. *For any basis* **B** *of* **U**, *the system*

$$I_{\mathbf{U}}\mathbf{B}I_{\mathbf{U}} = \{I_{\mathbf{U}}UI_{\mathbf{U}}: U \in \mathbf{B}\}$$

is a basis of **U**.

Proof. Since $U \leqq I_{\mathbf{U}} U I_{\mathbf{U}}$, we have $I_{\mathbf{U}} U I_{\mathbf{U}} \in \mathbf{U}$ for every $U \in \mathbf{U}$. For any $U \in \mathbf{U}$ we can find a symmetric $U_1 \in \mathbf{U}$ such that $U_1{}^3 \leqq U$, and $V \in \mathbf{B}$ such that $V \leqq U_1$. Then we have $I_{\mathbf{U}} V I_{\mathbf{U}} \leqq U_1{}^3 \leqq U$. Therefore $I_{\mathbf{U}} \mathbf{B} I_{\mathbf{U}}$ is a basis of $\mathbf{U}$.

Let U be a discrete connector on S. Then the system xU $(x \in S)$ gives a partition of S by Theorem 1.7. Therefore, considering each set xU $(x \in S)$ a point, we obtain a space, which will be called the *partition space* of S by U. The atom $I_{\mathbf{U}}$ of $\mathbf{U}$ is a discrete connector by Theorem 2.4. The partition space of S by $I_{\mathbf{U}}$ is called the *purification* of S by $\mathbf{U}$ and denoted by $S(\mathbf{U})$, that is, $S(\mathbf{U}) = \{xI_{\mathbf{U}}: x \in S\}$. Setting $xP = xI_{\mathbf{U}}$ $(x \in S)$ we obtain a full mapping P from S to $S(\mathbf{U})$, which is called the *purifying mapping* for $\mathbf{U}$ and denoted by $P_{\mathbf{U}}$. With this definition, we obviously have

(1) $xP_{\mathbf{U}} = xI_{\mathbf{U}}$ for $x \in S$

(2) $XP_{\mathbf{U}}P_{\mathbf{U}}{}^{-1} = XI_{\mathbf{U}}$ for $X \subset S$,

(3) $AP_{\mathbf{U}}{}^{-1} = AP_{\mathbf{U}}{}^{-1}I_{\mathbf{U}}$ for $A \subset S(\mathbf{U})$.

Theorem 13.2. *For any connector V on $S(\mathbf{U})$, its inverse image $P_{\mathbf{U}}VP_{\mathbf{U}}{}^{-1}$ by $P_{\mathbf{U}}$ is a topological connector on S, and for any topological connector U on S, there exists uniquely a connector V on $S(\mathbf{U})$ such that $U = P_{\mathbf{U}}VP_{\mathbf{U}}{}^{-1}$.*

Proof. $xP_{\mathbf{U}}VP_{\mathbf{U}}{}^{-1}$ is a topological set for every $x \in S$ by (3). Thus $P_{\mathbf{U}}VP_{\mathbf{U}}{}^{-1}$ is a topological connector by (1). For a topological connector U on S for $\mathbf{U}$, if $xP_{\mathbf{U}} = yP_{\mathbf{U}}$, then $xI_{\mathbf{U}} = yI_{\mathbf{U}}$ by (1), and hence $xU = xI_{\mathbf{U}}U = yI_{\mathbf{U}}U = yU$. Therefore, putting $xP_{\mathbf{U}}V = xUP_{\mathbf{U}}$ for every $x \in S$, we obtain a connector V on $S(\mathbf{U})$, and we have $xP_{\mathbf{U}}VP_{\mathbf{U}}{}^{-1} = xUI_{\mathbf{U}} = xU$ for every $x \in S$ by (2). Furthermore, $P_{\mathbf{U}}WP_{\mathbf{U}}{}^{-1} = U$ implies $xP_{\mathbf{U}}W = xUP_{\mathbf{U}}$ for every $x \in S$ by Theorem 11.1. Thus such V is determined uniquely.

For the purifying mapping $P_{\mathbf{U}}$, putting

(4) $\mathbf{U}_P = \{U: P_{\mathbf{U}}UP_{\mathbf{U}}{}^{-1} \in \mathbf{U}\}$

we obtain a uniformity $\mathbf{U}_P$ on $S(\mathbf{U})$. Because $\mathbf{U}_P$ obviously satisfies the uniformity condition (1), since $U \leqq V$ implies $P_{\mathbf{U}}UP_{\mathbf{U}}{}^{-1} \leqq P_{\mathbf{U}}VP_{\mathbf{U}}{}^{-1}$.

It is clear by (12) in 11 that $\mathbf{U}_P$ satisfies condition 2). Referring to Theorems 13.1, 13.2 and 11.2, we see easily that $\mathbf{U}_P$ satisfies condition 3). This uniformity $\mathbf{U}_P$ on $S(\mathbf{U})$ is called the *purification* of $\mathbf{U}$.

The purification of $\mathbf{U}$ is pure. Because, if $xP_{\mathbf{U}} \neq yP_{\mathbf{U}}$, then $xI_{\mathbf{U}} \neq yI_{\mathbf{U}}$, and hence there is $U \in \mathbf{U}$ such that $xU \not\ni y$. For such $U \in \mathbf{U}$ we can find a symmetric $V \in \mathbf{U}$ such that $V^3 \leqq U$. Then $xI_{\mathbf{U}}VI_{\mathbf{U}} \subset xV^3 \subset xU$, and hence $xI_{\mathbf{U}}VI_{\mathbf{U}} \not\ni y$. On the other hand, there is $W \in \mathbf{U}_P$ by Theorem 13.2 such that $I_{\mathbf{U}}VI_{\mathbf{U}} = P_{\mathbf{U}}WP_{\mathbf{U}}^{-1}$. Thus $xP_{\mathbf{U}}WP_{\mathbf{U}}^{-1} \not\ni y$, that is, $xP_{\mathbf{U}}W \not\ni yP_{\mathbf{U}}$. It is obvious by (4) that the purifying mapping $P_{\mathbf{U}}$ is uniformly continuous for $\mathbf{U}_P$.

From Theorems 13.1 and 13.2, we conclude immediately

Theorem 13.3. *For the purification* $\mathbf{U}_P$ *of* $\mathbf{U}$, *the system* $\{P_{\mathbf{U}}UP_{\mathbf{U}}^{-1}: U \in \mathbf{U}_P\}$ *is a basis of* $\mathbf{U}$.

A set $X \subset S$ is said to be *pure,* if the relative uniformity $\mathbf{U}^X$ is pure, that is, if $I_{\mathbf{U}}^X = I^X$, or if $xI_{\mathbf{U}} \cap X = \{x\}$ for every $x \in X$. A set $X \subset S$ is said to be *full,* if $XI_{\mathbf{U}} = S$. We see easily by Choice Axiom that for any uniformity there is a full pure set.

A uniformity $\mathbf{U}$ on a space S is said to be *unimorphic* to a uniformity $\mathbf{V}$ on a space R, if there is a transformation T from S to R such that both T and its inverse transformation T^{-1} are uniformly continuous. Such a transformation T is called a *unimorphism* from $\mathbf{U}$ to $\mathbf{V}$.

Theorem 13.4. *For a full pure set* $X \subset S$ *for* $\mathbf{U}$, *the relative uniformity* $\mathbf{U}^X$ *is unimorphic to the purification* $\mathbf{U}_P$ *of* $\mathbf{U}$ *by the relative mapping* $P_{\mathbf{U}}^X$ *of the purifying mapping* $P_{\mathbf{U}}$.

Proof. It is obvious by definition that $P_{\mathbf{U}}^X$ is a transformation from X to $S(\mathbf{U})$, and $P_{\mathbf{U}}^X$ is uniformly continuous by Theorem 12.6. For any $U \in \mathbf{U}$ there is $V \in \mathbf{U}_P$ by Theorem 13.3 such that $U \geqq P_{\mathbf{U}}VP_{\mathbf{U}}^{-1}$. Then we have $U^X \geqq P_{\mathbf{U}}^X V (P_{\mathbf{U}}^X)^{-1}$ by (17) in 11, and hence

$$a(P_{\mathbf{U}}^X)^{-1}U^X \supset aV(P_{\mathbf{U}}^X)^{-1} \quad \text{for every } a \in S(\mathbf{U}).$$

Thus $(P_{\mathbf{U}}^X)^{-1}$ also is uniformly continuous by definition.

14. **Uniformly Open Mappings.** Let $\mathbf{U}$ be a uniformity on a space S, and let $\mathbf{V}$ be a uniformity on a space R. A full mapping M from S to R is

said to be *open at* a point $x \in S$, if for any $U \in \mathbf{U}$ we can find $V \in \mathbf{V}$ such that $xUM \supset xMV$. M is said to be *open,* if M is open at every point of S. Then we clearly have by the definition of open sets

Theorem 14.1. *A full mapping M from S to R is open, if and only if $XM \in \mathbf{T}(\mathbf{V})$ for every $X \in \mathbf{T}(\mathbf{U})$.*

A full mapping M from S to R is said to be *uniformly open,* if for any $U \in \mathbf{U}$ we can find $V \in \mathbf{V}$ such that $xUM \supset xMV$ for every $x \in S$. Uniformly open mappings are obviously open by definition.

Let M be a mapping from a space S to a space R, and let N be a mapping from R to a space Q. Setting

$$x(MN) = xMN \quad \text{for every} \quad x \in S,$$

we obtain a mapping MN from S to Q. This mapping MN is called the *composition* of M and N. With this definition we obviously have

(1) $X(MN) = XMN$ for every $X \subset S$.

(2) $A(MN)^{-1} = AN^{-1}M^{-1}$ for every $A \subset Q$.

Because we have $x \in A(MN)^{-1}$ if and only if $xMN \in A$, or if and only if $x \in AN^{-1}M^{-1}$.

For a connector U on Q we have

(3) $MNU(MN)^{-1} = M(NUN^{-1})M^{-1}$.

Because $x(MNU(MN)^{-1}) = xMNUN^{-1}M^{-1} = xM(NUN^{-1})M^{-1}$ for every $x \in S$.

Let $\mathbf{U}$, $\mathbf{V}$, $\mathbf{W}$ be uniformities respectively on S, R, Q. Referring to Theorem 12.2, we obtain by (2)

Theorem 14.2. *If both M and N are continuous, then MN also is continuous.*

From Theorem 12.4 we conclude immediately from (3)

Theorem 14.3. *If both M and N are uniformly continuous, then MN also is uniformly continuous.*

Theorem 14.4. *If M is uniformly open and if MN is uniformly continuous, then N is uniformly continuous.*

Proof. Since MN is uniformly continuous by assumption, for any $W \in \mathbf{W}$ we can find $U \in \mathbf{U}$ such that $xUMN \subset xMNW$ for every $x \in S$. As M is uniformly open by assumption, for such $U \in \mathbf{U}$ we can find $V \in \mathbf{V}$ such that $xUM \supset xMV$ for every $x \in S$. Since M is full by assumption, we hence obtain $yVN \subset yNW$ for every $y \in R$. Therefore N is uniformly continuous by definition.

Theorem 14.5. *The purifying mapping $P_{\mathbf{U}}$ for a uniformity* **U** *on a space S is uniformly continuous and uniformly open.*

Proof. We need only to prove that $P_{\mathbf{U}}$ is uniformly open. For any $U \in \mathbf{U}$ there is $V \in \mathbf{U}_P$ by Theorem 13.3 such that $U \geqq P_{\mathbf{U}} V P_{\mathbf{U}}^{-1}$. Then we obtain by Theorem 11.1

$$xUP_{\mathbf{U}} \supset xP_{\mathbf{U}}VP_{\mathbf{U}}^{-1}P_{\mathbf{U}} = xP_{\mathbf{U}}V \quad \text{for every } x \in S.$$

Therefore $P_{\mathbf{U}}$ is uniformly open by definition.

Theorem 14.6. *If a mapping M from a space S with a uniformity* **U** *to a space R with a pure uniformity* **V** *is uniformly continuous, then there exists uniquely a mapping N from the purification $S(\mathbf{U})$ to R such that $xP_{\mathbf{U}}N = xM$ for every $x \in S$ for the purifying mapping $P_{\mathbf{U}}$ of* **U**, *and such N is uniformly continuous.*

Proof. Since M is uniformly continuous by assumption, for any $V \in \mathbf{V}$ we can find $U \in \mathbf{U}$ such that $xUM \subset xMV$ for every $x \in S$. Thus $xI_{\mathbf{U}} \ni y$ implies $yM \in xMV$ for every $V \in \mathbf{V}$, because $I_{\mathbf{U}} \leqq U$ for every $U \in \mathbf{U}$. Since **V** is pure by assumption, we hence obtain $xM = yM$ for $xI_{\mathbf{U}} \ni y$. Therefore, setting $xP_{\mathbf{U}}N = xM$ for every $x \in S$, we obtain a mapping N from $S(\mathbf{U})$ to R. The uniqueness of such a mapping N is clear. Since M is uniformly continuous and $P_{\mathbf{U}}$ is uniformly open by Theorem 14.5, we conclude by Theorem 14.4 that N is uniformly continuous.

15. **Equi-Continuous Systems.** Let **U** be a uniformity on a space S and let **V** be a uniformity on a space R. A system of mappings M_λ $(\lambda \in \Lambda)$ from S to R is said to be *equi-continuous,* if for any $V \in \mathbf{V}$ we can find $U \in \mathbf{U}$ such that $xUM_\lambda \subset xM_\lambda V$ for every $x \in S$, $\lambda \in \Lambda$. Since we have $xUM_\lambda \subset xM_\lambda V$ if and only if $xU \subset xM_\lambda VM_\lambda^{-1}$, we conclude immediately from definition

Theorem 15.1. *M_λ $(\lambda \in \Lambda)$ is equi-continuous if and only if*

$$\bigcap_{\lambda \in \Lambda} M_\lambda VM_\lambda^{-1} \in \mathbf{U} \quad \text{for every } V \in \mathbf{V}.$$

It is clear by definition that if M_λ $(\lambda \in \Lambda)$ is equi-continuous, then each M_λ is uniformly continuous. Furthermore we see easily by definition:

If M_λ $(\lambda \in \Lambda)$ is equi-continuous, then M_λ $(\lambda \in \Lambda_0)$ also is equi-continuous for $\emptyset \neq \Lambda_0 \subset \Lambda$. If M_λ $(\lambda \in \Lambda_\nu)$ is equi-continuous for every $\nu = 1, 2, \ldots, n$ and $\Lambda = \bigcup_{\nu=1}^{n} \Lambda_\nu$, then M_λ $(\lambda \in \Lambda)$ also is equi-continuous.

Lemma. *Let U_ν $(\nu = 1, 2, \ldots, n)$ be a finite system of connectors on a space S. For a set $A \subset S$, if $A \subset \bigcup_{\mu=1}^{m_\nu} a_{\nu,\mu} U_\nu$ $(\nu = 1, 2, \ldots, n)$ for a finite system of points $a_{\nu,\mu} \in A$ $(\mu = 1, 2, \ldots, m_\nu,\ \nu = 1, 2, \ldots, n)$, then there is a finite system of points $a_\rho \in A$ $(\rho = 1, 2, \ldots, k)$ such that*

$$A \subset \bigcup_{\rho=1}^{k} a_\rho \bigcap_{\nu=1}^{n} (U_\nu^{-1} U_\nu).$$

Proof. By assumption we have

$$A \subset \bigcap_{\nu=1}^{n} \bigcup_{\mu=1}^{m_\nu} a_{\nu,\mu} U_\nu = \bigcup \{ \bigcap_{\nu=1}^{n} a_{\nu,\mu_\nu} U_\nu : 1 \leqq \mu_\nu \leqq m_\nu,\ \nu = 1, 2, \ldots, n \}.$$

For a point $a \in \bigcap_{\nu=1}^{n} a_{\nu,\mu_\nu} U_\nu \cap A$, we obviously have $a \in a_{\nu,\mu_\nu} U_\nu$ for every $\nu = 1, 2, \ldots, n$. Thus we obtain by Theorem 1.2

$$a_{\nu,\mu_\nu} U_\nu \subset a U_\nu^{-1} U_\nu \quad \text{for every } \nu = 1, 2, \ldots, n,$$

and hence $\bigcap_{\nu=1}^{n} a_{\nu,\mu_\nu} U_\nu \subset a \bigcap_{\nu=1}^{n} U_\nu^{-1} U_\nu$. Therefore there exists a finite system of points $a_\rho \in A$ $(\rho = 1, 2, \ldots, k)$ such that

$$\bigcup \{ \bigcap_{\nu=1}^{n} a_{\nu,\mu_\nu} U_\nu : 1 \leqq \mu_\nu \leqq m_\nu,\ \nu = 1, 2, \ldots, n \} \subset \bigcup_{\rho=1}^{k} a_\rho \bigcap_{\nu=1}^{n} U_\nu^{-1} U_\nu .$$

As a generalization of the so-called Ascoli's theorem about a system of functions on a closed interval, we have

Theorem 15.2. *If M_λ $(\lambda \in \Lambda)$ is equi-continuous, $\mathbf{U}$ is totally bounded, and $\{xM_\lambda : \lambda \in \Lambda\}$ is totally bounded for $\mathbf{V}$ for every $x \in S$, then for any $V \in \mathbf{V}$ we can find a finite system $\lambda_\rho \in \Lambda$ $(\rho = 1, 2, \ldots, k)$ such that for any $\lambda \in \Lambda$ there is λ_ρ for which $xM_\lambda \in xM_{\lambda_\rho} V$ for every $x \in S$.*

Proof. For any $V \in \mathbf{V}$ there is a symmetric $W \in \mathbf{V}$ by Theorem 2.1 such that $W^4 \leqq V$. Since M_λ $(\lambda \in \Lambda)$ is equi-continuous by assumption, we have $\bigcap_{\lambda \in \Lambda} M_\lambda W M_\lambda^{-1} \in \mathbf{U}$ by Theorem 15.1. As $\mathbf{U}$ is totally bounded by assumption, we can find a finite system of points $x_\nu \in S$ $(\nu = 1,$

2, ..., n) such that $S = \bigcup_{\nu=1}^{n} \bigcap_{\lambda \in \Lambda} x_\nu M_\lambda W M_\lambda^{-1}$. For such $x_\nu \in S$ ($\nu = 1, 2, \ldots, n$), setting

$$\lambda N_\nu = x_\nu M_\lambda \quad \text{for } \lambda \in \Lambda,\ \nu = 1, 2, \ldots, n,$$

we obtain a system of mappings N_ν ($\nu = 1, 2, \ldots, n$) from Λ to R. Then ΛN_ν is totally bounded for $\mathbf{V}$ for every $\nu = 1, 2, \ldots, n$ by assumption, and hence we can find $\lambda_{\nu,\mu} \in \Lambda$ ($\mu = 1, 2, \ldots, m_\nu$; $\nu = 1, 2, \ldots, n$) such that

$$\Lambda N_\nu \subset \bigcup_{\mu=1}^{m_\nu} \lambda_{\nu,\mu} N_\nu W \quad \text{for every } \nu = 1, 2, \ldots, n,$$

that is,

$$\Lambda = \bigcup_{\mu=1}^{m_\nu} \lambda_{\nu,\mu} N_\nu W N_\nu^{-1} \quad \text{for every } \nu = 1, 2, \ldots, n.$$

Thus we can find $\lambda_\rho \in \Lambda$ ($\rho = 1, 2, \ldots, k$) by the Lemma such that

$$\Lambda = \bigcup_{\rho=1}^{k} \bigcap_{\nu=1}^{n} \lambda_\rho (N_\nu W N_\nu^{-1})^{-1} (N_\nu W N_\nu^{-1}).$$

Since $(N_\nu W N_\nu^{-1})^{-1}(N_\nu W N_\nu^{-1}) \leqq N_\nu W^2 N_\nu^{-1}$ by (13), (14) in **11**, we obtain

$$\Lambda = \bigcup_{\rho=1}^{k} \bigcap_{\nu=1}^{n} \lambda_\rho N_\nu W^2 N_\nu^{-1}.$$

Therefore for any $\lambda \in \Lambda$ there is λ_ρ such that

$$\lambda \in \lambda_\rho N_\nu W^2 N_\nu^{-1}, \text{ namely } \lambda N_\nu \in \lambda_\rho N_\nu W^2 \quad \text{for every } \nu = 1, 2, \ldots, n,$$

and hence

$$x_\nu M_\lambda \in x_\nu M_{\lambda_\rho} W^2 \quad \text{for every } \nu = 1, 2, \ldots, n.$$

On the other hand, for any $x \in S$ there is x_ν such that

$$x \in x_\nu M_\lambda W M_\lambda^{-1}, \text{ namely } x M_\lambda \in x_\nu M_\lambda W \quad \text{for every } \lambda \in \Lambda,$$

and hence we obtain

$$x M_\lambda \in x_\nu M_{\lambda_\rho} W^3 \subset x M_{\lambda_\rho} W^4 \subset x M_{\lambda_\rho} V.$$

Thus $x M_\lambda \in x M_{\lambda_\rho} V$ for every $x \in S$.

For $\emptyset \neq X \subset S$, a system of mappings M_λ ($\lambda \in \Lambda$) from S to R is said to be *equi-continuous* on X, if the system of the relative mappings M_λ^X ($\lambda \in \Lambda$) is equi-continuous for the relative uniformity $\mathbf{U}^X$. Thus, if M_λ ($\lambda \in \Lambda$) is equi-continuous, then M_λ ($\lambda \in \Lambda$) also is equi-continuous on any set $X \neq \emptyset$ of S.

As a generalization of Theorem 12.7, we have

Theorem 15.3. *If* M_λ $(\lambda \in \Lambda)$ *is equi-continuous on a set* $X \subset S$ *and if for any* $x \in S$ *and for any* $\lambda \in \Lambda$ *we can find a convergent system* $X \ni x_\delta \xrightarrow[\delta\in\Delta]{} x$ *such that* $x_\delta M_\lambda \xrightarrow[\delta\in\Delta]{} xM_\lambda$, *then* M_λ $(\lambda \in \Lambda)$ *is equi-continuous.*

Proof. For any $V \in \mathbf{V}$ there is a symmetric $W \in \mathbf{V}$ by Theorem 2.1 such that $W^3 \leqq V$. As M_λ $(\lambda \in \Lambda)$ is equi-continuous on X by assumption, we can find $U_0 \in \mathbf{U}$ by Theorem 15.1 such that $U_0{}^X \leqq \bigcap_{\lambda\in\Lambda} M_\lambda{}^X W (M_\lambda{}^X)^{-1}$. For such $U_0 \in \mathbf{U}$ there is a symmetric $U \in \mathbf{U}$ such that $U^3 \leqq U_0$. For any $x \in S$ and for any $\lambda \in \Lambda$, we can find $x_\lambda \in X$ such that $x_\lambda \in xU$ and $x_\lambda M_\lambda \in xM_\lambda W$, because there is a convergent system $X \ni x_\delta \xrightarrow[\delta\in\Delta]{} x$ such that $x_\delta M_\lambda \xrightarrow[\delta\in\Delta]{} xM$. If $x \in yU$, then for any $x_\lambda, y_\lambda \in X$ such that $x_\lambda \in xU$, $y_\lambda \in yU$, $x_\lambda M_\lambda \in xM_\lambda W$ and $y_\lambda M_\lambda \in yM_\lambda W$, we have $x_\lambda \in xU \subset yU^2 \subset y_\lambda U^3 \subset y_\lambda U_0$, and hence $x_\lambda \in y_\lambda M_\lambda{}^X W (M_\lambda{}^X)^{-1}$, that is, $x_\lambda M_\lambda = x_\lambda M_\lambda{}^X \in y_\lambda M_\lambda{}^X W = y_\lambda M_\lambda W$. Thus we obtain

$$xM_\lambda \in x_\lambda M_\lambda W \subset y_\lambda M_\lambda W^2 \subset yM_\lambda W^3 \subset yM_\lambda V.$$

Consequently, $x \in yU$ implies $xM_\lambda \in yM_\lambda V$ for every $\lambda \in \Lambda$, that is,

$$yUM_\lambda \subset yM_\lambda V \quad \text{for every } y \in S \text{ and } \lambda \in \Lambda.$$

Therefore M_λ $(\lambda \in \Lambda)$ is equi-continuous by definition.

Referring to Theorems 7.3 and 12.1, we conclude immediately from Theorem 15.3

Theorem 15.4. *If* M_λ $(\lambda \in \Lambda)$ *is equi-continuous on a set* $X \subset S$, $X^{\mathbf{U}-} = S$, *and each* M_λ *is continuous, then* M_λ $(\lambda \in \Lambda)$ *is equi-continuous.*

M_λ $(\lambda \in \Lambda)$ is said to be *equi-continuous at* a point $x \in S$, if for any $V \in \mathbf{V}$ we can find $U \in \mathbf{U}$ such that $xUM_\lambda \subset xM_\lambda V$ for every $\lambda \in \Lambda$. If M_λ $(\lambda \in \Lambda)$ is equi-continuous, then it is obviously equi-continuous at every point.

Theorem 15.5. *If* M_λ $(\lambda \in \Lambda)$ *is equi-continuous at every point of a compact set* $X \subset S$, *then* M_λ $(\lambda \in \Lambda)$ *is equi-continuous on* X.

Proof. For any $V \in \mathbf{V}$ we can find a system $U_x \in \mathbf{U}$ $(x \in X)$ by assumption such that $xU_x M_\lambda \subset xM_\lambda V$ for every $\lambda \in \Lambda$. For such $U_x \in \mathbf{U}$

$(x \in X)$ there is a symmetric $W_x \in \mathbf{U}$ $(x \in X)$ such that $W_x{}^2 \leqq U_x$. As X is compact by assumption, we can find a finite system $x_\nu \in X$ $(\nu = 1, 2, \ldots, n)$ such that $X \subset \bigcup_{\nu=1}^{n} x_\nu W_{x_\nu}$. Then, for any $x \in X$ there is x_ν such that $x \in x_\nu W_{x_\nu}$, and hence, setting $U = \bigcap_{\nu=1}^{n} W_{x_\nu}$, we have $U \in \mathbf{U}$ and $xU \subset x_\nu W_{x_\nu} U \subset x_\nu W_{x_\nu}{}^2 \subset x_\nu U_{x_\nu}$. Thus we obtain

$$xUM_\lambda \subset x_\nu U_{x_\nu} M_\lambda \subset x_\nu M_\lambda V \subset xM_\lambda V^{-1}V,$$

because $xM_\lambda \in x_\nu M_\lambda V$ implies $x_\nu M_\lambda \in xM_\lambda V^{-1}$. Therefore we obtain

$$xU^X M_\lambda{}^X \subset xM_\lambda{}^X V^{-1}V \quad \text{for every } \lambda \in \Lambda,\ x \in X.$$

Since $V \in \mathbf{V}$ is arbitrary, we hence conclude that M_λ $(\lambda \in \Lambda)$ is equi-continuous on X.

16. **Binary Mappings.** For two spaces S, R, the space of all pairs (x, y) $(x \in S,\ y \in R)$ is called the *product space* of S and R, and denoted by $S \times R$. A mapping from the product space $S \times R$ to a space Q is called a *binary mapping*, and denoted by $(x, y) \in Q$ $(x \in S,\ y \in R)$. Here (x, y) also denotes the image of the pair (x, y) by the binary mapping.

For sets $X \subset S$, $Y \subset R$, we make use of the notation

$$(X, Y) = \{(x, y) \colon x \in X,\ y \in Y\} \subset Q.$$

Then we obviously have

(1) $\left(\bigcup_{\lambda \in \Lambda} X_\lambda,\ \bigcup_{\gamma \in \Gamma} Y_\gamma\right) = \bigcup_{\lambda \in \Lambda,\, \gamma \in \Gamma} (X_\lambda, Y_\gamma).$

Setting $yM_x = (x, y)$, we obtain a system of mappings M_x $(x \in S)$ from R to Q, and putting $xN_y = (x, y)$, we obtain a system of mappings N_y $(y \in R)$ from S to Q, that is,

(2) $yM_x = xN_y = (x, y)$ for $x \in S$, $y \in R$.

We also make use of the notation

(3) $(X, y) = XN_y$, $(x, Y) = YM_x$ for $X \subset S$, $Y \subset R$.

Let $\mathbf{U}$, $\mathbf{V}$, $\mathbf{W}$ be uniformities respectively on S, R, Q. A binary mapping $(x, y) \in Q$ $(x \in S,\ y \in R)$ is said to be *uniformly continuous*, if for any $W \in \mathbf{W}$ we can find $U \in \mathbf{U}$ and $V \in \mathbf{V}$ such that

$$(xU, yV) \subset (x, y)W \quad \text{for every } x \in S,\ y \in R.$$

Theorem 16.1. *$(x, y) \in Q$ $(x \in S, y \in R)$ is uniformly continuous, if and only if both systems M_x $(x \in S)$ and N_y $(y \in R)$ are equi-continuous.*

Proof. If both M_x $(x \in S)$ and N_y $(y \in R)$ are equi-continuous, then for any $W \in \mathbf{W}$ we can find $U \in \mathbf{U}$ and $V \in \mathbf{V}$ such that

$$yVM_x \subset yM_xW, \; xUN_y \subset xN_yW \quad \text{for every } x \in S, \; y \in R,$$

and hence we have

$$(xU, yV) = \bigcup_{z \epsilon xU} (z, yV) = \bigcup_{z \epsilon xU} yVM_z \subset \bigcup_{z \epsilon xU} yM_zW$$
$$= (xU, y)W = xUN_yW \subset xN_yW^2 = (x, y)W^2.$$

Thus (x, y) $(x \in S, y \in R)$ is uniformly continuous by definition.

Conversely if (x, y) $(x \in S, y \in R)$ is uniformly continuous, then both M_x $(x \in S)$ and N_y $(y \in R)$ are equi-continuous, because

$$yVM_x = (x, yV) \subset (xU, yV), \; xUN_y = (xU, y) \subset (xU, yV)$$

for every $x \in S$, $y \in R$, $U \in \mathbf{U}$, $V \in \mathbf{V}$.

Theorem 16.2. *If $(x, y) \in Q$ $(x \in S, y \in R)$ is uniformly continuous, then for any totally bounded sets $X \subset S$ and $Y \subset R$ respectively for $\mathbf{U}$ and $\mathbf{V}$, the image $(X, Y) \subset Q$ also is totally bounded for $\mathbf{W}$.*

Proof. If (x, y) $(x \in S, y \in R)$ is uniformly continuous, then for any $W \in \mathbf{W}$ we can find $U \in \mathbf{U}$ and $V \in \mathbf{V}$ by definition such that $(xU, yV) \subset (x, y)W$ for every $x \in S$, $y \in R$. If both sets $X \subset S$ and $Y \subset R$ are totally bounded, we can find a finite system $x_\nu \in X$, $y_\mu \in Y$ $(\nu = 1, 2, \ldots, n;$ $\mu = 1, 2, \ldots, m)$ such that

$$X \subset \bigcup_{\nu=1}^{n} x_\nu U, \quad Y \subset \bigcup_{\mu=1}^{m} y_\mu V.$$

Then we have by (1)

$$(X, Y) \subset \bigcup_{\nu,\mu} (x_\nu U, y_\mu V) \subset \bigcup_{\nu,\mu} (x_\nu, y_\mu)W.$$

Therefore (X, Y) is totally bounded.

Theorem 16.3. *If the system N_y $(y \in R)$ is equi-continuous, and if M_x is uniformly continuous for every $x \in S$, then the system M_x $(x \in X)$ is equi-continuous for any totally bounded set $X \neq \emptyset$ of S.*

Proof. For any $W \in \mathbf{W}$, we can find a symmetric $U \in \mathbf{U}$ and a system $V_x \in \mathbf{V}$ $(x \in S)$ by assumption such that

$$(xU,\ y) = xUN_y \subset xN_yW = (x,\ y)W,$$
$$(x,\ yV_x) = yV_xM_x \subset yM_xW = (x,\ y)W$$

for every $x \in S$ and $y \in R$. If a set $\emptyset \neq X \subset S$ is totally bounded, then we can find a finite system $x_\nu \in X$ $(\nu = 1, 2, \ldots, n)$ such that $X \subset \bigcup_{\nu=1}^{n} x_\nu U$. For such $x_\nu \in X$ $(\nu = 1, 2, \ldots, n)$, setting $V = \bigcap_{\nu=1}^{n} V_{x_\nu}$, we have $V \in \mathbf{V}$, and for any $x \in X$ there is x_ν such that $x \in x_\nu U$. Thus we have

$$yVM_x = (x,\ yV) \subset (x_\nu U,\ yV_{x_\nu}) \subset (x_\nu,\ yV_{x_\nu})W$$
$$\subset (x_\nu,\ y)W^2 \subset (xU,\ y)W^2 \subset (x,\ y)W^3 = yM_xW^3$$

for every $y \in R$, because $x \in x_\nu U$ implies $x_\nu \in xU$. Here $x \in X$ and $W \in \mathbf{W}$ are arbitrary. Therefore M_x $(x \in X)$ is equi-continuous by definition.

Theorem 16.4. *If N_y $(y \in R)$ is equi-continuous and if M_x is uniformly continuous for every $x \in S$, then (X, Y) is totally bounded for* $\mathbf{W}$ *for any totally bounded set $X \subset S$ for* $\mathbf{U}$ *and for any totally bounded set $Y \subset R$ for* $\mathbf{V}$.

Proof. If $X \neq \emptyset$ is totally bounded for $\mathbf{U}$, then the system M_x $(x \in X)$ is equi-continuous by Theorem 16.3. Thus the binary mapping $(x, y) \in Q$ $(x \in X,\ y \in R)$ is uniformly continuous by Theorem 16.1. Consequently (X, Y) is totally bounded for $\mathbf{W}$ by Theorem 16.2.

17. **Convergence of Mappings.** Let S be a space and let R be a uniform space with a uniformity $\mathbf{V}$. A directed system of mappings M_δ $(\delta \in \Delta)$ from S to R is said to be *convergent to* a mapping M and we write $M_\delta \xrightarrow[\delta\in\Delta]{} M$, if $xM_\delta \xrightarrow[\delta\in\Delta]{} xM$ for $\mathbf{V}$ for every $x \in S$.

A system of mappings $\mathbf{M}$ from S to R is said to be *closed,* if $\mathbf{M} \ni M_\delta \xrightarrow[\delta\in\Delta]{} M$ implies $\mathbf{M} \ni M$. For a system of mappings $\mathbf{M}$ from S to R, setting

(1) $\overline{\mathbf{M}} = \{M\colon M_\delta \xrightarrow[\delta\in\Delta]{} M$ for some $M_\delta \in \mathbf{M}$ $(\delta \in \Delta)\}$,

we obtain a closed system $\overline{\mathbf{M}}$. Because, if $\overline{\mathbf{M}} \ni \overline{M}_\delta \xrightarrow[\delta\in\Delta]{} \overline{M}$, then for any $V \in \mathbf{V}$ and for any finite system of points $F \subset S$, there is $\delta_0 \in \Delta$ such that

$$x\overline{M}_{\delta_0} \in x\overline{M}V \text{ for every } x \in F.$$

For such $\overline{M}_{\delta_0}$ we can find $M_{(F,V)} \in \mathbf{M}$ such that $xM_{(F,V)} \in x\overline{M}_{\delta_0}V$ for every $x \in F$, and hence

$$xM_{(F,V)} \in x\overline{M}V^2 \text{ for every } x \in F.$$

For two finite systems $F_1, F_2 \subset S$ we define $F_1 \geqq F_2$ to mean $F_1 \subset F_2$, and for $V_1, V_2 \in \mathbf{V}$ we also define $(F_1, V_1) \geqq (F_2, V_2)$ to mean that $F_1 \geqq F_2$ and $V_1 \geqq V_2$. Then we obtain a directed system $M_{(F,V)} \in \mathbf{M}$ $(F \subset S,\ V \in \mathbf{V})$ such that

$$xM_{(F,V)} \in x\overline{M}V^2 \text{ for } x \in F \subset S,\ V \in \mathbf{V}.$$

Thus $M_{(F,V)} \xrightarrow[F\subset S,V\in\mathbf{V}]{} \overline{M}$ by definition, and hence $\overline{\mathbf{M}} \ni \overline{M}$ by (1). This closed system $\overline{\mathbf{M}}$ is called the *closure* of $\mathbf{M}$. It is obvious that $\overline{\mathbf{M}} \supset \mathbf{M}$, because, setting $M_\delta = M$ for every $\delta \in \Delta$, we have always $M_\delta \xrightarrow[\delta\in\Delta]{} M$.

M_δ $(\delta \in \Delta)$ is said to be *uniformly convergent to* M and we write $M_\delta \overset{\delta\in\Delta}{\Longrightarrow} M$, if for any $V \in \mathbf{V}$ we can find $\delta_0 \in \Delta$ such that $xM_\delta \in xMV$ for every $x \in S$ and $\delta \leqq \delta_0$. With this definition, $M_\delta \overset{\delta\in\Delta}{\Longrightarrow} M$ obviously implies $M_\delta \xrightarrow[\delta\in\Delta]{} M$.

A system of mappings $\mathbf{M}$ is said to be *uniformly closed,* if $\mathbf{M} \ni M_\delta \overset{\delta\in\Delta}{\Longrightarrow} M$ implies $\mathbf{M} \ni M$. For a system of mappings $\mathbf{M}$, setting

(2) $\widetilde{\mathbf{M}} = \{M\colon M_\delta \overset{\delta\in\Delta}{\Longrightarrow} M \text{ for some } M_\delta \in \mathbf{M}\ (\delta \in \Delta)\}$,

we obtain a uniformly closed system $\widetilde{\mathbf{M}}$. Because, if $\widetilde{\mathbf{M}} \ni \widetilde{M}_\delta \overset{\delta\in\Delta}{\Longrightarrow} \widetilde{M}$, then for any $V \in \mathbf{V}$ there is $\delta_0 \in \Delta$ such that $x\widetilde{M}_{\delta_0} \in x\widetilde{M}V$ for every $x \in S$. For such $\delta_0 \in \Delta$ we can find $M_V \in \mathbf{M}$ such that $xM_V \in xM_{\delta_0}V$ for every $x \in S$, and hence $xM_V \in x\widetilde{M}V^2$ for every $x \in S$. Thus we conclude by definition $M_V \overset{V\in\mathbf{V}}{\Longrightarrow} \widetilde{M}$. Therefore we obtain $\widetilde{M} \in \widetilde{\mathbf{M}}$ by (2). This uniformly closed system $\widetilde{\mathbf{M}}$ is called the *uniform closure* of $\mathbf{M}$. We have obviously $\widetilde{\mathbf{M}} \subset \overline{\mathbf{M}}$ by definition.

Now we consider S a uniform space with a uniformity $\mathbf{U}$.

Theorem 17.1. *If a system of mappings* $\mathbf{M}$ *from* S *to* R *is equi-continuous, then its closure* $\overline{\mathbf{M}}$ *also is equi-continuous.*

Proof. If $\mathbf{M}$ is equi-continuous, then for any $V \in \mathbf{V}$ there is $U \in \mathbf{U}$ such that $xUM \subset xMV$ for every $x \in S$ and $M \in \mathbf{M}$. For any $\overline{M} \in \overline{\mathbf{M}}$ we can find $M_\delta \in \mathbf{M}$ $(\delta \in \Delta)$ by (1) such that $M_\delta \underset{\delta \in \Delta}{\longrightarrow} \overline{M}$. For any two $x, y \in S$ there is $\delta \in \Delta$ for which $xM_\delta \in x\overline{M}V$, $yM_\delta \in y\overline{M}V$, and if $y \in xU$, then we have

$$y\overline{M} \in yM_\delta V^{-1} \subset xUM_\delta V^{-1} \subset xM_\delta VV^{-1} \subset x\overline{M}V^2V^{-1}.$$

Thus we obtain $xU\overline{M} \subset x\overline{M}V^2V^{-1}$. For any $W \in \mathbf{V}$ we can find a symmetric $V \in \mathbf{V}$ such that $V^3 \leqq W$. Therefore $\overline{\mathbf{M}}$ is equi-continuous.

Theorem 17.2. *For a system of uniformly continuous mappings* $\mathbf{M}$ *from* S *to* R, *its uniform closure* $\widetilde{\mathbf{M}}$ *consists of uniformly continuous mappings.*

Proof. For any $\widetilde{M} \in \widetilde{\mathbf{M}}$ we can find $M_\delta \in \mathbf{M}$ $(\delta \in \Delta)$ by (2) such that $M_\delta \underset{\delta \in \Delta}{\Longrightarrow} \widetilde{M}$. Then for any $V \in \mathbf{V}$ there is $\delta \in \Delta$ such that $xM_\delta \in x\widetilde{M}V$ for every $x \in S$. Since M_δ is uniformly continuous by assumption, we can find $U \in \mathbf{U}$ such that $xUM_\delta \subset xM_\delta V$ for every $x \in S$, and hence

$$xU\widetilde{M} \subset xUM_\delta V^{-1} \subset xM_\delta VV^{-1} \subset x\widetilde{M}V^2V^{-1} \quad \text{for every } x \in S.$$

Since for any $W \in \mathbf{V}$ there is a symmetric $V \in \mathbf{V}$ such that $V^3 \leqq W$, $\widetilde{M}$ is therefore uniformly continuous.

A directed system of mappings M_δ $(\delta \in \Delta)$ is called a *Cauchy system,* if xM_δ $(\delta \in \Delta)$ is a Cauchy system for $\mathbf{V}$ for every $x \in S$. M_δ $(\delta \in \Delta)$ is called a *uniform Cauchy system,* if for any $V \in \mathbf{V}$ we can find $\delta_0 \in \Delta$ such that $xM_\delta \in xM_{\delta_0}V$ for every $x \in S$ and $\delta \leqq \delta_0$.

Theorem 17.3. *If* M_δ $(\delta \in \Delta)$ *is equi-continuous and if the system of the relative mappings* $M_\delta{}^X$ $(\delta \in \Delta)$ *is a Cauchy system for a set* X *such that* $X^{\mathbf{U}-} = S$, *then* M_δ $(\delta \in \Delta)$ *also is a Cauchy system.*

Proof. If M_δ $(\delta \in \Delta)$ is equi-continuous, then for any $V \in \mathbf{V}$ we can find a symmetric $U \in \mathbf{U}$ such that $xUM_\delta \subset xM_\delta V$ for every $x \in S$ and $\delta \in \Delta$. Since $S = X^{\mathbf{U}-} = XU$ by (4) in 4, for any $x \in S$ there is $x_0 \in X$ such that $x \in x_0U$. For such $x_0 \in X$ we can find $\delta_0 \in \Delta$ by assumption such that $x_0M_\delta \in x_0M_{\delta_0}V$ for every $\delta \leqq \delta_0$. Then we have

$$xM_\delta \in x_0UM_\delta \subset x_0M_\delta V \subset x_0M_{\delta_0}V^2 \subset xUM_{\delta_0}V^2 \subset xM_{\delta_0}V^3$$

for every $\delta \leqq \delta_0$. Thus we conclude by Theorem 2.1 that M_δ $(\delta \in \Delta)$ is a Cauchy system.

Theorem 17.4. *For a directed system of uniformly continuous mappings M_δ $(\delta \in \Delta)$ from S to R, if the system of the relative mappings $M_\delta{}^X$ $(\delta \in \Delta)$ is a uniform Cauchy system for a set X such that $X^{\mathbf{U}-} = S$, then M_δ $(\delta \in \Delta)$ also is a uniform Cauchy system.*

Proof. If $M_\delta{}^X$ $(\delta \in \Delta)$ is a uniform Cauchy system, then for any $V \in \mathbf{V}$ there is $\delta_0 \in \Delta$ such that $xM_\delta \in xM_{\delta_0}V$ for every $x \in X$ and $\delta \leqq \delta_0$. For any $\delta \leqq \delta_0$, as M_δ is uniformly continuous by assumption, there is a symmetric $U \in \mathbf{U}$ such that

$$yUM_\delta \subset yM_\delta V, \quad yUM_{\delta_0} \subset yM_{\delta_0}V \quad \text{for every } y \in S.$$

Since $X^{\mathbf{U}-} = S$ by assumption, for any $y \in S$ we can find $x \in X$ by (4) in 4 such that $y \in xU$, and hence

$$yM_\delta \in xUM_\delta \subset xM_\delta V \subset xM_{\delta_0}V^2 \subset yUM_{\delta_0}V^2 \subset yM_{\delta_0}V^3,$$

because $y \in xU$ implies $x \in yU$. Thus we have $yM_\delta \in yM_{\delta_0}V^3$ for every $y \in S$ and $\delta \leqq \delta_0$. Therefore we conclude by Theorem 2.1 that M_δ $(\delta \in \Delta)$ is a uniform Cauchy system.

Theorem 17.5. *If M_δ $(\delta \in \Delta)$ is a uniform Cauchy system, then $M_\delta \xrightarrow[\delta\in\Delta]{} M$ implies $M_\delta \underset{\delta\in\Delta}{\Longrightarrow} M$.*

Proof. For any $V \in \mathbf{V}$ there is a symmetric $W \in \mathbf{V}$ by Theorem 2.1 such that $W^3 \leqq V$. For such $W \in \mathbf{V}$ we can find $\delta_0 \in \Delta$ such that $xM_\delta \in xM_{\delta_0}W$ for every $x \in S$ and $\delta \leqq \delta_0$, because M_δ $(\delta \in \Delta)$ is a uniform Cauchy system by assumption. If $M_\delta \xrightarrow[\delta\in\Delta]{} M$, then for any $x \in S$ we can find $\delta_x \in \Delta$ such that $xM_\delta \in xMW$ for $\delta \leqq \delta_x$. Then for any $\delta_1 \leqq \delta_0, \delta_x$ we have

$$xM_\delta \in xM_{\delta_0}W \subset xM_{\delta_1}W^2 \subset xMW^3 \subset xMV \quad \text{for every } \delta \leqq \delta_0,$$

and hence $xM \in xMV$ for every $x \in S$ and $\delta \leqq \delta_0$, that is, $M_\delta \underset{\delta\in\Delta}{\Longrightarrow} M$.

Theorem 17.6. *For a binary mapping $(x, y) \in Q$ $(x \in S, y \in R)$, $xN_y = yM_x = (x, y)$ with uniformities $\mathbf{U}$, $\mathbf{V}$, $\mathbf{W}$ respectively on S, R, Q, if N_y*

$(y \in R)$ is equi-continuous, then M_{x_δ} $(\delta \in \Delta)$ is a uniform Cauchy system for any Cauchy system $x_\delta \in S$ $(\delta \in \Delta)$ for **U**, *and $S \ni x_\delta \xrightarrow[\delta \in \Delta]{} x$ implies $M_{x_\delta} \underset{\delta \in \Delta}{\Longrightarrow} M_x$.*

Proof. For any $W \in \mathbf{W}$, setting $U = \bigcap_{y \in R} N_y W N_y^{-1}$, we have $U \in \mathbf{U}$, because N_y $(y \in R)$ is equi-continuous by assumption. If $S \ni x_\delta \xrightarrow[\delta \in \Delta]{} x$, then for such $U \in \mathbf{U}$ we can find $\delta_0 \in \Delta$ such that $x_\delta \in xU$ for $\delta \leqq \delta_0$. Thus we obtain

$$yM_{x_\delta} = x_\delta N_y \in xUN_y \subset xN_y W N_y^{-1} N_y \subset xN_y W = yM_x W$$

for every $y \in R$ and $\delta \leqq \delta_0$. Therefore we have $M_{x_\delta} \underset{\delta \in \Delta}{\Longrightarrow} M_x$ by definition.

If $x_\delta \in S$ $(\delta \in \Delta)$ is a Cauchy system for **U**, then we can find $\delta_0 \in \Delta$ such that $x_\delta \in x_{\delta_0} U$ for $\delta \leqq \delta_0$. Thus we obtain quite similarly $yM_{x_\delta} \in yM_{x_{\delta_0}} W$ for every $y \in R$ and $\delta \leqq \delta_0$. Therefore M_{x_δ} $(\delta \in \Delta)$ is a uniform Cauchy system by definition.

18. **Uniformly Continuous Functions.** A mapping from a space S to the space of all real numbers **R** is called a *function* on S. For a function ϕ on S, the image of $x \in S$ is called the *value* of ϕ *at* x, and denoted by $\phi(x)$. A function ϕ on S is said to be *bounded* if

$$-\infty < \inf_{x \in \mathbf{R}} \phi(x) \leqq \sup_{x \in \mathbf{R}} \phi(x) < +\infty,$$

that is, if there is a positive number γ such that $|\phi(x)| \leqq \gamma$ for every $x \in S$. A function ϕ is said to be *bounded on* a set $X \subset S$, if the relative mapping ϕ^X is bounded as a function on X.

For two functions ϕ, ψ on S and for two real numbers α, β, setting

$$\omega(x) = \alpha\, \phi(x) + \beta\, \psi(x) \quad \text{for every } x \in S,$$

we obtain a function ω on S. This function ϕ will be denoted by $\alpha\phi + \beta\psi$. We define also $\phi \vee \psi$ and $\phi \wedge \psi$ by

$$\phi \vee \psi(x) = \mathrm{Max}\,\{\phi(x), \psi(x)\}, \quad \phi \wedge \psi(x) = \mathrm{Min}\,\{\phi(x), \psi(x)\}.$$

The *product* $\phi\psi$ is defined by $\phi\psi(x) = \phi(x)\,\psi(x)$. We write $\phi \geqq \psi$ if $\phi(x) \geqq \psi(x)$ for every $x \in S$.

Lemma. *Let U_ν ($\nu = 0, 1, 2, \ldots$) be a sequence of symmetric connectors on S such that $U_\nu^2 \leqq U_{\nu-1}$ for every $\nu = 1, 2, \ldots$. For any set $X \neq \emptyset$ of S we can find a function ϕ on the subspace $\bigcup_{\mu=1}^{\infty} XU_0^\mu$ such that for any $x \in \bigcup_{\mu=1}^{\infty} XU_0^\mu$ we have*

1) $y \in xU_\nu$ *implies* $|\phi(x) - \phi(y)| \leqq \frac{1}{2^{\nu-1}}$ *for every* $\nu = 1, 2, \ldots,$
2) $\phi(x) = 0$ *for* $x \in X$,
3) $\phi(x) \geqq \frac{1}{2^\nu}$ *for* $x \bar{\in} XU_\nu$,
4) $\phi(x) \geqq \mu$ *for* $x \bar{\in} XU_0^\mu$,
5) $0 \leqq \phi(x) \leqq \mu$ *for* $x \in XU_0^\mu$,

Proof. Setting $V_\tau = U_0^\mu U_1^{\varepsilon_1} U_2^{\varepsilon_2} \ldots U_n^{\varepsilon_n}$,

$$\tau = \mu + \sum_{\nu=1}^{n} \frac{\varepsilon_\nu}{2^\nu}, \quad \xi_\nu = 0, 1, \quad \nu = 1, 2, \ldots, n; \quad \mu = 0, 1, 2, \ldots,$$

we will prove by induction on ν that $\tau = \frac{a}{2^\nu}$, $\tau' = \frac{a+1}{2^\nu}$, $a \geqq 0$ implies $V_{\tau'} \geqq V_\tau U_\nu$. This is obviously true for $\nu = 0$. We assume that it is true for $0, 1, 2, \ldots, \nu - 1$. If a is even, then we obviously have $V_{\tau'} = V_\tau U_\nu$. If a is odd, then, setting $a = 2\beta + 1$, $\sigma = \frac{\beta}{2^{\nu-1}}$, we have $\tau' = \frac{\beta+1}{2^{\nu-1}}$, and hence $V_{\tau'} \geqq V_\sigma U_{\nu-1}$ by assumption. As $U_{\nu-1} \geqq U_\nu^2$, we obtain therefore $V_{\tau'} \geqq V_\sigma U_\nu^2 = V_\tau U_\nu$, because $\sigma + \frac{1}{2^\nu} = \tau$. Thus our assertion is proved. From this relation we conclude immediately that $\sigma > \tau \geqq 0$ implies $V_\sigma \geqq V_\tau$.

For every point $x \in \bigcup_{\mu=1}^{\infty} XU_0^\mu$, setting

$$\phi(x) = \inf_{XV_\tau \ni x} \tau,$$

we obtain a function ϕ on $\bigcup_{\mu=1}^{\infty} XU_0^\mu$. This function ϕ clearly satisfies 2), 3), 4), 5). For each point $x \in \bigcup_{\mu=1}^{\infty} XU_0^\mu$ and for any ν we can find ϕ such that $\frac{\phi}{2^\nu} - \frac{1}{2^\nu} \leqq \phi(x) < \frac{\phi}{2^\nu}$. Then, putting $\tau = \frac{\phi}{2^\nu}$, we obviously have $x \in XV_\tau$, and hence $y \in xU_\nu$ implies $y \in XV_\tau U_\nu \subset XV_{\tau'}$, because $V_\tau U_\nu \leqq V_{\tau'}$, as just proved above. Therefore we obtain by the definition of ϕ

$$\phi(y) \leqq \tau' = \frac{a}{2^\nu} + \frac{1}{2^\nu} \leqq \phi(x) + \frac{1}{2^{\nu-1}}$$

Since U_ν is symmetric by assumption, we obtain likewise

$$\phi(x) \leqq \phi(y) + \frac{1}{2^{\nu-1}}.$$

Thus we conclude 1): $y \in xU_\nu$ implies $|\phi(x) - \phi(y)| \leqq \frac{1}{2^{\nu-1}}$.

Now we define a uniformity on the space of real numbers **R**. For any $\varepsilon > 0$, setting

$$\xi V_\varepsilon = \{\eta : |\xi - \eta| < \varepsilon\}$$

we obtain a connector V_ε on **R**, which will be called an *interval connector* with *radius* ε. About interval connectors, we can easily prove

(1) $V_\varepsilon \cap V_\delta = V_{\mathrm{Min}\{\varepsilon,\delta\}}$

(2) $V_\varepsilon^{-1} = V_\varepsilon$

(3) $V_\varepsilon V_\varepsilon = V_{\varepsilon+\delta}$.

Thus the system V_ε $(\varepsilon > 0)$ satisfies the basis conditions, and hence there exists uniquely a uniformity on **R** for which V_ε $(\varepsilon > 0)$ is a basis. This uniformity on **R** is called the *natural uniformity*. For the natural uniformity on **R**, the sequence of interval connectors $V_{1/\nu}$ $(\nu = 1, 2, \ldots)$ is obviously a basis. Thus the natural uniformity is sequential. Every Cauchy sequence on **R** is convergent by the so-called Cauchy's theorem. Therefore the natural uniformity is complete by Theorem 8.5. Furthermore we see easily that every interval connector is open and totally bounded. Therefore we can state

Theorem 18.1. *The natural uniformity on* **R** *is pure, sequential and complete. Every interval connector is open and totally bounded for the natural uniformity.*

Theorem 18.2. *For the natural uniformity, every bounded set is totally bounded, and a set* $A \subset$ **R** *is bounded if and only if* $A \subset \xi V_\varepsilon$ *for some* $\xi \in$ **R** *and* $\varepsilon > 0$, *that is,* $\sup_{\xi \in A} |\xi| < +\infty$.

Let S be a uniform space with a uniformity $\mathbf{U}$. A function ϕ on S is said to be *continuous* or *uniformly continuous,* if it is so as a mapping from S to $\mathbf{R}$ for the natural uniformity.

With this definition we obviously have

Theorem 18.3. *A function ϕ on S is uniformly continuous if and only if for any $\varepsilon > 0$ we can find $U \in \mathbf{U}$ such that $x \in yU$ implies*

$$|\phi(x) - \phi(y)| < \varepsilon.$$

A function ϕ on S is said to be *bounded* if $\sup_{x \in S} |\phi(x)| < +\infty$. We also can easily prove

Theorem 18.4. *For two uniformly continuous functions ϕ, ψ on S, we obtain uniformly continuous functions $\phi \vee \psi$, $\phi \wedge \psi$, $a\phi + \beta\psi$ for real numbers a, β, and $\phi\psi$ if both ϕ and ψ are bounded. If ϕ is uniformly continuous and* $\inf_{x \in S} |\phi(x)| > 0$, *then $1/\phi$ also is uniformly continuous.*

A function ϕ is said to be *bounded on* a set X, if $\sup_{x \in X} |\phi(x)| < +\infty$. With this definition we have

Theorem 18.5. *A set $A \neq \emptyset$ of S is bounded by* $\mathbf{U}$ *if and only if every uniformly continuous function is bounded on A.*

Proof. If A is bounded, then for any uniformly continuous function ϕ there is $U \in \mathbf{U}$ such that $x \in yU$ implies $|\phi(x) - \phi(y)| < 1$, and for such $U \in \mathbf{U}$ we can find a finite system $a_\nu \in A$ $(\nu = 1, 2, \ldots, n)$ such that $A \subset \bigcup_{\nu=1}^{n} a_\nu U^\sigma$ for some $\sigma = 1, 2, \ldots$. Thus we have

$$\sup_{x \in A} |\phi(x)| \leqq \operatorname*{Max}_{1 \leqq \nu \leqq n} |\phi(a_\nu)| + \sigma.$$

If A is not bounded, then we can find a symmetric $U_0 \in \mathbf{U}$ such that $A \neq A \cap \bigcup_{\nu=1}^{n} a_\nu U_0^{\sigma}$ for every $\sigma = 1, 2, \ldots$ and for every finite system $a_\nu \in A$ $(\nu = 1, 2, \ldots, n)$.

For such $U_0 \in \mathbf{U}$, two cases are considered. In the first case, where there is a point $a \in A$ such that

$$A \cap \bigcup_{\nu=1}^{\infty} aU_0^{\nu} \neq A \cap \bigcup_{\nu=1}^{\mu} aU_0^{\nu} \quad \text{for every } \mu = 1, 2, \ldots,$$

we can find a sequence of symmetric connectors $U_\nu \in \mathbf{U}$ $(\nu = 1, 2, \ldots)$ by Theorem 2.1 such that $U_\nu \geqq U_{\nu+1}{}^2$ for $\nu = 0, 1, 2, \ldots$. Then we can find a function ϕ on $\bigcup_{\nu=1}^{\infty} aU_0{}^\nu$ by the Lemma such that $x \in yU_\nu$ implies $|\phi(x) - \phi(y)| \leqq \frac{1}{2^{\nu-1}}$ and $\phi(x) \geqq \mu$ for $x \bar{\in} \bigcup_{\nu=1}^{\mu} aU_0{}^\nu$. For such a function ϕ, setting $\phi(x) = 0$ for $x \bar{\in} \bigcup_{\nu=1}^{\infty} aU_0{}^\nu$, we obtain a uniformly continuous function ϕ on S, because we have

$$(\bigcup_{\nu=1}^{\infty} aU_0{}^\nu)' U_\mu = (\bigcup_{\nu=1}^{\infty} aU_0{}^\nu)' \quad \text{for every } \mu = 0, 1, 2, \ldots$$

by Theorem 1.5. This uniformly continuous function ϕ is not bounded on A, because

$$\phi(x) \geqq \mu \quad \text{for } x \in (A \cap \bigcup_{\nu=1}^{\infty} aU_0{}^\nu) \cap (A \cap \bigcup_{\nu=1}^{\mu} aU_0{}^\nu)'.$$

In the second case, where there is no such point $a \in A$, we can find a sequence of points $a_\mu \in A$ $(\mu = 1, 2, \ldots)$ such that

$$\bigcup_{\nu=1}^{\infty} a_\mu U_0{}^\nu \cap \bigcup_{\nu=1}^{\infty} a_\rho U_0{}^\nu = \emptyset \quad \text{for } \mu \neq \rho,$$

because A is not bounded by assumption. Setting

$$\phi(x) = \begin{cases} \mu & \text{for } x \in \bigcup_{\nu=1}^{\infty} a_\mu U_0{}^\nu, \\ 0 & \text{for } x \bar{\in} \bigcup_{\mu=1}^{\infty} \bigcup_{\nu=1}^{\infty} a_\mu U_0{}^\nu, \end{cases}$$

we obtain a uniformly continuous function ϕ on S, because we have

$$(\bigcup_{\nu=1}^{\infty} a_\mu U_0{}^\nu) U_0 = \bigcup_{\nu=1}^{\infty} a_\mu U_0{}^\nu$$

by Theorem 1.5. This function ϕ is not bounded on A, because $\phi(a_\mu) \geqq \mu$ for $\mu = 1, 2, \ldots$. Therefore our assertion is established.

For a function ϕ on a directed space Δ, we make the definition:

$$\overline{\lim_{\delta \in \Delta}}\, \phi(\delta) = \inf_{\delta \in \Delta} \sup_{\delta \geqq \gamma \in \Delta} \phi(\gamma),$$

$$\underline{\lim_{\delta \in \Delta}}\, \phi(\delta) = \sup_{\delta \in \Delta} \inf_{\delta \geqq \gamma \in \Delta} \phi(\gamma).$$

With this definition we obviously have

$$-\infty \leqq \varliminf_{\delta\epsilon\Delta} \phi(\delta) \leqq \varlimsup_{\delta\epsilon\Delta} \phi(\delta) \leqq +\infty.$$

If $-\infty < \varliminf_{\delta\epsilon\Delta} \phi(\delta) = \varlimsup_{\delta\epsilon\Delta} \phi(\delta) < +\infty$, then the system $\phi(\delta)$ $(\delta \in \Delta)$ is said to be *convergent* and this common value is denoted by $\lim_{\delta\epsilon\Delta} \phi(\delta)$. This convergence coincides obviously with the convergence for the natural uniformity. If $\phi(\delta)$ $(\delta \in \Delta)$ is a Cauchy system for the natural uniformity, then $\phi(\delta)$ $(\delta \in \Delta)$ is convergent, because the natural uniformity is complete. We can easily prove

Theorem 18.6. *If* $\lim_{\delta\epsilon\Delta} \phi(\delta) = \lambda$, $\lim_{\delta\epsilon\Delta} \psi(\delta) = \rho$, *then*

$$\lim_{\delta\epsilon\Delta} (\alpha\phi(\delta) + \beta\psi(\delta)) = \alpha\lambda + \beta\rho.$$

If $\phi(\delta) \geqq \psi(\delta)$ $(\delta \leqq \delta_0)$ *for some* $\delta_0 \in \Delta$, *then* $\lim_{\delta\epsilon\Delta} \phi(\delta) \geqq \lim_{\delta\epsilon\Delta} \psi(\delta)$.

For any partial system $\delta_\gamma \in \Delta$ $(\gamma \in \Gamma)$, we obviously have by definition

$$\varliminf_{\delta\epsilon\Delta} \phi(\delta) \leqq \varliminf_{\gamma\epsilon\Gamma} \phi(\delta_\gamma) \leqq \varlimsup_{\gamma\epsilon\Gamma} \phi(\delta_\gamma) \leqq \varlimsup_{\delta\epsilon\Delta} \phi(\delta).$$

Thus we can state

Theorem 18.7. *If* $\lim_{\delta\epsilon\Delta} \phi(\delta) = \lambda$, *then* $\lim_{\gamma\epsilon\Gamma} \phi(\delta_\gamma) = \lambda$ *for any partial system* $\delta_\gamma \in \Delta$ $(\gamma \in \Gamma)$.

19. **Extension Theorems.** Let $\mathbf{U}$ be a uniformity on a space S. For any $U \in \mathbf{U}$ we can find a sequence of symmetric connectors $U_\nu \in \mathbf{U}$ $(\nu = 0, 1, 2, \ldots)$ by Theorem 2.1 such that $U_\nu^2 \leqq U_{\nu-1} \leqq U$ $(\nu = 1, 2, \ldots)$: For any set $X \neq \emptyset$ of S there is a function ϕ on $\bigcup_{\mu=1}^{\infty} XU_0^\mu$ by the Lemma in 18 such that $\phi(x) = 0$ for $x \in X$, $0 \leqq \phi(x) \leqq 1$ for $x \in XU_0$, $\phi(x) \geqq 1$ for $x \bar{\epsilon} XU_0$, and

$$xU_\nu \ni y \in \bigcup_{\mu=1}^{\infty} XU_0^\mu \text{ implies } |\phi(x) - \phi(y)| \leqq \frac{1}{2^{\nu-1}} \; (\nu = 1, 2, \ldots).$$

For such a function ϕ, setting $\phi_0(x) = 1$ for $x \bar{\epsilon} XU_0$ and $\phi_0(x) = \phi(x)$

for $x \in XU_0$, we obtain a function ϕ_0 on S such that $\phi_0(x) = 0$ for $x \in X$, $0 \leqq \phi_0(x) \leqq 1$ for $x \in S$, $\phi_0(x) = 1$ for $x \bar{\in} XU$, and

$$xU_\nu \ni y \text{ implies } |\phi_0(x) - \phi_0(y)| \leqq \frac{1}{2^{\nu-1}} \quad (\nu = 1, 2, \ldots).$$

Therefore we conclude

Theorem 19.1. *For any $U \in \mathbf{U}$ and for any system of sets $X_\lambda \neq \emptyset$ $(\lambda \in \Lambda)$ there is an equi-continuous system of functions ϕ_λ $(\lambda \in \Lambda)$ such that*

$$\phi_\lambda(x) = \begin{cases} 0 & \text{for } x \in X_\lambda \\ 1 & \text{for } x \bar{\in} X_\lambda U \end{cases} \quad \text{for every } \lambda \in \Lambda,$$

and $0 \leqq \phi_\lambda(x) \leqq 1$ for $x \in S$, $\lambda \in \Lambda$.

For two sets X, $Y \neq \emptyset$, if there is $U \in \mathbf{U}$ such that $XU \cap Y = \emptyset$, then we can find a uniformly continuous function ϕ by Theorem 19.1 such that $\phi(x) = 0$ for $x \in X$, $\phi(x) = 1$ for $x \in Y$, and $0 \leqq \phi(x) \leqq 1$ for $x \in S$. For such ϕ, setting $\psi = \frac{2}{3}(\phi - \frac{1}{2})$, we obtain a uniformly continuous function ψ such that $\psi(x) = -\frac{1}{3}$ for $x \in X$, $\psi(x) = \frac{1}{3}$ for $x \in Y$, and $-\frac{1}{3} \leqq \psi(x) \leqq \frac{1}{3}$ for $x \in S$.

Now let $\emptyset \neq A \subset S$ and let ϕ be a uniformly continuous function on A for the relative uniformity $\mathbf{U}^A$ such that

$$\sup_{x \in A} \phi(x) = 1, \quad \inf_{x \in A} \phi(x) = -1.$$

Since ϕ is uniformly continuous for $\mathbf{U}^A$, we can find $U \in \mathbf{U}$ such that

$$|\phi(x) - \phi(y)| < \frac{1}{3} \quad \text{for } x \in yU,\ x, y \in A.$$

For such $U \in \mathbf{U}$, setting

$$X = \{x: \phi(x) < -\frac{1}{3}\}, \quad Y = \{x: \phi(x) > \frac{1}{3}\},$$

we have $XU \cap Y = \emptyset$, because $x \in X$, $y \in xU$, $y \in A$ implies $\phi(x) < -\frac{1}{3}$, $|\phi(x) - \phi(y)| < \frac{1}{3}$, and hence $\phi(y) < 0$. Thus there is a uniformly continuous function ψ_1 on S such that $\psi_1(x) = -\frac{1}{3}$ for $x \in X$, $\psi_1(x) = \frac{1}{3}$

for $x \in Y$ and $-\frac{1}{3} \leqq \psi_1(x) \leqq \frac{1}{3}$ for $x \in S$. For such ψ_1, setting

$$\phi_1(x) = \frac{3}{2}(\phi(x) - \psi_1(x)) \text{ for } x \in A,$$

we obtain a uniformly continuous function ϕ_1 on A for $\mathbf{U}^A$ and we obviously have

$$\sup_{x \in A} \phi_1(x) = \sup_{x \in Y} \phi_1(x) = 1, \quad \inf_{x \in A} \phi_1(x) = \inf_{x \in X} \phi_1(x) = -1.$$

Similarly we consecutively obtain uniformly continuous functions ψ_ν on S for $\mathbf{U}$ and ϕ_ν on A for $\mathbf{U}^A$ ($\nu = 2, 3, \ldots$) such that

$$\phi_\nu(x) = \frac{3}{2}(\phi_{\nu-1}(x) - \psi_\nu(x)) \text{ for } x \in A,$$

$$|\phi_\nu(x)| \leqq 1 \text{ for } x \in A, \quad |\psi_\nu(x)| \leqq \frac{1}{3} \text{ for } x \in S$$

for $\nu = 2, 3, \ldots$. Then we have

$$\phi(x) = \sum_{\mu=1}^{\nu} \left(\frac{2}{3}\right)^{\mu-1} \psi_\mu(x) + \left(\frac{2}{3}\right) \phi_\nu(x)$$

for $x \in A$ and $\nu = 1, 2, \ldots$, and hence

$$\phi(x) = \sum_{\mu=1}^{\infty} \left(\frac{2}{3}\right)^{\mu-1} \psi_\mu(x) \text{ for } x \in A.$$

Here the series on the right side is obviously uniformly convergent on S. Thus, setting

$$\psi(x) = \sum_{\mu=1}^{\infty} \left(\frac{2}{3}\right)^{\mu-1} \psi_\mu(x) \text{ for } x \in S,$$

we obtain a uniformly continuous function ψ by Theorem 17.2 and $\psi(x) = \phi(x)$ for $x \in A$.

If ϕ is a uniformly continuous function on A for $\mathbf{U}^A$ such that

$$\sup_{x \in A} \phi(x) = \alpha, \quad \inf_{x \in A} \phi(x) = \beta, \quad \alpha > \beta,$$

then, setting $\phi_0 = \frac{1}{\alpha - \beta}(2\phi - \alpha - \beta)$, we obtain a uniformly continuous function ϕ_0 on A such that

$$\sup_{x \in A} \phi_0(x) = 1, \quad \inf_{x \in A} \phi_0(x) = -1.$$

Therefore there exists a uniformly continuous function ψ_0 on S such that $\psi_0(x) = \phi_0(x)$ for $x \in A$. Thus we can state

Theorem 19.2. *For any bounded, uniformly continuous function* ϕ

on a set $A \subset S$ for $\mathbf{U}^A$, there is a uniformly continuous function ψ on S such that $\psi(x) = \phi(x)$ for $x \in A$.

Remark. If $\mathbf{U}$ is bounded, then every uniformly continuous function on S is bounded by Theorem 18.5. If $\mathbf{U}$ is not totally bounded, then there is a set $A \subset S$ by Theorem 6.4 which is not bounded for the relative uniformity $\mathbf{U}^A$, and we can find a function ϕ on A by Theorem 18.5 such that ϕ is uniformly continuous for $\mathbf{U}^A$ but not bounded. Therefore, if $\mathbf{U}$ is bounded, but not totally bounded, then we can find a set $A \subset S$ and a function ϕ on A such that ϕ is uniformly continuous for $\mathbf{U}^A$ but not bounded, and hence there is no uniformly continuous extension of ϕ over S. Concerning bounded but not totally bounded uniformities, we shall find them in 25.

20. **Comparison of Uniformities.** Let $\mathbf{U}$ and $\mathbf{V}$ be two uniformities on a space S. We say that $\mathbf{U}$ is *stronger* than $\mathbf{V}$ or that $\mathbf{V}$ is *weaker* than $\mathbf{U}$, if $\mathbf{U} \supset \mathbf{V}$. Setting $xE = x$ $(x \in S)$, we obtain a transformation E from S to S, which is called the *identity* on S. It is obvious by definition that the identity E on S is uniformly continuous as a mapping from S with $\mathbf{U}$ to S with $\mathbf{V}$, if and only if $\mathbf{U} \supset \mathbf{V}$.

Referring to Theorem 4.4, we obtain immediately

Theorem 20.1. $\mathbf{U} \supset \mathbf{V}$ *implies* $\mathbf{T}(\mathbf{U}) \supset \mathbf{T}(\mathbf{V})$.

We also have clearly by definition

Theorem 20.2. *For two uniformities $\mathbf{U} \supset \mathbf{V}$ on S, if a set $A \subset S$ is bounded, totally bounded, compact or connected for $\mathbf{U}$, then A also is so for $\mathbf{V}$; $S \ni x_\delta \xrightarrow[\delta\in\Delta]{} x$ for $\mathbf{U}$ implies $x_\delta \xrightarrow[\delta\in\Delta]{} x$ for $\mathbf{V}$; and every Cauchy system for $\mathbf{U}$ is a Cauchy system for $\mathbf{V}$ too.*

Let Q be another uniform space with uniformity $\mathbf{W}$. We can conclude easily from definition

Theorem 20.3. *If a mapping M from S to Q is continuous or uniformly continuous for a uniformity $\mathbf{V}$ on S, then M also is so for every uniformity $\mathbf{U} \supset \mathbf{V}$ on S. If a system of mappings M_λ $(\lambda \in \Lambda)$ from S to Q is equi-continuous for a uniformity $\mathbf{V}$ on S, then M_λ $(\lambda \in \Lambda)$ also is equi-continuous for every uniformity $\mathbf{U} \supset \mathbf{V}$ on S.*

Theorem 20.4. *If every equi-continuous system of bounded functions on S for* **U** *is always equi-continuous for* **V**, *then* $\mathbf{U} \subset \mathbf{V}$.

Proof. If **V** is not stronger than **U**, then there is $U_0 \in \mathbf{U}$ by definition such that $U_0 \,\bar{\in}\, \mathbf{V}$. For such $U_0 \in \mathbf{U}$ we can find a system x_V, $y_V \in S$ $(V \in \mathbf{V})$ such that $x_V V \ni y_V$ but $x_V U_0 \,\bar{\ni}\, y_V$ for every $V \in \mathbf{V}$, because $xU_0 \supset xV$ fails for some $x \in S$. Then we can find a system of functions ϕ_V $(V \in \mathbf{V})$ by Theorem 19.1 such that $\phi_V(x_V) = 0$, $\phi_V(y_V) = 1$, $0 \leqq \phi_V(x) \leqq 1$ for every $x \in S$ and the system ϕ_V $(V \in \mathbf{V})$ is equi-continuous for **U**. But this system ϕ_V $(V \in \mathbf{V})$ is not equi-continuous for **V**, because $x_V V \ni y_V$ for every $V \in \mathbf{V}$.

Theorem 20.5. *If* **U** *is totally bounded and if every uniformly continuous function on S for* **U** *also is uniformly continuous for* **V**, *then* $\mathbf{U} \subset \mathbf{V}$.

Proof. If **V** is not stronger than **U**, then we can find $U_0 \in \mathbf{U}$ and x_V, $y_V \in S$ $(V \in \mathbf{V})$ such that $x_V V \ni y_V$ but $x_V U_0 \,\bar{\ni}\, y_V$ for every $V \in \mathbf{V}$, as proved just above. For such $U_0 \in \mathbf{U}$ there is a symmetric $U \in \mathbf{U}$ by Theorem 2.1 such that $U^3 \leqq U_0$. If **U** is totally bounded, then we can find a finite system of points $a_\nu \in S$ $(\nu = 1, 2, \ldots, n)$ such that $S = \bigcup_{\nu=1}^{n} a_\nu U$, and there is ν such that $\{V\colon x_V \in a_\nu U\}$ is a basis of **V**. Because if $\{V\colon x_V \in a_\nu U\}$ is not basis of **V** for every $\nu = 1, 2, \ldots, n$, then we can find $V_\nu \in \mathbf{V}$ $(\nu = 1, 2, \ldots, n)$ such that $x_V \in a_\nu U$ implies $V \not\leqq V_\nu$ and hence $V \not\leqq \bigcap_{\mu=1}^{n} V_\mu \in \mathbf{V}$ for every $\nu = 1, 2, \ldots, n$, contradicting $\mathbf{V} = \bigcup_{\nu=1}^{n} \{V\colon x_V \in a_\nu U\}$. If $\{V\colon x_V \in a_\nu U\}$ is a basis of **V**, then setting

$$X = \{x_V\colon x_V \in a_\nu U\}, \quad Y = \{y_V\colon x_V \in a_\nu U\},$$

we have $XU \subset a_\nu U^2 \subset x_V U^3 \subset x_V U_0$ for $x_V \in a_\nu U$, and hence $XU \subset \bigcap_{x_V \in a_\nu U} x_V U_0$. Consequently we obtain $XU \cap Y = \emptyset$. Thus there exists a uniformly continuous ϕ on S for **U** by Theorem 19.1 such that $\phi(x) = 0$ for $x \in X$ and $\phi(x) = 1$ for $x \in Y$. But this function ϕ is not uniformly continuous for **V**, because $\phi(x_V) = 0$, $\phi(y_V) = 1$, $x_V V \ni y_V$ for $x_V \in a_\nu U$ and $\{V\colon x_V \in a_\nu U\}$ is a basis of **V**.

Theorem 20.6. *For two uniformities* $\mathbf{U} \supset \mathbf{V}$ *on* S, *if* $\mathbf{U}^A = \mathbf{V}^A$ *for a set* A *such that* $A^{\mathbf{U}-} = S$, *then* $\mathbf{U} = \mathbf{V}$.

Proof. Considering the identity E on S as a mapping from S with $\mathbf{V}$ to S with $\mathbf{U}$, the relative mapping E^A is uniformly continuous, because $\mathbf{U}^A = \mathbf{V}^A$ by assumption. Since $A^{\mathbf{U}-} = S$, for any $x \in S$ we can find a system $x_\delta \in A$ $(\delta \in \Delta)$ by Theorem 7.3 such that $x_\delta \xrightarrow[\delta\in\Delta]{} x$ for $\mathbf{U}$ and hence $x_\delta \xrightarrow[\delta\in\Delta]{} x$ for $\mathbf{V}$ by Theorem 20.2. Thus E is uniformly continuous by Theorem 12.7. Therefore $\mathbf{V} \supset \mathbf{U}$.

Theorem 20.7. *If the relative uniformity* $\mathbf{U}^A$ *is sequential for a set* A *such that* $A^{\mathbf{U}-} = S$, *then* $\mathbf{U}$ *also is sequential.*

Proof. If $\mathbf{U}^A$ is sequential and $U_\nu{}^A$ $(\nu = 1, 2, \ldots)$ is a basis of $\mathbf{U}^A$ such that $U_\nu \in \mathbf{U}$ $(\nu = 1, 2, \ldots)$, then we can find a sequence of symmetric $V_\nu \in \mathbf{U}$ $(\nu = 1, 2, \ldots)$ such that $U_\nu \geqq V_\nu \geqq V_{\nu+1}{}^2$ $(\nu = 1, 2, \ldots)$. Then $V_\nu \in \mathbf{U}$ $(\nu = 1, 2, \ldots)$ obviously satisfies the basis conditions, and hence there exists uniquely a uniformity $\mathbf{V}$ on S such that V_ν $(\nu = 1, 2, \ldots)$ is a basis of $\mathbf{V}$. For such a sequential uniformity $\mathbf{V}$ on S, we obviously have that $\mathbf{U} \supset \mathbf{V}$ and $\mathbf{U}^A = \mathbf{V}^A$. Therefore we obtain $\mathbf{U} = \mathbf{V}$ by Theorem 20.6, and consequently $\mathbf{U}$ is sequential.

For a set $X \neq \emptyset$ of S, we say that $\mathbf{U}$ is *stronger* than $\mathbf{V}$ on X, or that $\mathbf{V}$ is *weaker* than $\mathbf{U}$ on X, if $\mathbf{U}^X \supset \mathbf{V}^X$. Referring to Theorem 12.10, we conclude immediately from definition

Theorem 20.8. *For a finite system of sets* $X_\nu \neq \emptyset$ $(\nu = 1, 2, \ldots, n)$ *and* $U \in \mathbf{U}$, *if* $\mathbf{U}$ *is stronger than* $\mathbf{V}$ *on* $X_\nu U$ *for every* $\nu = 1, 2, \ldots, n$, *then* $\mathbf{U}$ *is stronger than* $\mathbf{V}$ *on* $\bigcup_{\nu=1}^{n} X_\nu$.

III. EQUI-UNIFORMITIES

21. Weakest Stronger Uniformities. Let S be a space. The pure discrete uniformity on S is obviously stronger than any uniformity on S. For a system of uniformities $\mathbf{U}_\lambda$ $(\lambda \in \Lambda)$ on S, there is the weakest among the uniformities which are stronger than every $\mathbf{U}_\lambda$ $(\lambda \in \Lambda)$. Because, if we set

$$\mathbf{B} = \{ \bigcap_{\nu=1}^{n} U_\nu : U_\nu \in \mathbf{U}_{\lambda_\nu}, \lambda_\nu \in \Lambda \ (\nu = 1, 2, \ldots, n), n = 1, 2, \ldots \},$$

then $\mathbf{B}$ obviously satisfies the basis condition 1). Since

$$(\bigcap_{\nu=1}^{n} U_\nu)^{-1} (\bigcap_{\nu=1}^{n} V_\nu) \leqq \bigcap_{\nu=1}^{n} U_\nu^{-1} V_\nu ,$$

for connectors U_ν, V_ν $(\nu = 1, 2, \ldots, n)$, $\mathbf{B}$ also satisfies 2). Thus there exists uniquely a uniformity $\mathbf{U}_0$ on S such that $\mathbf{B}$ is a basis of $\mathbf{U}_0$. Then we obviously have $\mathbf{U}_0 \supset \mathbf{B} \supset \mathbf{U}_\lambda$ for every $\lambda \in \Lambda$. If $\mathbf{U} \supset \mathbf{U}_\lambda$ $(\lambda \in \Lambda)$ for some uniformity $\mathbf{U}$ on S, then $\mathbf{U} \ni \bigcap_{\nu=1}^{n} U_\nu$ for any finite system $U_\nu \in \mathbf{U}_{\lambda_\nu}$ $(\nu = 1, 2, \ldots, n)$ by the uniformity condition 2), and hence $\mathbf{U} \supset \mathbf{B}$. On the other hand $\mathbf{U} \supset \mathbf{B}$ implies $\mathbf{U} \supset \mathbf{U}_0$ by the uniformity condition 1). Therefore $\mathbf{U}_0$ is the weakest among the uniformities which are stronger than every $\mathbf{U}_\lambda$ $(\lambda \in \Lambda)$. This uniformity $\mathbf{U}_0$ is called the *weakest stronger uniformity* of $\mathbf{U}_\lambda$ $(\lambda \in \Lambda)$ and denoted by $\bigvee_{\lambda \in \Lambda} \mathbf{U}_\lambda$. Thus we can state

Theorem 21.1. *We have* $U \in \bigvee_{\lambda \in \Lambda} \mathbf{U}_\lambda$ *if and only if we can find a finite system* $U_\nu \in \mathbf{U}_{\lambda_\nu}$ $(\nu = 1, 2, \ldots, n)$ *such that* $U \geqq \bigcap_{\nu=1}^{n} U_\nu$.

Theorem 21.2. *For a topology* $\mathbf{T}$ *on* S *we have* $\mathbf{T} \supset \mathbf{T}(\bigvee_{\lambda \epsilon \Lambda} \mathbf{U}_\lambda)$ *if and only if* $\mathbf{T} \supset \mathbf{T}(\mathbf{U}_\lambda)$ *for every* $\lambda \epsilon \Lambda$.

Proof. For any $U \epsilon \bigvee_{\lambda \epsilon \Lambda} \mathbf{U}_\lambda$ there is a finite system $U_\nu \epsilon \mathbf{U}_{\lambda_\nu}$ ($\nu = 1, 2, \ldots, n$) by Theorem 21.1 such that $U \geqq \bigcap_{\nu=1}^{n} U_\nu$. If $\mathbf{T} \supset \mathbf{T}(\mathbf{U}_\lambda)$ for every $\lambda \epsilon \Lambda$, then we have $x \epsilon (xU_\nu)^{\mathbf{T}\circ}$ for every $x \epsilon S$ and $\nu = 1, 2, \ldots, n$ by Theorem 4.2. On the other hand we have by Theorem 3.1

$$(xU)^{\mathbf{T}\circ} \supset (\bigcap_{\nu=1}^{n} xU_\nu)^{\mathbf{T}\circ} = \bigcap_{\nu=1}^{n} (xU_\nu)^{\mathbf{T}\circ} \text{ for every } x \epsilon S.$$

Thus we also have $x \epsilon (xU)^{\mathbf{T}\circ}$ for every $x \epsilon S$. Consequently $\mathbf{T} \supset \mathbf{T}(\bigvee_{\lambda \epsilon \Lambda} \mathbf{U}_\lambda)$ by Theorem 4.2. Conversely $\mathbf{T}(\bigvee_{\lambda \epsilon \Lambda} \mathbf{U}_\lambda) \supset \mathbf{T}(\mathbf{U}_\gamma)$ for every $\gamma \epsilon \Lambda$ by Theorem 20.1.

Theorem 21.3. *For any set* $X \neq \emptyset$ *of* S *we have*

$$(\bigvee_{\lambda \epsilon \Lambda} \mathbf{U}_\lambda)^X = \bigvee_{\lambda \epsilon \Lambda} \mathbf{U}_\lambda{}^X.$$

Proof. For any $U \epsilon \bigvee_{\lambda \epsilon \Lambda} \mathbf{U}_\lambda$ we can find a finite system $U_\nu \epsilon \mathbf{U}_{\lambda_\nu}$ ($\nu = 1, 2, \ldots, n$) by Theorem 21.1 such that $U \geqq \bigcap_{\nu=1}^{n} U_\nu$, and hence $U^X \geqq \bigcap_{\nu=1}^{n} U_\nu{}^X$. Thus we obtain $(\bigvee_{\lambda \epsilon \Lambda} \mathbf{U}_\lambda)^X \subset \bigvee_{\lambda \epsilon \Lambda} \mathbf{U}_\lambda{}^X$ by Theorem 21.1. On the other hand, $(\bigvee_{\lambda \epsilon \Lambda} \mathbf{U}_\lambda)^X \supset \mathbf{U}_\gamma{}^X$ for every $\gamma \epsilon \Lambda$ implies $(\bigvee_{\lambda \epsilon \Lambda} \mathbf{U}_\lambda)^X \supset \bigvee_{\lambda \epsilon \Lambda} \mathbf{U}_\lambda{}^X$.

We also can prove easily by Theorem 21.1

Theorem 21.4. *We have* $x_\delta \xrightarrow[\delta \epsilon \Delta]{} x$ *for* $\bigvee_{\lambda \epsilon \Lambda} \mathbf{U}_\lambda$ *if and only if* $x_\delta \xrightarrow[\delta \epsilon \Delta]{} x$ *for* $\mathbf{U}_\lambda$ *for every* $\lambda \epsilon \Lambda$. $x_\delta \epsilon S$ ($\delta \epsilon \Delta$) *is a Cauchy system for* $\bigvee_{\lambda \epsilon \Lambda} \mathbf{U}_\lambda$ *if and only if it is so for* $\mathbf{U}_\lambda$ *for every* $\lambda \epsilon \Lambda$.

Theorem 21.5. *A set* A *is totally bounded for* $\bigvee_{\lambda \epsilon \Lambda} \mathbf{U}_\lambda$ *if and only if* A *is so for* $\mathbf{U}_\lambda$ *for every* $\lambda \epsilon \Lambda$.

Proof. If A is totally bounded for $\bigvee_{\lambda \epsilon \Lambda} \mathbf{U}_\lambda$, then A also is so for every $\mathbf{U}_\lambda$ by Theorem 20.2. Conversely we suppose that A is totally bounded for $\mathbf{U}_\lambda$ for every $\lambda \in \Lambda$. For any $U \in \bigvee_{\lambda\in\Lambda} \mathbf{U}_\lambda$ there is a finite system $U_\nu \in \mathbf{U}_{\lambda_\nu}$ $(\nu = 1, 2, \ldots, n)$ by Theorem 21.1 such that $U \geqq \bigcap_{\nu=1}^{n} U_\nu$. For such U_ν we can find symmetric $W_\nu \in \mathbf{U}_{\lambda_\nu}$ $(\nu = 1, 2, \ldots, n)$ by Theorem 2.1 such that $W_\nu{}^2 \leqq U_\nu$ $(\nu = 1, 2, \ldots, n)$. Since A is totally for every $\mathbf{U}_\lambda$ by assumption, we can find a finite system $a_{\nu,\mu} \in A$ $(\mu = 1, 2, \ldots, m_\nu; \nu = 1, 2, \ldots, n)$ such that $A \subset \bigcup_{\mu=1}^{m_\nu} a_{\nu,\mu} W_\nu$, and hence there is a finite system $a_\rho \in A$ $(\rho = 1, 2, \ldots, k)$ by the Lemma in 15 such that

$$A \subset \bigcup_{\rho=1}^{k} a_\rho \bigcap_{\nu=1}^{n} W_\nu{}^2 \subset \bigcup_{\rho=1}^{k} a_\rho U.$$

Therefore A is totally bounded for $\bigvee_{\lambda\in\Lambda} \mathbf{U}_\lambda$.

For two uniformities $\mathbf{U}$, $\mathbf{V}$ on S, the weakest stronger uniformity of $\mathbf{U}$ and $\mathbf{V}$ is denoted by $\mathbf{U} \vee \mathbf{V}$.

Theorem 21.6. *For two uniformities* $\mathbf{U}$, $\mathbf{V}$ *on* S *and a set* A *such that* $A^{(\mathbf{U}\vee\mathbf{V})-} = S$, *if* $\mathbf{U}^A \supset \mathbf{V}^A$, *then* $\mathbf{U} \supset \mathbf{V}$.

Proof. We obviously have $\mathbf{U} \vee \mathbf{V} \supset \mathbf{U}$ by definition, and $\mathbf{U}^A \supset \mathbf{V}^A$ implies $\mathbf{U}^A = \mathbf{U}^A \vee \mathbf{V}^A = (\mathbf{U} \vee \mathbf{V})^A$ by Theorem 21.3. Thus we conclude by Theorem 20.6 that $\mathbf{U}^A \supset \mathbf{V}^A$ implies $\mathbf{U} = \mathbf{U} \vee \mathbf{V}$, that is, $\mathbf{U} \supset \mathbf{V}$.

If $\mathbf{T}(\mathbf{U}) \supset \mathbf{T}(\mathbf{V})$, then we have $\mathbf{T}(\mathbf{U} \vee \mathbf{V}) = \mathbf{T}(\mathbf{U})$ by Theorem 4.4. Thus we conclude immediately from Theorem 21.6.

Theorem 21.7. *For two uniformities* $\mathbf{U}$, $\mathbf{V}$ *on* S, *if* $\mathbf{T}(\mathbf{U}) \supset \mathbf{T}(\mathbf{V})$ *and* $\mathbf{U}^A \supset \mathbf{V}^A$ *for a set* $A \subset S$ *such that* $A^{\mathbf{U}-} = S$, *then* $\mathbf{U} \supset \mathbf{V}$.

Setting $xI_\infty = S$ for every $x \in S$, we obtain a connector I_∞ on S, which will be called the *trivial connector* on S. About the trivial connector I_∞, we obviously have $I_\infty I_\infty = I_\infty$, $I_\infty{}^{-1} = I_\infty$, and $I_\infty \geqq U$ for every connector U on S. Thus the trivial connector constitutes alone a uniformity which is weaker than every uniformity on S. This uniformity is called the *trivial uniformity* on S. The atom of the trivial uniformity is obviously the trivial connector itself.

For a system of uniformities $\mathbf{U}_\lambda$ $(\lambda \in \Lambda)$ on S there is the strongest among the uniformities which are weaker than every $\mathbf{U}_\lambda$ $(\lambda \in \Lambda)$. Because, setting

$$\mathbf{U}_0 = \vee\{\mathbf{U}: \mathbf{U} \subset \mathbf{U}_\lambda \quad \text{for every } \lambda \in \Lambda\},$$

we see easily that $\mathbf{U}_0 \subset \mathbf{U}_\lambda$ for every $\lambda \in \Lambda$, and $\mathbf{U} \subset \mathbf{U}_\lambda$ for every $\lambda \in \Lambda$ implies $\mathbf{U}_0 \supset \mathbf{U}$. This $\mathbf{U}_0$ is called the *strongest weaker uniformity* of $\mathbf{U}_\lambda$ $(\lambda \in \Lambda)$ and denoted by $\bigwedge_{\lambda\in\Lambda} \mathbf{U}_\lambda$.

22. Local Unimorphisms. Let S be a space and let $\mathbf{U}$, $\mathbf{V}$ be two uniformities on S. $\mathbf{U}$ is said to be *locally stronger* than $\mathbf{V}$, if there is $U \in \mathbf{U}$ such that $\mathbf{U}^{xU} \supset \mathbf{V}^{xU}$ for every $x \in S$. If $\mathbf{U}$ is stronger than $\mathbf{V}$, then $\mathbf{U}$ is locally stronger than $\mathbf{V}$ by definition.

Theorem 22.1. *If* $\mathbf{U}$ *is locally stronger than* $\mathbf{V}$, *then every totally bounded set for* $\mathbf{U}$ *also is totally bounded for* $\mathbf{V}$, *and there is a symmetric* $U \in \mathbf{U}$ *such that* $\mathbf{U}^{XU} \supset \mathbf{V}^{XU}$ *for every totally bounded set* X *for* $\mathbf{U}$.

Proof. We suppose that there is $U_0 \in \mathbf{U}$ such that $\mathbf{U}^{xU_0} \supset V^{xU_0}$ for every $x \in S$. For such $U_0 \in \mathbf{U}$ we can find a symmetric $U \in \mathbf{U}$ such that $U^3 \leqq U_0$. If $X \neq \emptyset$ is totally bounded for $\mathbf{U}$, then we can find a finite system $x_\nu \in X$ $(\nu = 1, 2, ..., n)$ such that $X \subset \bigcup_{\nu=1}^{n} x_\nu U$. Since $U^3 \leqq U_0$ and $\mathbf{U}^{x_\nu U_0} \supset \mathbf{V}^{x_\nu U_0}$ for every $\nu = 1, 2, ..., n$, $\mathbf{U}$ is stronger than $\mathbf{V}$ on $\bigcup_{\nu=1}^{n} x_\nu U^2$ by Theorem 20.8, and hence $\mathbf{U}^{XU} \supset \mathbf{V}^{XU}$, because $XU \subset \bigcup_{\nu=1}^{n} x_\nu U^2$. Since $X \subset XU$ and X is totally bounded for $\mathbf{U}$, X also is totally bounded for $\mathbf{V}$ by Theorem 20.2.

Referring to Theorem 4.4 we conclude immediately from definition

Theorem 22.2. *If* $\mathbf{U}$ *is locally stronger than* $\mathbf{V}$, *then* $\mathbf{T}(\mathbf{U}) \supset \mathbf{T}(\mathbf{V})$.

We also easily obtain by Theorem 20.2

Theorem 22.3. *If* $\mathbf{U}$ *is locally stronger than* $\mathbf{V}$, *then* $S \ni x_\delta \xrightarrow[\delta\in\Delta]{} x$ *for* $\mathbf{U}$ *implies* $x_\delta \xrightarrow[\delta\in\Delta]{} x$ *for* $\mathbf{V}$, *and every Cauchy system for* $\mathbf{U}$ *is a Cauchy system for* $\mathbf{V}$ *too.*

Theorem 22.4. *If* $\mathbf{U}$ *is locally stronger than* $\mathbf{V}$, $\mathbf{V}$ *is locally stronger than* $\mathbf{W}$, *and* $\mathbf{U}$ *is locally totally bounded, then* $\mathbf{U}$ *is locally stronger than* $\mathbf{W}$.

Proof. If $\mathbf{U}$ is locally totally bounded, then there is $U \in \mathbf{U}$ such that xU is totally bounded for every $x \in S$ by definition. Then we have $\mathbf{U}^{xU} \supset \mathbf{V}^{xU}$ and $\mathbf{V}^{xU} \supset \mathbf{W}^{xU}$ by Theorem 22.1, and hence $\mathbf{U}^{xU} \supset \mathbf{W}^{xU}$ for every $x \in S$.

Theorem 22.5. *If* $\mathbf{U}$ *is locally totally bounded and locally stronger than* $\mathbf{U}_\lambda$ *for every* $\lambda \in \Lambda$, *then* $\mathbf{U}$ *is locally stronger than* $\bigvee_{\lambda \in \Lambda} \mathbf{U}_\lambda$.

Proof. As $\mathbf{U}$ is locally totally bounded by assumption, there is $U \in \mathbf{U}$ such that xU is totally bounded for $\mathbf{U}$ for every $x \in S$. Since $\mathbf{U}$ is locally stronger than $\mathbf{U}_\lambda$ for every $\lambda \in \Lambda$ by assumption, we have $\mathbf{U}^{xU} \supset \mathbf{U}_\lambda{}^{xU}$ for every $\lambda \in \Lambda$ by Theorem 22.1, and hence

$$\mathbf{U}^{xU} \supset \bigvee_{\lambda \in \Lambda} \mathbf{U}_\lambda{}^{xU} = (\bigvee_{\lambda \in \Lambda} \mathbf{U}_\lambda)^{xU}$$

for every $x \in S$ by Theorem 21.3. Thus $\mathbf{U}$ is locally stronger than $\bigvee_{\lambda \in \Lambda} \mathbf{U}_\lambda$ by definition.

$\mathbf{U}$ is said to be *locally semi-unimorphic* to $\mathbf{V}$, if there is $U \in \mathbf{U}$ such that $\mathbf{U}^{xU} = \mathbf{V}^{xU}$ for every $x \in S$. If $\mathbf{U}$ is locally semi-unimorphic to $\mathbf{V}$, then $\mathbf{U}$ is obviously locally stronger than $\mathbf{V}$.

$\mathbf{U}$ is said to be *locally unimorphic* to $\mathbf{V}$ and we write $\mathbf{U} \sim \mathbf{V}$, if $\mathbf{U}$ is locally stronger than $\mathbf{V}$ and $\mathbf{V}$ is locally stronger than $\mathbf{U}$. It is obvious by definition that $\mathbf{U} \sim \mathbf{V}$ implies $\mathbf{V} \sim \mathbf{U}$. If $\mathbf{U} \sim \mathbf{V}$ and $\mathbf{U}$ is locally totally bounded, then $\mathbf{U}$ is locally semi-unimorphic to $\mathbf{V}$. Because for $U \in \mathbf{U}$ such that xU is totally bounded for $\mathbf{U}$ for every $x \in S$, xU also is totally bounded for $\mathbf{V}$ and $\mathbf{U}^{xU} \subset \mathbf{V}^{xU}$ by Theorem 22.1.

We obviously have by Theorem 22.2

Theorem 22.6. $\mathbf{U} \sim \mathbf{V}$ *implies* $\mathbf{T}(\mathbf{U}) = \mathbf{T}(\mathbf{V})$.

We conclude from Theorem 22.3

Theorem 22.7. *If* $\mathbf{U} \sim \mathbf{V}$ *and* $\mathbf{U}$ *is complete, then* $\mathbf{V}$ *also is complete.*

We also obviously have by Theorem 22.1

Theorem 22.8. *For two locally totally bounded uniformities* $\mathbf{U}, \mathbf{V}$ *on* S, *we have* $\mathbf{U} \sim \mathbf{V}$, *if and only if* $\mathbf{U}^X = \mathbf{V}^X$ *for any* $\emptyset \neq X \subset S$ *which is totally bounded for one of* $\mathbf{U}, \mathbf{V}$.

Referring to Theorem 22.4, we obtain

Theorem 22.9. *For two locally totally bounded uniformities* $\mathbf{U}$, $\mathbf{V}$ *on* S *we have* $\mathbf{U} \sim \mathbf{V}$ *if there is a uniformity* $\mathbf{W}$ *on* S *such that* $\mathbf{U} \sim \mathbf{W}$ *and* $\mathbf{V} \sim \mathbf{W}$.

A locally totally bounded uniformity $\mathbf{U}$ is said to be *primitive,* if $\mathbf{U} \sim \mathbf{V}$ implies $\mathbf{U} \supset \mathbf{V}$.

Theorem 22.10. *For any locally totally bounded uniformity* $\mathbf{U}$ *on* S *there is a primitive uniformity* $\mathbf{W}$ *on* S *such that* $\mathbf{W} \sim \mathbf{U}$.

Proof. Setting $\mathbf{W} = \bigvee_{\mathbf{V} \sim \mathbf{U}} \mathbf{V}$, we have $\mathbf{W} \supset \mathbf{U}$, because $\mathbf{U} \sim \mathbf{U}$. On the other hand, $\mathbf{U}$ is locally stronger than $\mathbf{W}$ by Theorem 22.5. Thus, for $U \in \mathbf{U}$ such that xU is totally bounded for $\mathbf{U}$ for every $x \in S$, xU also is totally bounded for $\mathbf{W}$ by Theorem 22.1, and $U \in \mathbf{W}$. Therefore $\mathbf{W}$ is locally totally bounded, and $\mathbf{W} \sim \mathbf{U}$. If $\mathbf{W} \sim \mathbf{V}$, then $\mathbf{U}$ is locally stronger than $\mathbf{V}$ by Theorem 22.4, and hence $\mathbf{U} \sim \mathbf{V} \vee \mathbf{U}$ by Theorem 22.5. Consequently we obtain $\mathbf{W} \supset \mathbf{V} \vee \mathbf{U} \supset \mathbf{V}$.

23. **Weak-Uniformities.** Let M be a mapping from a space S to a uniform space R with uniformity $\mathbf{V}$. There is a uniformity $\mathbf{U}$ on S such that M is uniformly continuous for $\mathbf{U}$. For instance, if we consider the pure discrete uniformity on S, which consists of all connectors on S, then M is obviously uniformly continuous. If M is uniformly continuous for a uniformity $\mathbf{U}$ on S, then M also is uniformly continuous for any uniformity on S which is stronger than $\mathbf{U}$. Making use of the notation

$$M\mathbf{V}M^{-1} = \{MVM^{-1}: V \in \mathbf{V}\}$$

we can show easily by (12), (13), (14) in 11 that $M\mathbf{V}M^{-1}$ satisfies the basis conditions. Thus there exists uniquely a uniformity $\mathbf{U}_0$ on S such that $M\mathbf{V}M^{-1}$ is a basis of $\mathbf{U}_0$. Then M is uniformly continuous for $\mathbf{U}_0$ by Theorem 12.4. If M is uniformly continuous for a uniformity $\mathbf{U}$ on S, then we have $\mathbf{U} \supset M\mathbf{V}M^{-1}$ by Theorem 12.4, and hence $\mathbf{U} \supset \mathbf{U}_0$. Therefore $\mathbf{U}_0$ is the weakest among the uniformities on S for which M is uniformly continuous. This uniformity $\mathbf{U}_0$ on S is called the *weak-uniformity* on S by M. For the weak-uniformities we can hence state

Theorem 23.1. *For a mapping* M *from* S *to* R *with uniformity* $\mathbf{V}$, $M\mathbf{V}M^{-1}$ *is a basis of the weak-uniformity on* S *by* M.

Theorem 23.2. *If a mapping M from S to R with $\mathbf{V}$ is full, then M is uniformly open for the weak-uniformity on S by M.*

Proof. Let $\mathbf{U}_0$ be the weak-uniformity on S by M. For any $U \in \mathbf{U}_0$ we can find $V \in \mathbf{V}$ by Theorem 23.1 such that $U \geqq MVM^{-1}$, and hence

$$xUM \supset xMVM^{-1}M = xMV \quad \text{for every } x \in S$$

by Theorem 11.1. Therefore M is uniformly open by definition.

We can prove easily by Theorem 23.1

Theorem 23.3. *For the weak-uniformity $\mathbf{U}$ on S by M, we have $S \ni x_\delta \xrightarrow[\delta\in\Lambda]{} x$ for $\mathbf{U}$ if and only if $x_\delta M \xrightarrow[\delta\in\Delta]{} xM$ for $\mathbf{V}$; $x_\delta \in S$ $(\delta \in \Delta)$ is a Cauchy system for $\mathbf{U}$, if and only if $x_\delta M$ $(\delta \in \Delta)$ is a Cauchy system for $\mathbf{V}$; $MI_{\mathbf{V}}M^{-1} = I_{\mathbf{U}}$; and a set $X \subset S$ is totally bounded, complete, connected or compact for $\mathbf{U}$, if and only if XM is so for $\mathbf{V}$.*

Referring to (17) in 11, we obtain

Theorem 23.4. *For the weak-uniformity $\mathbf{U}$ on S by M, the relative uniformity $\mathbf{U}^X$ is the weak-uniformity on X by the relative mapping M^X.*

As an immediate consequence of Theorem 13.3, we have

Theorem 23.5. *Every uniformity $\mathbf{U}$ on S is the weak-uniformity on S by the purifying mapping $P_{\mathbf{U}}$.*

We consider now a system of mappings M_λ $(\lambda \in \Lambda)$ from a space S to R_λ with uniformity $\mathbf{V}_\lambda$ for every $\lambda \in \Lambda$. If $\mathbf{U}_\lambda$ denotes the weak-uniformity on S by M_λ, then $\bigvee_{\lambda\in\Lambda} \mathbf{U}_\lambda$ is obviously the weakest among the uniformities for which M_λ is uniformly continuous for every $\lambda \in \Lambda$. This uniformity $\bigvee_{\lambda\in\Lambda} \mathbf{U}_\lambda$ is called the *weak-uniformity* on S by the system M_λ $(\lambda \in \Lambda)$.

With this definition we obviously have by Theorems 21.1 and 23.1

Theorem 23.6. *For the weak-uniformity $\mathbf{U}$ on S by M_λ $(\lambda \in \Lambda)$, we have $U \in \mathbf{U}$ if and only if we can find a finite system $V_\nu \in \mathbf{V}_{\lambda_\nu}$, $\lambda_\nu \in \Lambda$ $(\nu = 1, 2, \dots, n)$ such that $U \geqq \bigcap_{\nu=1}^{n} M_{\lambda_\nu} V_\nu M_{\lambda_\nu}^{-1}$.*

We also conclude from Theorems 21.4 and 23.3

Theorem 23.7. *For the weak-uniformity on S by* M_λ $(\lambda \in \Lambda)$ *we have* $S \ni x_\delta \underset{\delta\in\Lambda}{\longrightarrow} x$ *if and only if* $x_\delta M_\lambda \underset{\delta\in\Lambda}{\longrightarrow} xM_\lambda$ *for* $\mathbf{V}_\lambda$ *for every* $\lambda \in \Lambda$, *and* $x_\delta \in S$ $(\delta \in \Delta)$ *is a Cauchy system if and only if* $x_\delta M_\lambda$ $(\delta \in \Delta)$ *is a Cauchy system for* $\mathbf{V}_\lambda$ *for every* $\lambda \in \Lambda$.

Referring to Theorem 21.5, we obtain by Theorem 23.3

Theorem 23.8. *A set* $X \subset S$ *is totally bounded for the weak-uniformity on S by* M_λ $(\lambda \in \Lambda)$ *if and only if* XM_λ *is totally bounded for* $\mathbf{V}_\lambda$ *for every* $\lambda \in \Lambda$.

Theorem 23.9. *Let* $\mathbf{V}_\lambda$ *be complete for every* $\lambda \in \Lambda$. *In order that a set* $X \subset S$ *be complete for the weak-uniformity on S by* M_λ $(\lambda \in \Lambda)$, *it is necessary and sufficient that for a system of points* $a_\lambda \in R_\lambda$ $(\lambda \in \Lambda)$, *if*

$$X \cap \bigcap_{\nu=1}^{n} a_{\lambda_\nu} V_\nu M_{\lambda_\nu}^{-1} \neq \emptyset \text{ for any finite system } V_\nu \in \mathbf{V}_{\lambda_\nu}$$

$\lambda_\nu \in \Lambda$ $(\nu = 1, 2, \ldots, n)$, *then there is a point* $x \in S$ *such that* $xM_\lambda \in a_\lambda I_{\mathbf{V}_\lambda}$ *for every* $\lambda \in \Lambda$.

Proof. We suppose that X is complete for the weak-uniformity on S by M_λ $(\lambda \in \Lambda)$ and $X \cap \bigcap_{\nu=1}^{n} a_{\lambda_\nu} V_\nu M_{\lambda_\nu}^{-1} \neq \emptyset$ for every finite system $V_\nu \in \mathbf{V}_{\lambda_\nu}$, $\lambda_\nu \in \Lambda$ $(\nu = 1, 2, \ldots, n)$. Now we define order among the finite systems $(V_\nu \in \mathbf{V}_{\lambda_\nu}: \nu = 1, 2, \ldots, n)$ with $\lambda_\nu \neq \lambda_\rho$ for $\nu \neq \rho$ by

$$(V_\nu \in \mathbf{V}_{\lambda_\nu}: \nu = 1, 2, \ldots, n) \geqq (W_\nu \in \mathbf{V}_{\lambda_\nu}: \nu = 1, 2, \ldots, m)$$

if $V_\nu \geqq W_\nu$ $(\nu = 1, 2, \ldots, n)$ and $n \leqq m$. Then we obtain a directed system of points $x(V_1, \ldots, V_n) \in X$ $(V_\nu \in \mathbf{V}_{\lambda_\nu};\ \nu = 1, 2, \ldots, n;\ n = 1, 2, \ldots)$ such that

$$x(V_1, \ldots, V_n) \in X \cap \bigcap_{\nu=1}^{n} a_{\lambda_\nu} V_\nu M_{\lambda_\nu}^{-1},$$

and we have $x(V_1, \ldots, V_n)M_\lambda \underset{(V_1,\ldots,V_n)}{\longrightarrow} a_\lambda$ for every $\lambda \in \Lambda$, because

$$x(V_1, \ldots, V_n)M_{\lambda_\nu} \in a_{\lambda_\nu} V_\nu \quad \text{for every } \nu = 1, 2, \ldots, n.$$

Therefore $x(V_1, \ldots, V_n)M_\lambda (V_\nu \in \mathbf{V}_{\lambda_\nu};\ \nu = 1, 2, \ldots, n;\ n = 1, 2, \ldots)$ is a Cauchy system for $\mathbf{V}_\lambda$ for every $\lambda \in \Lambda$ and hence $x(V_1, \ldots, V_n)$ is also a Cauchy system for the weak-uniformity on S by M_λ $(\lambda \in \Lambda)$ by

Theorem 23.7. Thus we can find $x \in X$ such that $x(V_1, \ldots, V_n) \xrightarrow[(V_1,\ldots,V_n)]{} x$ for the weak-uniformity on S by M_λ $(\lambda \in \Lambda)$. Then we also have $x(V_1, \ldots, V_n)M_\lambda \xrightarrow[(V_1,\ldots,V_n)]{} xM_\lambda$ for $\mathbf{V}_\lambda$ for every $\lambda \in \Lambda$ by Theorem 23.7, and hence $xM_\lambda \in a_\lambda I_{\mathbf{V}_\lambda}$ for every $\lambda \in \Lambda$ by Theorem 7.1.

Conversely we assume that the condition in Theorem 23.9 is satisfied. If $x_\delta \in X$ $(\delta \in \Delta)$ is a Cauchy system for the weak-uniformity on S by M_λ $(\lambda \in \Lambda)$, then $x_\delta M_\lambda$ $(\delta \in \Delta)$ is a Cauchy system for $\mathbf{V}_\lambda$ by Theorem 23.7, and hence we can find $a_\lambda \in R_\lambda$ such that $x_\delta M_\lambda \xrightarrow[\delta\in\Delta]{} a_\lambda$, because $\mathbf{V}_\lambda$ is complete by assumption. Then for any finite system $V_\nu \in \mathbf{V}_{\lambda_\nu}$, $\lambda_\nu \in \Lambda$ $(\nu = 1, 2, \ldots, n)$ we can find $\delta_0 \in \Delta$ such that $x_\delta M_{\lambda_\nu} \in a_{\lambda_\nu} V_\nu$ for $\delta \leqq \delta_0$, $\nu = 1, 2, \ldots, n$, and hence

$$x_\delta \in \bigcap_{\nu=1}^{n} a_{\lambda_\nu} V_\nu M_{\lambda_\nu}^{-1} \quad \text{for } \delta \leqq \delta_0.$$

Therefore there is a point $x \in X$ by assumption such that $xM_\lambda \in a_\lambda I_{\mathbf{V}_\lambda}$ for every $\lambda \in \Lambda$. For such $x \in X$ we have $x_\delta M_\lambda \xrightarrow[\delta\in\Delta]{} xM_\lambda$ for every $\lambda \in \Lambda$ by Theorem 7.1. Consequently $x_\delta \xrightarrow[\delta\in\Delta]{} x$ for the weak-uniformity on S by M_λ $(\lambda \in \Lambda)$ by Theorem 23.7.

Referring to Theorems 23.4 and 21.3, we clearly obtain

Theorem 23.10. *For the weak-uniformity* $\mathbf{U}$ *on* S *by* M_λ $(\lambda \in \Lambda)$, *the relative uniformity* $\mathbf{U}^X$ *is the weak-uniformity on* X *by the system of the relative mappings* $M_\lambda{}^X$ $(\lambda \in \Lambda)$.

Referring to (3) in 14, we conclude easily from Theorem 23.6

Theorem 23.11. *Let* M_λ *be a mapping from* S *to* R_λ *for each* $\lambda \in \Lambda$ *and let* $N_{\lambda,\gamma}$ *be a mapping from* R_λ *to* $Q_{\lambda,\gamma}$ *with uniformity* $\mathbf{V}_{\lambda,\gamma}$ *for each* $\gamma \in \Gamma_\lambda$, $\lambda \in \Lambda$. *The weak-uniformity on* S *by* M_λ $(\lambda \in \Lambda)$ *for the weak-uniformity on* R_λ *by* $N_{\lambda,\gamma}$ $(\gamma \in \Gamma_\lambda)$ *for every* $\lambda \in \Lambda$, *is the weak-uniformity on* S *by* $M_\lambda N_{\lambda,\gamma}$ $(\gamma \in \Gamma_\lambda, \lambda \in \Lambda)$.

Theorem 23.12. *Let* $\mathbf{U}$ *be the weak-uniformity on* S *by* M_λ $(\lambda \in \Lambda)$ *and let* Q *be a space with uniformity* $\mathbf{W}$. *A mapping* N *from* Q *to* S *is* *uniformly continuous if and only if* NM_λ *is uniformly continuous for every* $\lambda \in \Lambda$.

Proof. If N is uniformly continuous, then NM_λ is uniformly continuous for every $\lambda \in \Lambda$ by Theorem 14.3. Conversely, if NM_λ is uniformly continuous for every $\lambda \in \Lambda$, then for any $U \in \mathbf{U}$ we can find a finite system $V_\nu \in \mathbf{V}_{\lambda_\nu}$, $\lambda_\nu \in \Lambda$ $(\nu = 1, 2, \ldots, n)$ by Theorem 23.6 such that $U \geqq \bigcap_{\nu=1}^{n} M_{\lambda_\nu} V_\nu M_{\lambda_\nu}^{-1}$ and hence

$$NUN^{-1} \geqq \bigcap_{\nu=1}^{n} NM_{\lambda_\nu} V_\nu (NM_{\lambda_\nu})^{-1} \in \mathbf{W}$$

by (12) in 11 and (3) in 14. Therefore N is uniformly continuous by Theorem 12.4.

24. Products of Uniformities. Let S_λ $(\lambda \in \Lambda)$ be a system of subspaces of a space S. The space of all mappings x from Λ to S such that $x(\lambda) \in S_\lambda$ for every $\lambda \in \Lambda$, is called the *product* of S_λ $(\lambda \in \Lambda)$ and denoted by $\prod_{\lambda\in\Lambda} S_\lambda$. Here $x(\lambda)$ represents the image of λ by a mapping x. The product of two subspaces S_1 and S_2 is denoted by $S_1 \times S_2$.

Setting $xP_\lambda = x(\lambda)$ for $x \in \prod_{\lambda\in\Lambda} S_\lambda$, $\lambda \in \Lambda$, we obtain a mapping P_λ from $\prod_{\lambda\in\Lambda} S_\lambda$ to S_λ for each $\lambda \in \Lambda$. This mapping P_λ is called the *projection* from $\prod_{\lambda\in\Lambda} S_\lambda$ to S_λ. With this definition we obviously have that $xP_\lambda = yP_\lambda$ for every $\lambda \in \Lambda$ implies $x = y$.

Theorem 24.1. *The projection* P_λ *is a full mapping for every* $\lambda \in \Lambda$ *and* $S_\gamma \supset X_\gamma \neq \emptyset$ $(\gamma \in \Gamma)$, $\Gamma \subset \Lambda$, *implies*

$$(\bigcap_{\gamma\in\Gamma} X_\gamma P_\gamma^{-1}) P_\lambda = \begin{cases} X_\lambda & \text{for } \lambda \in \Gamma \\ S_\lambda & \text{for } \lambda \,\overline{\in}\, \Gamma. \end{cases}$$

Proof. We consider first the case where $\Gamma = \Lambda$. For any $x_\gamma \in X_\gamma$ we can find a system $x_\lambda \in X_\lambda$ $(\gamma \neq \lambda \in \Lambda)$ by Choice Axiom. Then setting $x(\lambda) = x_\lambda$ $(\lambda \in \Lambda)$, we obtain a point $x \in \prod_{\lambda\in\Lambda} S_\lambda$ and we have $x \in X_\lambda P_\lambda^{-1}$ for every $\lambda \in \Lambda$. Thus $x \in \bigcap_{\lambda\in\Lambda} X_\lambda P_\lambda^{-1}$ and hence

$$x_\gamma = xP_\gamma \in (\bigcap_{\lambda\in\Lambda} X_\lambda P_\lambda^{-1})P_\gamma.$$

Therefore $X_\gamma \subset (\bigcap_{\lambda\in\Lambda} X_\lambda P_\lambda^{-1})P_\gamma \subset X_\gamma P_\gamma^{-1}P_\gamma \subset X_\gamma$ by (9) in 11, that is,

$$(\bigcap_{\lambda\in\Lambda} X_\lambda P_\lambda^{-1})P_\gamma = X_\gamma \quad \text{for every } \gamma \in \Lambda.$$

In particular, we have $(\bigcap_{\lambda\in\Lambda} S_\lambda P_\lambda^{-1})P_\gamma = S_\gamma$ for every $\gamma \in \Lambda$, and hence P_λ is full for every $\lambda \in \Lambda$.

In the other case, where $\Gamma \neq \Lambda$, setting $X_\lambda = S_\lambda$ for $\lambda \bar{\in} \Gamma$, we have

$$\bigcap_{\gamma\in\Gamma} X_\gamma P_\gamma^{-1} = \bigcap_{\lambda\in\Lambda} X_\lambda P_\lambda^{-1}$$

since $S_\lambda P_\lambda^{-1} = \prod_{\lambda\in\Lambda} S_\lambda$ for $\lambda \in \Lambda$. Thus $(\bigcap_{\gamma\in\Gamma} X_\gamma P_\gamma^{-1})P_\lambda = X_\lambda$ for every $\lambda \in \Lambda$, as just proved above.

Now we consider a uniformity $\mathbf{U}_\lambda$ on S_λ for each $\lambda \in \Lambda$. The weak-uniformity on the product $\prod_{\lambda\in\Lambda} S_\lambda$ by the system of the projections P_λ $(\lambda \in \Lambda)$ is called the *product* of $\mathbf{U}_\lambda$ $(\lambda \in \Lambda)$ and denoted by $\prod_{\lambda\in\Lambda} \mathbf{U}_\lambda$. Then every projection P_λ is obviously uniformly continuous for $\prod_{\lambda\in\Lambda} \mathbf{U}_\lambda$. Furthermore P_λ is uniformly open. Because for any $U \in \prod_{\lambda\in\Lambda} \mathbf{U}_\lambda$ we can find a finite system $U_\nu \in \mathbf{U}_{\lambda_\nu}$, $\lambda_\nu \in \Lambda$ $(\nu = 1, 2, \ldots, n)$ by Theorem 23.6 such that $U \geqq \bigcap_{\nu=1}^{n} P_{\lambda_\nu} U_\nu P_{\lambda_\nu}^{-1}$, and we have by Theorem 24.1

$$(\bigcap_{\nu=1}^{n} xP_{\lambda_\nu} U_\nu P_{\lambda_\nu}^{-1})P_\lambda = \begin{cases} xP_{\lambda_\nu} U_\nu & \text{for } \lambda = \lambda_\nu \ (\nu = 1, 2, \ldots, n) \\ S_\lambda & \text{for } \lambda \neq \lambda_\nu \text{ for every } \nu. \end{cases}$$

Thus we can state

Theorem 24.2 *Every projection P_λ is uniformly continuous and uniformly open for the product $\prod_{\lambda\in\Lambda} \mathbf{U}_\lambda$.*

Theorem 24.3. $\prod_{\lambda\in\Lambda} \mathbf{U}_\lambda$ *is complete if and only if every $\mathbf{U}_\lambda$ is complete.*

Proof. For any system $a_\lambda \in S_\lambda$ $(\lambda \in \Lambda)$, setting $x(\lambda) = a_\lambda$ $(\lambda \in \Lambda)$, we obtain a point $x \in \prod_{\lambda\in\Lambda} S_\lambda$ such that $xP_\lambda = a_\lambda$ for every $\lambda \in \Lambda$. Therefore, if every $\mathbf{U}_\lambda$ is complete, then $\prod_{\lambda\in\Lambda} \mathbf{U}_\lambda$ is complete by Theorem 23.9. Conversely, if $\prod_{\lambda\in\Lambda} \mathbf{U}_\lambda$ is complete, then for any Cauchy system $a_\delta \in S_\gamma$ $(\delta \in \Delta)$ for $\mathbf{U}_\gamma$ we can find a system $x_\delta \in \prod_{\lambda\in\Lambda} S_\lambda$ $(\delta \in \Delta)$ such that $x_\delta P_\gamma = a_\delta$ $(\delta \in \Delta)$ and $x_\delta P_\lambda = x_{\delta'} P_\lambda$ for every $\lambda \neq \gamma$, and $\delta, \delta' \in \Delta$, and hence x_δ $(\delta \in \Delta)$ is a Cauchy system for $\prod_{\lambda\in\Lambda} \mathbf{U}_\lambda$ by Theorem 23.7. Consequently there is a point $x \in \prod_{\lambda\in\Lambda} S_\lambda$ such that $x_\delta \xrightarrow[\delta\in\Delta]{} x$ for $\prod_{\lambda\in\Lambda} \mathbf{U}_\lambda$, and we obtain $a_\delta = x_\delta P_\gamma \xrightarrow[\delta\in\Delta]{} xP_\gamma$ by Theorem 23.7. Therefore $\mathbf{U}_\gamma$ is complete by definition.

For a finite system $U_\nu \in \mathbf{U}_{\lambda_\nu}$ $(\nu = 1, 2, \ldots, n)$ setting $U = \bigcap_{\nu=1}^{n} P_{\lambda_\nu} U_\nu P_{\lambda_\nu}^{-1}$ we have by Theorem 24.1 that $x \in yU$ if and only if $xP_{\lambda_\nu} \in yP_{\lambda_\nu} U_\nu$ for every $\nu = 1, 2, \ldots, n$. Therefore we conclude easily

Theorem 24.4. $\prod_{\lambda\in\Lambda} \mathbf{U}_\lambda$ *is connected if and only if* $\mathbf{U}_\lambda$ *is connected for every* $\lambda \in \Lambda$. $\prod_{\lambda\in\Lambda} \mathbf{U}_\lambda$ *is bounded if and only if* $\mathbf{U}_\lambda$ *is bounded for every* $\lambda \in \Lambda$.

Referring to Theorem 23.8, we obtain by definition

Theorem 24.5. $\prod_{\lambda\in\Lambda} \mathbf{U}_\lambda$ *is totally bounded if and only if* $\mathbf{U}_\lambda$ *is totally bounded for every* $\lambda \in \Lambda$.

Theorem 24.6. *For the atom* $I_{\prod_\lambda \mathbf{U}_\lambda}$ *of* $\prod_{\lambda\in\Lambda} \mathbf{U}_\lambda$ *we have*

$$I_{\prod_\lambda \mathbf{U}_\lambda} = \bigcap_{\lambda\in\Lambda} P_\lambda I_{\mathbf{U}_\lambda} P_\lambda^{-1}.$$

Proof. Since every P_λ is uniformly continuous by Theorem 24.2, we have $xP_\lambda U_\lambda P_\lambda^{-1} \supset xI_{\prod_\lambda \mathbf{U}_\lambda}$ for $x \in \prod_{\lambda\in\Lambda} S_\lambda$, $U_\lambda \in \mathbf{U}_\lambda$, that is, $xP_\lambda U_\lambda \supset xI_{\prod_\lambda \mathbf{U}_\lambda} P_\lambda$ for any $U_\lambda \in \mathbf{U}_\lambda$. Therefore we obtain $xP_\lambda I_{\mathbf{U}_\lambda} \supset xI_{\prod_\lambda \mathbf{U}_\lambda} P_\lambda$, and hence $P_\lambda I_{\mathbf{U}_\lambda} P_\lambda^{-1} \geqq I_{\prod_\lambda \mathbf{U}_\lambda}$ for every $\lambda \in \Lambda$. On the other hand, since P_λ is uniformly open by Theorem 24.2, $xUP_\lambda \supset xP_\lambda I_{\mathbf{U}_\lambda}$ for $x \in \prod_{\lambda\in\Lambda} S_\lambda$, $U \in \prod_{\lambda\in\Lambda} \mathbf{U}_\lambda$, and hence $I_{\prod_\lambda \mathbf{U}_\lambda} \geqq P_\lambda I_{\mathbf{U}_\lambda} P_\lambda^{-1}$ for every $\lambda \in \Lambda$.

As an immediate consequence of this theorem, we have

Theorem 24.7. $\prod_{\lambda\in\Lambda} \mathbf{U}_\lambda$ *is pure if and only if* $\mathbf{U}_\lambda$ *is pure for every* $\lambda \in \Lambda$.

For a system of mappings M_λ from S to R_λ $(\lambda \in \Lambda)$, setting

$$xN(\lambda) = xM_\lambda \in R_\lambda \ (\lambda \in \Lambda),$$

we obtain a mapping N from S to $\prod_{\lambda\in\Lambda} R_\lambda$. This mapping N is called the *product* of M_λ $(\lambda \in \Lambda)$ and denoted by $\prod_{\lambda\in\Lambda} M_\lambda$. Then we obviously have

$$M_\gamma = (\prod_{\lambda\in\Lambda} M_\lambda)P_\gamma \quad (\gamma \in \Lambda)$$

for the projection P_γ from $\prod_{\lambda\in\Lambda} R_\lambda$ to R_γ. Therefore we obtain by Theorem 23.12

Theorem 24.8. *For a system of mappings* M_λ *from* S *to uniform spaces* R_λ *with uniformities* $\mathbf{U}_\lambda$ $(\lambda \in \Lambda)$, *the weak-uniformity on* S *by* M_λ $(\lambda \in \Lambda)$ *is the weak-uniformity on* S *by the product* $\prod_{\lambda\in\Lambda} M_\lambda$.

25. **Strong Powers of Uniformities.** If $S_\lambda = S$ for every $\lambda \in \Lambda$, then the product $\prod_{\lambda\in\Lambda} S_\lambda$ is called the *power* of S by Λ and denoted by S^Λ. Thus S^Λ consists of all mappings from Λ to S and we have

$$xP_\lambda = x(\lambda) \in S \ \text{ for } x \in S^\Lambda$$

for the projections P_λ $(\lambda \in \Lambda)$.

For a uniformity $\mathbf{U}$ on S, setting $\mathbf{U}_\lambda = \mathbf{U}$ for every $\lambda \in \Lambda$, we obtain the product $\prod_{\lambda\in\Lambda} \mathbf{U}_\lambda$ on S^Λ. This product is called the *weak-power* of $\mathbf{U}$ by Λ and denoted by $\prod_\Lambda \mathbf{U}$, that is, $\prod_\Lambda \mathbf{U}$ is the weak-uniformity on S^Λ by the system of all projections P_λ $(\lambda \in \Lambda)$.

For a connector U on S, setting

(1) $xU^\Lambda = \{y\colon y(\lambda) \in x(\lambda)U \text{ for every } \lambda \in \Lambda\}$ $(x, y \in S)$,

we obtain a connector U^{Λ} on the power S^{Λ}. This connector U^{Λ} is called the *power* of U by Λ. From (1) we conclude immediately

(2) $U^{\Lambda} = \bigcap_{\lambda\in\Lambda} P_{\lambda} U P_{\lambda}^{-1}$.

Therefore we have by Theorem 24.1

(3) $xU^{\Lambda}P_{\lambda} = xP_{\lambda}U$ for every $\lambda \in \Lambda$ and $x \in S$.

Furthermore we obtain by (12) in 11

(4) $(\bigcap_{\lambda\in\Lambda} U_{\lambda})^{\Lambda} = \bigcap_{\lambda\in\Lambda} U_{\lambda}^{\Lambda}$.

Since P_{λ} is full by Theorem 24.1, we conclude easily from (3)

(5) $U^{\Lambda} \leqq V^{\Lambda}$ if and only if $U \leqq V$.

For two connectors U, V on S, we have by (2) and Theorem 24.1

$$xU^{\Lambda}V^{\Lambda} = \bigcap_{\gamma\in\Lambda} (\bigcap_{\lambda\in\Lambda} xP_{\lambda}UP_{\lambda}^{-1})P_{\gamma}VP_{\gamma}^{-1} = \bigcap_{\gamma\in\Lambda} xP_{\gamma}UVP_{\gamma}^{-1}.$$

Therefore we obtain

(6) $U^{\Lambda}V^{\Lambda} = (UV)^{\Lambda}$

Referring to (13) in 11, we obtain

$$(\bigcap_{\lambda\in\Lambda} P_{\lambda}UP_{\lambda}^{-1})^{-1} = \bigcap_{\lambda\in\Lambda} (P_{\lambda}UP_{\lambda}^{-1})^{-1} = \bigcap_{\lambda\in\Lambda} P_{\lambda}U^{-1}P_{\lambda}^{-1}.$$

Thus we have

(7) $(U^{\Lambda})^{-1} = (U^{-1})^{\Lambda}$.

For a uniformity $\mathbf{U}$ on S, making use of the notation

$$\mathbf{U}^{\Lambda} = \{U^{\Lambda}: U \in \mathbf{U}\},$$

we can show easily by (3), (4), (5) that $\mathbf{U}^{\Lambda}$ satisfies the basis conditions. Therefore there exists uniquely a uniformity on the power S^{Λ}, of which $\mathbf{U}^{\Lambda}$ is a basis. This uniformity is called the *strong-power* of $\mathbf{U}$ by Λ and denoted by $\mathbf{U}(\Lambda)$. $\mathbf{U}(\Lambda)$ is obviously stronger than $\Pi_{\Lambda}\mathbf{U}$ by definition. Thus the projections P_{λ} $(\lambda \in \Lambda)$ are uniformly continuous for $\mathbf{U}(\Lambda)$. In addition, (3) shows that P_{λ} is uniformly open for $\mathbf{U}(\Lambda)$ for every $\lambda \in \Lambda$. Therefore we can state

Theorem 25.1. *Every projection P_{λ} is uniformly continuous and uniformly open for the strong-power* $\mathbf{U}(\Lambda)$ *of* $\mathbf{U}$.

Theorem 25.2. $\mathbf{U}(\Lambda) = \Pi_{\Lambda}\mathbf{U}$ *if and only if Λ is finite or* $\mathbf{U}$ *is a trivial uniformity.*

Proof. If Λ is finite, or if $\mathbf{U}$ is a trivial uniformity, then we have $\mathbf{U}(\Lambda) = \Pi_\Lambda \mathbf{U}$ obviously by definition. If $\mathbf{U}$ is not trivial, then we can find $U \in \mathbf{U}$ and two points $a, b \in S$ such that $b \bar{\in} aU$. If $\mathbf{U}(\Lambda) \subset \Pi_\Lambda \mathbf{U}$, then for any $U \in \mathbf{U}$ we can find $V \in \mathbf{U}$ and a finite system $\lambda_\nu \in \Lambda$ ($\nu = 1, 2, \ldots, n$) such that $U^\Lambda \geqq \bigcap_{\nu=1}^{n} P_{\lambda_\nu} V P_{\lambda_\nu}{}^{-1}$. If $\Lambda \ni \gamma \neq \lambda_\nu$ for every $\nu = 1, 2, \ldots, n$, then considering $x \in S^\Lambda$ such that $x(\lambda) = a$ for every $\lambda \in \Lambda$, we obtain by Theorem 24.1

$$aU = xU^\Lambda P_\gamma \supset (\bigcap_{\nu=1}^{n} aVP_{\lambda_\nu}{}^{-1})P_\gamma = S,$$

contradicting $b \bar{\in} aU$ for some $a, b \in S$ and $U \in \mathbf{U}$. Thus $\Lambda = \{\lambda_1, \lambda_2, \ldots, \lambda_n\}$.

Theorem 25.3. $\mathbf{U}(\Lambda)$ *is complete if and only if* $\mathbf{U}$ *is complete.*

Proof. For a Cauchy system $x_\delta \in S^\Lambda$ $(\delta \in \Delta)$ for $\mathbf{U}(\Lambda)$, $x_\delta P_\lambda \in S$ $(\delta \in \Delta)$ also is a Cauchy system for $\mathbf{U}$ for every $\lambda \in \Lambda$ by Theorem 12.5. If $\mathbf{U}$ is complete, then we can find $a_\lambda \in S$ $(\lambda \in \Lambda)$ such that $x_\delta P_\lambda \xrightarrow[\delta \in \Lambda]{} a_\lambda$ for every $\lambda \in \Lambda$. For any $U \in \mathbf{U}$ there is a symmetric $V \in \mathbf{U}$ such that $V^3 \leqq U$, and we can find $\delta_0 \in \Delta$ such that $x_\delta \in x_{\delta_0} V^\Lambda$ for $\delta \leqq \delta_0$. Then we have by (3)

$$x_\delta P_\lambda \in x_{\delta_0} V^\Lambda P_\lambda = x_{\delta_0} P_\lambda V \quad \text{for } \delta \leqq \delta_0, \lambda \in \Lambda.$$

Since $x_\delta P_\lambda \xrightarrow[\delta \in \Lambda]{} a_\lambda$, for any $\lambda \in \Lambda$ we can find $\delta_\lambda \in \Delta$ such that $x_{\delta_\lambda} P_\lambda \in a_\lambda V$ and $\delta_\lambda \leqq \delta_0$. For such $\delta_\lambda \in \Delta$ we have $x_{\delta_0} P_\lambda \in x_{\delta_\lambda} P_\lambda V \subset a_\lambda V^2$, and hence

$$x_\delta P_\lambda \in x_{\delta_0} P_\lambda V \subset a_\lambda V^3 \subset a_\lambda U \quad \text{for every } \lambda \in \Lambda, \delta \leqq \delta_0.$$

For a point $x \in S^\Lambda$ such that $x(\lambda) = a_\lambda$ $(\lambda \in \Lambda)$, we therefore have

$$x_\delta \in \bigcap_{\lambda \in \Lambda} a_\lambda U P_\lambda{}^{-1} = \bigcap_{\lambda \in \Lambda} x P_\lambda U P_\lambda{}^{-1} = xU^\Lambda \quad \text{for } \delta \leqq \delta_0.$$

Consequently $x_\delta \xrightarrow[\delta \in \Lambda]{} x$ for $\mathbf{U}(\Lambda)$. Thus $\mathbf{U}(\Lambda)$ is complete.

Conversely, if $\mathbf{U}(\Lambda)$ is complete, then for any Cauchy system $a_\delta \in S$ $(\delta \in \Delta)$, setting $x_\delta(\lambda) = a_\delta$ for every $\lambda \in \Lambda$, we obtain a Cauchy system $x_\delta \in S^\Lambda$ $(\delta \in \Delta)$ for $\mathbf{U}(\Lambda)$ by (1), and hence there is $x \in S^\Lambda$ such that

$x_\delta \xrightarrow[\delta\epsilon\Lambda]{} x$ for $\mathbf{U}(\Lambda)$. For such $x \in S^\Lambda$, we have $x_\delta P_\lambda \xrightarrow[\delta\epsilon\Lambda]{} xP_\lambda$ by Theorem 12.1, that is, $a_\delta \xrightarrow[\delta\epsilon\Lambda]{} xP_\lambda$ for $\mathbf{U}$.

Theorem 25.4. $\mathbf{U}(\Lambda)$ *is bounded and connected if and only if* $\mathbf{U}$ *is bounded and connected.*

Proof. If $\mathbf{U}$ is bounded and connected, then for any $U \in \mathbf{U}$ we can find $\sigma = 1, 2, \ldots$ by Theorem 10.8 such that $aU^\sigma = S$ for every $a \in S$, and hence for any $x \in S^\Lambda$ we have by (2), (6)

$$x(U^\Lambda)^\sigma = x(U^\sigma)^\Lambda = \bigcap_{\lambda\epsilon\Lambda} xP_\lambda U^\sigma P_\lambda^{-1} = \bigcap_{\lambda\epsilon\Lambda} SP_\lambda^{-1} = S^\Lambda.$$

Therefore $\mathbf{U}(\Lambda)$ is bounded and connected by Theorem 10.8. Conversely, if S^Λ is bounded and connected, then S also is so by Theorem 12.5, because $S = S^\Lambda P_\lambda$ for every $\lambda \in \Lambda$.

Theorem 25.5. *If* $\mathbf{U}(\Lambda)$ *is totally bounded, then* Λ *is finite or* $\mathbf{U}$ *is a trivial uniformity.*

Proof. We suppose that $\mathbf{U}$ is not trivial. Then we can find $U \in \mathbf{U}$ and $a, b \in S$ such that $bU \not\ni a$. Setting $x_\gamma(\lambda) = a$ for $\lambda \neq \gamma$ and $x_\gamma(\gamma) = b$, we obtain a system of points $x_\gamma \in S^\Lambda$ $(\gamma \in \Lambda)$. If $\mathbf{U}(\Lambda)$ is totally bounded, then we can find a finite system $\gamma_\nu \in \Lambda$ $(\nu = 1, 2, \ldots, n)$ such that $x_\gamma \in \bigcup_{\nu=1}^{n} x_{\gamma_\nu} U^\Lambda$ for every $\gamma \in \Lambda$. If $\gamma \neq \gamma_\nu$ for every $\nu = 1, 2, \ldots, n$; then we have $a = x_\gamma(\gamma_\nu)$, $b = x_{\gamma_\nu}(\gamma_\nu)$, and hence $x_\gamma P_{\gamma_\nu} \bar{\epsilon}\, x_{\gamma_\nu} P_{\gamma_\nu} U$. Since $U^\Lambda \leqq P_{\gamma_\nu} U P_{\gamma_\nu}^{-1}$ for every $\nu = 1, 2, \ldots, n$ by (2), we hence obtain $x_\gamma \bar{\epsilon}\, x_{\gamma_\nu} U^\Lambda$ for every $\nu = 1, 2, \ldots, n$, contradicting $x_\gamma \in \bigcup_{\nu=1}^{n} x_{\gamma_\nu} U^\Lambda$. Therefore $\Lambda = \{\gamma_1, \gamma_2, \ldots, \gamma_n\}$.

Every projection P_λ is uniformly continuous and uniformly open by Theorem 25.1. Using a proof similar to that in Theorem 24.6, one can prove

Theorem 25.6. *For the atom* $I_{\mathbf{U}(\Lambda)}$ *of* $\mathbf{U}(\Lambda)$ *we have*

$$I_{\mathbf{U}(\Lambda)} = \bigcap_{\lambda\epsilon\Lambda} P_\lambda I_{\mathbf{U}} P_\lambda^{-1},$$

$$xI_{\mathbf{U}(\Lambda)} P_\lambda = xP_\lambda I_{\mathbf{U}} \quad \textit{for } x \in S^\Lambda.$$

The next theorem follows immediately

Theorem 25.7. $\mathbf{U}(\Lambda)$ *is pure if and only if* $\mathbf{U}$ *is pure.*

Theorem 25.8. *If* $\mathbf{U}(\Lambda)$ *is sequential if and only if* $\mathbf{U}$ *is sequential.*

Proof. If $\mathbf{U}(\Lambda)$ is sequential, then we can find a sequence $U_\nu \in \mathbf{U}$ ($\nu = 1, 2, \ldots$) such that $U_\nu{}^\Lambda$ ($\nu = 1, 2, \ldots$) is a basis of $\mathbf{U}(\Lambda)$, because $\mathbf{U}^\Lambda$ is a basis of $\mathbf{U}(\Lambda)$. Such $U_\nu \in \mathbf{U}$ ($\nu = 1, 2, \ldots$) also is a basis of $\mathbf{U}$, because for any $U \in \mathbf{U}$ there is $\nu = 1, 2, \ldots$ such that $U_\nu{}^\Lambda \leqq U^\Lambda$, and hence $U_\nu \leqq U$ by (5). Conversely, if $\mathbf{U}$ is sequential and $U_\nu \in \mathbf{U}$ ($\nu = 1, 2, \ldots$) is a basis of $\mathbf{U}$, then $U_\nu{}^\Lambda$ ($\nu = 1, 2, \ldots$) is a basis of $\mathbf{U}(\Lambda)$, because for any $W \in \mathbf{U}(\Lambda)$ we can find $U \in \mathbf{U}$ such that $W \geqq U^\Lambda$ and hence $W \geqq U_\nu{}^\Lambda$ for some $\nu = 1, 2, \ldots$.

Remark. If a uniformity $\mathbf{U}$ is bounded, connected and not trivial, then the strong power $\mathbf{U}(\Lambda)$ is bounded by Theorem 25.4, but not totally bounded for an infinite Λ by Theorem 25.5. For instance, the relative uniformity $\mathbf{U}$ of the natural uniformity on the interval (0, 1) is obviously bounded and connected. Thus the strong power $\mathbf{U}(1, 2, \ldots)$ is bounded but not totally bounded. For the pure and discrete uniformity $\mathbf{U}$ on a space of two points $\{a, b\}$, $\mathbf{U}(1, 2, \ldots)$ also is bounded, but not totally bounded.

26. **Single Equi-Uniformities.** Let M_λ $(\lambda \in \Lambda)$ be a system of mappings from a space S to a space R with uniformity $\mathbf{V}$. For the pure discrete uniformity on S, M_λ $(\lambda \in \Lambda)$ is obviously equi-continuous. If M_λ $(\lambda \in \Lambda)$ is equi-continuous for a uniformity $\mathbf{U}$ on S, then M_λ $(\lambda \in \Lambda)$ also is equi-continuous for any uniformity on S which is stronger than $\mathbf{U}$. There exists the weakest among the uniformities for which M_λ $(\lambda \in \Lambda)$ is equi-continuous. Because, setting

$$\mathbf{B} = \{ \bigcap_{\lambda \in \Lambda} M_\lambda V M_\lambda{}^{-1} : V \in \mathbf{V} \}$$

we obtain a system of connectors $\mathbf{B}$ on S. It is obvious by (12) in 11 that $\mathbf{B}$ satisfies the basis condition 1). Since

$$(\bigcap_{\lambda \in \Lambda} M_\lambda V M_\lambda{}^{-1})^{-1} (\bigcap_{\lambda \in \Lambda} M_\lambda V M_\lambda{}^{-1}) \leqq M_\gamma V^{-1} M_\gamma{}^{-1} M_\gamma V M_\gamma{}^{-1} \leqq M_\gamma V^{-1} V M_\gamma{}^{-1}$$

for every $\gamma \in \Lambda$ by (13), (14) in 11, we obtain

$$(\bigcap_{\lambda \in \Lambda} M_\lambda V M_\lambda{}^{-1})^{-1} (\bigcap_{\lambda \in \Lambda} M_\lambda V M_\lambda{}^{-1}) \leqq \bigcap_{\lambda \in \Lambda} M_\lambda V^{-1} V M_\lambda{}^{-1}.$$

Thus **B** also satisfies the basis condition 2). Therefore there exists uniquely a uniformity **U** on S such that **B** is a basis of **U**. For this uniformity **U**, M_λ $(\lambda \in \Lambda)$ is equi-continuous by Theorem 15.1. If M_λ $(\lambda \in \Lambda)$ is equi-continuous for a uniformity $\mathbf{U}_0$ on S, then $\mathbf{U}_0 \supset \mathbf{B}$ by Theorem 15.1, and hence $\mathbf{U}_0 \supset \mathbf{U}$. Therefore **U** is the weakest among the uniformities, for which M_λ $(\lambda \in \Lambda)$ is equi-continuous. Such a uniformity **U** is called the *single equi-uniformity* on S by M_λ $(\lambda \in \Lambda)$. Thus we can state

Theorem 26.1. *For the single equi-uniformity* **U** *on* S *by* M_λ $(\lambda \in \Lambda)$, *we have* $U \in \mathbf{U}$ *if and only if there is* $V \in \mathbf{V}$ *such that* $U \geqq \bigcap_{\lambda \in \Lambda} M_\lambda V M_\lambda^{-1}$.

It is obvious by definition that the single equi-uniformity on S by M_λ $(\lambda \in \Lambda)$ is stronger than the weak-uniformity on S by M_λ $(\lambda \in \Lambda)$.

Theorem 26.2. *The single equi-uniformity on* S *by* M_λ $(\lambda \in \Lambda)$ *is the weak-uniformity on* S *by the product* $\prod_{\lambda \in \Lambda} M_\lambda$ *from* S *to the power* R^Λ *for the strong power* $\mathbf{V}(\Lambda)$ *of* **V**.

Proof. Setting $M = \prod_{\lambda \in \Lambda} M_\lambda$, we have $M_\lambda = MP_\lambda$ for the projection P_λ $(\lambda \in \Lambda)$ by definition. Thus for $V \in \mathbf{V}$ we have by (12) in 11

$$\bigcap_{\lambda \in \Lambda} M_\lambda V M_\lambda^{-1} = \bigcap_{\lambda \in \Lambda} MP_\lambda V P_\lambda^{-1} M^{-1} = MV^\Lambda M^{-1}.$$

Therefore we conclude Theorem 26.2 from Theorems 26.1 and 23.1.

As a special case of Theorem 26.2, we have

Theorem 26.3. *The strong power* $\mathbf{U}(\Lambda)$ *of a uniformity* **U** *on* S *by* Λ *is the single equi-uniformity on the power* S^Λ *by the system of all projections* P_λ $(\lambda \in \Lambda)$.

Theorem 26.4. *If* **V** *is complete, then in order that the single equi-uniformity on* S *by* M_λ $(\lambda \in \Lambda)$ *be complete, it is necessary and sufficient that for a system of points* $a_\lambda \in R_\lambda$ $(\lambda \in \Lambda)$, *if* $\bigcap_{\lambda \in \Lambda} a_\lambda V M_\lambda^{-1} \neq \emptyset$ *for every* $V \in \mathbf{V}$, *then there exists* $x \in S$ *such that* $xM_\lambda \in a_\lambda I_V$ *for every* $\lambda \in \Lambda$.

Proof. If **V** is complete, then the strong power $\mathbf{V}(\Lambda)$ of **V** by Λ also is complete by Theorem 25.3. Setting $M = \prod_{\lambda \in \Lambda} M_\lambda$, we hence have by Theorem 23.9 that the weak-uniformity on S by M is complete if and only if for any $a \in R^\Lambda$ such that $aV^\Lambda M^{-1} \neq \emptyset$ for every $V \in \mathbf{V}$, we can find $x \in S$ such that $xM \in aI_{\mathbf{V}^\Lambda}$. On the other hand, we have by (2) in 25

$$aV^\Lambda M^{-1} = \bigcap_{\lambda \in \Lambda} aP_\lambda VP_\lambda^{-1} M^{-1} = \bigcap_{\lambda \in \Lambda} aP_\lambda VM_\lambda^{-1},$$

and we have by Theorem 25.6 that $xM \in aI_{\mathbf{V}(\Lambda)}$ if and only if $xMP_\lambda \in aI_{\mathbf{V}(\Lambda)}P$ for every $\lambda \in \Lambda$, that is, if and only if $xM_\lambda \in aP_\lambda I_{\mathbf{V}}$ for every $\lambda \in \Lambda$. Thus we obtain Theorem 26.4 by Theorem 26.2.

For $\emptyset \neq X \subset S$, we obviously have by definition

$$(\prod_{\lambda \in \Lambda} M_\lambda)^X = \prod_{\lambda \in \Lambda} M_\lambda{}^X.$$

Therefore we obtain by Theorems 23.4 and 26.2

Theorem 26.5. *For $\emptyset \neq X \subset S$, the relative uniformity of the single equi-uniformity by M_λ ($\lambda \in \Lambda$) on X is the single equi-uniformity on X by the system of relative mappings $M_\lambda{}^X$ ($\lambda \in \Lambda$).*

Referring to Theorem 25.8, we obtain by Theorems 26.2 and 23.1

Theorem 26.6. *If* $\mathbf{V}$ *is sequential, then the single equi-uniformity on S by M_λ ($\lambda \in \Lambda$) also is sequential.*

Theorem 26.7. *If the single equi-uniformity* $\mathbf{U}$ *on S by M_λ ($\lambda \in \Lambda$) is totally bounded, and if $\{xM_\lambda: \lambda \in \Lambda\}$ is totally bounded for* $\mathbf{V}$ *for every $x \in S$, then* $\mathbf{U}$ *is the weak-uniformity on S by M_λ ($\lambda \in \Lambda$).*

Proof. For any $V \in \mathbf{V}$ there is a symmetric $W \in \mathbf{V}$ such that $W^3 \leqq V$. Under the assumption of Theorem 26.7, we can find a finite system $\lambda_\nu \in \Lambda$ ($\nu = 1, 2, \ldots, n$) by Theorem 15.2 such that for any $\lambda \in \Lambda$ there is λ_ν for which $xM_\lambda \in xM_{\lambda_\nu} W$ for every $x \in S$. Then $yM_{\lambda_\nu} \in xM_{\lambda_\nu} W$ implies

$$yM_\lambda \in yM_{\lambda_\nu} W \subset xM_{\lambda_\nu} W^2 \subset xM_\lambda W^3 \subset xM_\lambda V$$

and hence $M_{\lambda_\nu} WM_{\lambda_\nu}{}^{-1} \leqq M_\lambda VM_\lambda{}^{-1}$. Therefore $\bigcap_{\nu=1}^{n} M_{\lambda_\nu} WM_{\lambda_\nu}{}^{-1} \leqq M_\lambda VM_\lambda{}^{-1}$ for every $\lambda \in \Lambda$. Consequently $\bigcap_{\nu=1}^{n} M_{\lambda_\nu} WM_{\lambda_\nu}{}^{-1} \leqq \bigcap_{\lambda \in \Lambda} M_\lambda VM_\lambda{}^{-1}$. Referring to Theorem 23.6, we hence conclude that $\mathbf{U}$ is the weak-uniformity on S by M_λ ($\lambda \in \Lambda$).

Theorem 26.8. *For a binary mapping $(x, y) \in Q$ $(x \in S,\ y \in R)$ from $S \times R$ to a uniform space Q with uniformity* **W** *such that (x, R) and (S, y) are totally bounded for* **W** *for every $x \in S$ and $y \in R$, the single equi-uniformity on S by N_y $(y \in R)$ is totally bounded if and only if the single equi-uniformity on R by M_x $(x \in S)$ is totally bounded. Here $xN_y = yM_x = (x, y)$.*

Proof. Let **U** be the single equi-uniformity on S by N_y $(y \in R)$. Then N_y $(y \in R)$ is equi-continuous for **U** by definition. If **U** is totally bounded, then for any $W \in \mathbf{W}$ we can find a finite system $a_\nu \in R$ $(\nu = 1, 2, \ldots, n)$ by Theorem 15.2 such that for any $y \in R$ there is a_ν for which $xN_y \in xN_{a_\nu}W$ for every $x \in S$. Thus $yM_x \in a_\nu M_x W$ for every $x \in S$, and hence

$$y \in a_\nu \bigcap_{x \in S} M_x W M_x^{-1}$$

Therefore $R = \bigcup_{\nu=1}^{n} a_\nu \bigcap_{x \in S} M_x W M_x^{-1}$. Referring to Theorem 26.1, we hence conclude that R is totally bounded for the single equi-uniformity on R by M_x $(x \in S)$. The converse can be proved quite similarly.

27. **Multiple Equi-Uniformities.** Let $M_{\lambda,\gamma}$ $(\gamma \in \Gamma_\lambda,\ \lambda \in \Lambda)$ be a *double system* of mappings from S to R_λ $(\lambda \in \Lambda)$ such that $M_{\lambda,\gamma}$ $(\gamma \in \Gamma_\lambda)$ is a system of mappings from S to R_λ for each $\lambda \in \Lambda$. We consider a uniformity $\mathbf{V}_\lambda$ on R_λ for each $\lambda \in \Lambda$. The weakest uniformity on S among the uniformities for which $M_{\lambda,\gamma}$ $(\gamma \in \Gamma_\lambda)$ is equi-continuous for every $\lambda \in \Lambda$, is called the *multiple equi-uniformity* on S by a double system $M_{\lambda,\gamma}$ $(\gamma \in \Gamma_\lambda,\ \lambda \in \Lambda)$. Making $\mathbf{U}_\lambda$ denote the single equi-uniformity on S by $M_{\lambda,\gamma}$ $(\gamma \in \Gamma_\lambda)$ for each $\lambda \in \Lambda$, we obviously have by definition that $\bigvee_{\lambda \in \Lambda} \mathbf{U}_\lambda$ is the multiple equi-uniformity on S by $M_{\lambda,\gamma}$ $(\gamma \in \Gamma_\lambda,\ \lambda \in \Lambda)$. Therefore we can state by Theorems 21.1 and 26.1

Theorem 27.1. *For the multiple equi-uniformity* **U** *on S by a double system $M_{\lambda,\gamma}$ $(\gamma \in \Gamma_\lambda,\ \lambda \in \Lambda)$, we have $U \in \mathbf{U}$ if and only if there is a finite system $V_\nu \in \mathbf{V}_{\lambda_\nu}$, $\lambda_\nu \in \Lambda$ $(\nu = 1, 2, \ldots, n)$ such that*

$$U \geqq \bigcap_{\nu=1}^{n} \bigcap_{\gamma \in \Gamma_{\lambda_\nu}} M_{\lambda_\nu,\gamma} V_\nu M_{\lambda_\nu,\gamma}^{-1}.$$

Referring to Theorem 26.2, we obviously have by definition

Theorem 27.2. *The multiple equi-uniformity on S by* $M_{\lambda,\gamma}$ $(\gamma \in \Gamma_\lambda, \lambda \in \Lambda)$ *is the weak-uniformity on S by the system of the products* $\prod_{\gamma \in \Gamma_\lambda} M_{\lambda,\gamma}$ $(\lambda \in \Lambda)$ *for the strong powers* $\mathbf{V}_\lambda$ (Γ_λ) *on the powers* $R_\lambda^{\Gamma_\lambda}$ $(\lambda \in \Lambda)$.

Therefore we conclude from Theorem 23.9

Theorem 27.3. *If* $\mathbf{V}_\lambda$ *is complete for every* $\lambda \in \Lambda$, *then the multiple equi-uniformity on S by* $M_{\lambda,\gamma}$ $(\gamma \in \Gamma_\lambda, \lambda \in \Lambda)$ *is complete if and only if for any system of points* $a_{\lambda,\gamma} \in R_\lambda$ $(\gamma \in \Gamma_\lambda, \lambda \in \Lambda)$ *such that*

$$\bigcap_{\nu=1}^{n} \bigcap_{\gamma \in \Gamma_{\lambda_\nu}} a_{\lambda_\nu,\gamma} V_\nu M_{\lambda_\nu,\gamma}^{-1} \neq \emptyset$$

for any finite system $V_\nu \in \mathbf{V}_{\lambda_\nu}$, $\lambda_\nu \in \Lambda$ $(\nu = 1, 2, \ldots, n)$, *there exists* $x \in S$ *such that* $xM_{\lambda,\gamma} \in a_{\lambda,\gamma} I_{\mathbf{V}_\lambda}$ *for every* $\gamma \in \Gamma_\lambda$, $\lambda \in \Lambda$.

We also obviously have by Theorems 21.3 and 27.2

Theorem 27.4. *For* $\emptyset \neq X \subset S$, *the relative uniformity of the multiple equi-uniformity by* $M_{\lambda,\gamma}$ $(\gamma \in \Gamma_\lambda, \lambda \in \Lambda)$ *on X is the multiple equi-uniformity on X by the double system of the relative mappings* $M_{\lambda,\gamma}^{\ x}$ $(\gamma \in \Gamma_\lambda, \lambda \in \Lambda)$.

Theorem 27.5. *Let* **U** *denote the multiple equi-uniformity on S by* $M_{\lambda,\gamma}$ $(\gamma \in \Gamma_\lambda, \lambda \in \Lambda)$. *A system of mappings* N_δ $(\delta \in \Delta)$ *from a uniform space Q with uniformity* **W** *to S with uniformity* **U** *is equi-continuous if and only if the system of the composed mappings* $N_\delta M_{\lambda,\gamma}$ $(\delta \in \Delta, \gamma \in \Gamma_\lambda)$ *is equi-continuous for every* $\lambda \in \Lambda$.

Proof. Since for any finite system $V_\nu \in \mathbf{V}_{\lambda_\nu}$, $\lambda_\nu \in \Lambda$ $(\nu = 1, 2, \ldots, n)$ we have

$$\bigcap_{\delta \in \Lambda} N_\delta \Big(\bigcap_{\nu=1}^{n} \bigcap_{\gamma \in \Gamma_{\lambda_\nu}} M_{\lambda_\nu,\gamma} V_\nu M_{\lambda_\nu,\gamma}^{-1} \Big) N_\delta^{-1}$$

$$= \bigcap_{\nu=1}^{n} \bigcap_{\delta \in \Lambda} \bigcap_{\gamma \in \Gamma_{\lambda_\nu}} N_\delta M_{\lambda_\nu,\gamma} V_\nu (N_\delta M_{\lambda_\nu,\gamma})^{-1},$$

we conclude Theorem 27.5 from Theorems 15.1 and 27.1.

Now we consider a binary mapping $(x, y) \in Q$ $(x \in S,\ y \in R)$ from $S \times R$ to a space Q with uniformity $\mathbf{W}$. Let $X_\lambda \subset S$ $(\lambda \in \Lambda)$ be a system of sets such that $S = \bigcup_{\lambda \in \Lambda} X_\lambda$ and for any $\lambda_1, \lambda_2 \in \Lambda$ we can find $\lambda \in \Lambda$ for which $X \supset X_{\lambda_1} \cup X_{\lambda_2}$. We also make use of the notation:

$$yM_x = xN_y = (x, y) \quad \text{for} \quad x \in S,\ y \in R.$$

Then we obviously have by Theorem 27.1

Theorem 27.6. *For the multiple equi-uniformity* $\mathbf{V}$ *on* R *by the double system* M_x $(x \in X_\lambda,\ \lambda \in \Lambda)$, *we have* $V \in \mathbf{V}$ *if and only if we can find* $W \in \mathbf{W}$ and $\lambda \in \Lambda$ *such that* $V \geqq \bigcap_{x \in X_\lambda} M_x W M_x^{-1}$.

We conclude easily from Theorem 27.3

Theorem 27.7. *If* $\mathbf{W}$ *is complete, then the multiple equi-uniformity on* R *by* M_x $(x \in X_\lambda,\ \lambda \in \Lambda)$ *is complete if and only if for any system of points* $a_x \in Q$ $(x \in S)$ *such that* $\bigcap_{x \in X_\lambda} a_x W M_x^{-1} \neq \emptyset$ *for any* $W \in \mathbf{W}$ *and* $\lambda \in \Lambda$, *we can find* $y \in R$ *such that* $yM_x \in a_x I_{\mathbf{W}}$ *for every* $x \in S$.

Theorem 27.8. *If there is a uniformity* $\mathbf{U}$ *on* S *such that* X_λ *is totally bounded,* N_y $(y \in R)$ *is equi-continuous on* X_λ *for every* $\lambda \in \Lambda$, *and* (x, R) *is totally bounded for* $\mathbf{W}$ *for every* $x \in S$, *then the multiple equi-uniformity on* R *by* M_x $(x \in X_\lambda,\ \lambda \in \Lambda)$ *is totally bounded and coincides with the weak-uniformity on* R *by the system* M_x $(x \in X_\lambda,\ \lambda \in \Lambda)$.

Proof. Let $\mathbf{V}_\lambda$ be the single equi-uniformity on R by M_x $(x \in X_\lambda)$ for each $\lambda \in \Lambda$. Then $\mathbf{V}_\lambda$ is totally bounded by Theorem 26.8 and coincides with the weak-uniformity on R by M_x $(x \in X_\lambda)$ by Theorem 26.7, because (X_λ, y) is totally bounded for every $\lambda \in \Lambda$ and $y \in R$ by Theorem 12.5. Therefore $\bigvee_{\lambda \in \Lambda} \mathbf{V}_\lambda$ is totally bounded by Theorem 21.5 and coincides with the weak-uniformity on R by M_x $(x \in X_\lambda,\ \lambda \in \Lambda)$. On the other hand, $\bigvee_{\lambda \in \Lambda} \mathbf{V}_\lambda$ is the multiple equi-uniformity on R by the double system M_x $(x \in X_\lambda,\ \lambda \in \Lambda)$.

28. **Fundamental Theorems.** We defined interval connectors $V_\mathcal{E}$ $(\mathcal{E} > 0)$ on the real number space **R** in 18. For a function ϕ on a space S, the inverse image of $V_\mathcal{E}$ by ϕ will be denoted by $U(\mathcal{E}, \phi)$, namely

$$xU(\mathcal{E}, \phi) = \{y: |\phi(x) - \phi(y)| < \mathcal{E}\} \text{ for } x, y \in S.$$

For a system Φ of functions on S we make use of the notation

$$U(\mathcal{E}, \Phi) = \bigcap_{\phi \in \Phi} U(\mathcal{E}, \phi) \text{ for } \mathcal{E} > 0,$$

that is, we have $y \in xU(\mathcal{E}, \Phi)$ if and only if $|\phi(x) - \phi(y)| < \mathcal{E}$ for every $\phi \in \Phi$. Then we obviously have

$$U(\mathcal{E}, \Phi) \geqq U(\delta, \Phi) \text{ for } \mathcal{E} > \delta > 0.$$

Referring to Theorem 23.6, we can state that for a system of functions Φ on S

$$\{U(\mathcal{E}, \phi_1, \dots, \phi_n): \mathcal{E} > 0, \phi_\nu \in \Phi \ (\nu = 1, 2, \dots, n), n = 1, 2, \dots\}$$

is a basis of the weak-uniformity on S by Φ.

We conclude from Theorem 26.1 that

$$\{U(\mathcal{E}, \Phi): \mathcal{E} > 0\}$$

is a basis of the single equi-uniformity on S by Φ.

As an immediate consequence of Theorem 27.1 we have that for a double system of functions Φ_λ $(\lambda \in \Lambda)$

$$\{U(\mathcal{E}, \Phi_{\lambda_1}, \dots, \Phi_{\lambda_n}): \mathcal{E} > 0, \lambda_\nu \in \Lambda \ (\nu = 1, 2, \dots, n), n = 1, 2, \dots\}$$

is a basis of the multiple equi-uniformity on S by Φ_λ $(\lambda \in \Lambda)$.

Let **U** be an arbitrary uniformity on S. We consider a system Φ of bounded functions on S which is equi-continuous for **U**, that is, $U(\mathcal{E}, \Phi) \in \mathbf{U}$ for every $\mathcal{E} > 0$. Let Φ_λ $(\lambda \in \Lambda)$ be the system of all such systems of bounded functions on S. For the multiple equi-uniformity **V** on S by the double system Φ_λ $(\lambda \in \Lambda)$, we have $\mathbf{U} \supset \mathbf{V}$, because **V** is by definition the weakest among the uniformities for which Φ_λ is equi-continuous for every $\lambda \in \Lambda$. On the other hand, we have $\mathbf{U} \subset \mathbf{V}$ by Theorem 20.4, and hence $\mathbf{U} = \mathbf{V}$. Therefore we can state

Fundamental Theorem 1. *Every uniformity on S is a multiple equi-uniformity on S by a double system of bounded functions.*

We assume now that **U** is totally bounded. Let Φ be the system of all bounded, uniformly continuous functions on S for **U**. For the weak-uniformity **V** on S by Φ, we have $\mathbf{V} \subset \mathbf{U}$, because **V** is the weakest among the uniformities for which every function in Φ is uniformly continuous. On the other hand, we have $\mathbf{V} \supset \mathbf{U}$ by Theorem 20.5, and hence $\mathbf{V} = \mathbf{U}$.

Conversely, every weak-uniformity on S by a system of bounded functions is totally bounded by Theorem 23.8, because every bounded set of **R** is totally bounded for the natural uniformity by Theorem 18.2. Therefore we can state

Fundamental Theorem 2. *A uniformity on S is totally bounded if and only if it is a weak-uniformity on S by a system of bounded functions on S.*

If **U** is sequential, then we can find a sequence of symmetric connectors $U_\nu \in \mathbf{U}$ $(\nu = 1, 2, \ldots)$ such that $U_\nu \geqq U_{\nu+1}{}^2$ $(\nu = 1, 2, \ldots)$ and U_ν $(\nu = 1, 2, \ldots)$ is a basis of **U**. For such $U_\nu \in \mathbf{U}$ $(\nu = 1, 2, \ldots)$ we can find a system of functions ϕ_x $(x \in S)$ on S by the Lemma in 18 such that for every $x \in S$, 1) $y \in zU_{\nu+1}$ implies $|\phi_x(y) - \phi_x(z)| \leqq \frac{1}{2^{\nu-1}}$ $(\nu = 1, 2, \ldots)$, 2) $\phi_x(x) = 0$, 3) $\phi_x(y) \geqq \frac{1}{2^\nu}$ for $y \,\bar{\in}\, xU_{\nu+1}$, 4) $\phi_x(y) = 1$ for $y \,\bar{\in}\, xU_1$, 5) $0 \leqq \phi_x(y) \leqq 1$ for every $y \in S$. This system of functions ϕ_x $(x \in S)$ is equi-continuous for **U**, because 1) implies

$$U(\frac{1}{2^\nu}, \phi_x\ (x \in S)) \geqq U_{\nu+3} \in \mathbf{U}\ (\nu = 1, 2, \ldots).$$

Thus, for the single equi-uniformity **V** on S by ϕ_x $(x \in S)$, we have $\mathbf{V} \subset \mathbf{U}$. On the other hand, if $y \in zU(\frac{1}{2^{\nu+1}}, \phi_x\ (x \in S))$, that is, if $|\phi_x(y) - \phi_x(z)| < \frac{1}{2^{\nu+1}}$ for every $x \in S$, then setting $x = y$, we obtain $\phi_y(z) < \frac{1}{2^{\nu+1}}$ by 2) and 5), and hence $z \in yU_{\nu+1}$ by 3), that is, $y \in zU_{\nu+1}$. Therefore $U(\frac{1}{2^{\nu+1}}, \phi_x\ (x \in S)) \leqq U_{\nu+1}$ for $\nu = 1, 2, \ldots$. Since U_ν $(\nu = 1, 2, \ldots)$ is a basis of **U**, we hence conclude $\mathbf{U} \subset \mathbf{V}$, and consequently

$\mathbf{U} = \mathbf{V}$. Conversely, every single equi-uniformity by a system of functions is sequential by Theorem 26.6, because the natural uniformity on $\mathbf{R}$ is sequential by Theorem 18.1. Thus we can state

Fundamental Theorem 3. *A uniformity* $\mathbf{U}$ *on* S *is sequential if and only if it is a single equi-uniformity by a system of functions on* S, *and then there is a system of functions* $0 \leqq \phi_\lambda \leqq 1$ $(\lambda \in \Lambda)$ *such that* $\mathbf{U}$ *is the single equi-uniformity by* ϕ_λ $(\lambda \in \Lambda)$.

29. **Completions.** If a uniform space S with uniformity $\mathbf{U}$ is a subspace of another uniform space $\tilde{S}$ with uniformity $\tilde{\mathbf{U}}$ subject to the *completion conditions:*

1) $\tilde{\mathbf{U}}$ is complete,
2) $S^{\tilde{\mathbf{U}}-} = \tilde{S}$,
3) $\mathbf{U}$ is the relative uniformity $\tilde{\mathbf{U}}^S$.
4) $\tilde{\mathbf{U}}$ is pure on $\tilde{S} - S$,

then $\tilde{\mathbf{U}}$ is called a *completion* of $\mathbf{U}$ over $\tilde{S}$, and every point of $\tilde{S} - S$ is called an *adding point*. If $\mathbf{U}$ is complete, then $\mathbf{U}$ can be considered a completion of $\mathbf{U}$ itself. If $\mathbf{U}$ is pure, then every completion of $\mathbf{U}$ also is pure by definition.

If $\mathbf{U}$ is a weak-uniformity on S by a mapping M from S to a uniform space R with a pure, complete uniformity $\mathbf{V}$, then setting

$$\tilde{S} = S \cup ((SM)^{\mathbf{V}-} - SM),$$
$$x\tilde{M} = xM \text{ for } x \in S, \quad \tilde{x}\tilde{M} = \tilde{x} \text{ for } \tilde{x} \in ((XM)^{\mathbf{V}-} - SM),$$

we obtain a space $\tilde{S} \supset S$ and a mapping $\tilde{M}$ from $\tilde{S}$ to R such that $\tilde{M}^S = M$ and $\tilde{S}\tilde{M} = (SM)^{\mathbf{V}-}$. If $(SM)^{\mathbf{V}-} = SM$, then SM is complete by Theorem 8.2, and hence $\mathbf{U}$ is complete by Theorem 23.3. Thus we assume $(SM)^{\mathbf{V}-} \neq SM$. For the weak-uniformity $\tilde{\mathbf{U}}$ on $\tilde{S}$ by $\tilde{M}$, $\tilde{\mathbf{U}}$ is complete by Theorem 23.3, because $\tilde{S}\tilde{M} = (SM)^{\mathbf{V}-}$ is complete by Theorem 8.2. For any $\tilde{x} \in ((SM)^{\mathbf{V}-} - SM)$ we can find $x_\delta \in S$ $(\delta \in \Delta)$ by Theorem 7.3 such that $x_\delta M \xrightarrow[\delta \in \Lambda]{} \tilde{x} = \tilde{x}\tilde{M}$ for $\mathbf{V}$, and hence $x_\delta \xrightarrow[\delta \in \Lambda]{} \tilde{x}$ for $\tilde{\mathbf{U}}$ by Theorem 23.3. Therefore $S^{\tilde{\mathbf{U}}-} = \tilde{S}$ by Theorem 7.3. $\mathbf{U}$ is obviously the relative uniformity $\tilde{\mathbf{U}}^S$ by Theorem 23.4. Finally for any $\tilde{x} \in ((SM)^{\mathbf{V}-} - SM)$ we have by Theorem 23.3

$$\widetilde{x}I_{\mathbf{U}} = \widetilde{xM}I_{\mathbf{V}}\widetilde{M}^{-1} = \widetilde{x}I_{\mathbf{V}}\widetilde{M}^{-1} = \{\widetilde{x}\}$$

because $\widetilde{x}I_{\mathbf{V}} = \{\widetilde{x}\}$ by assumption. Therefore $\widetilde{\mathbf{U}}$ is a completion of **U**.

For an arbitrary uniformity **U** on S we can find a double system of bounded functions Φ_λ $(\lambda \in \Lambda)$ by Fundamental Theorem 1 in 28 such that **U** is the multiple equi-uniformity by Φ_λ $(\lambda \in \Lambda)$. A function ϕ on S is a mapping from S to the real number space **R** with the natural uniformity which will be denoted by $\mathbf{V}_0$ in this paragraph. According to Theorems 27.2 and 24.8, the multiple equi-uniformity on S by Φ_λ $(\lambda \in \Lambda)$ is the weak-uniformity on S by a mapping from S to $\prod_{\lambda\in\Lambda} \mathbf{R}^{\Phi_\lambda}$ for the uniformity $\prod_{\lambda\in\Lambda} \mathbf{V}_0{}^{\Phi_\lambda}$. Since the natural uniformity $\mathbf{V}_0$ is pure and complete by Theorem 18.1, $\prod_{\lambda\in\Lambda} \mathbf{V}_0{}^{\Phi_\lambda}$ also is pure and complete by Theorem 24.3, 24.7, 25.3, and 25.7. Therefore there is a completion of **U**, as proved just above. Thus we can state

Theorem 29.1. *Every uniformity has a completion.*

A uniformity **U** on a space S is said to be *unimorphic* to a uniformity **V** on a space R, if there is a transformation T from S to R such that T is uniformly continuous and uniformly open. Such a transformation T is called a *unimorphism* between **U** and **V**. If a transformation T is a unimorphism between **U** and **V**, then the inverse transformation T^{-1} is a unimorphism between **V** and **U**, because we have by definition that T is uniformly continuous if and only if $T\mathbf{V}T^{-1} \subset \mathbf{U}$, and that T is uniformly open if and only if $T^{-1}\mathbf{U}T \subset \mathbf{V}$, and hence that T is uniformly open if and only if the inverse transformation T^{-1} is uniformly continuous.

Theorem 29.2. *Between two completions* $\widetilde{\mathbf{U}}$ *and* $\hat{\mathbf{U}}$ *of a uniformity* **U** *on* S *there exists uniquely a unimorphism* T *between* $\widetilde{\mathbf{U}}$ *and* $\hat{\mathbf{U}}$ *such that* $xT = x$ *for* $x \in S$.

Proof. Let $\widetilde{S}$ and $\hat{S}$ be the spaces respectively of $\widetilde{\mathbf{U}}$ and $\hat{\mathbf{U}}$. For any adding point $\widetilde{x} \in \widetilde{S} - S$, there is a convergent system $S \ni x_\delta \xrightarrow[\delta\in\Lambda]{} \widetilde{x}$ for $\widetilde{\mathbf{U}}$ by Theorem 7.3, because $S^{\widetilde{\mathbf{U}}-} = \widetilde{S}$ by the completion condition 2). Such a system $x_\delta \in S$ $(\delta \in \Delta)$ is a Cauchy system for **U** by 3), and hence there exists a point $\hat{x} \in \hat{S}$ such that $x_\delta \xrightarrow[\delta\in\Lambda]{} \hat{x}$ for $\hat{\mathbf{U}}$, because $\hat{\mathbf{U}}$ is complete and $\mathbf{U} = \hat{\mathbf{U}}^S$ by 3). Therefore there exists a mapping T from $\tilde{S}$ to $\hat{S}$ such that $xT = x$ for $x \in S$, and for any $\tilde{x} \in \tilde{S}$ we can find a system $x_\delta \in S$ $(\delta \in \Delta)$ such that $x_\delta \xrightarrow[\delta \in \Delta]{} \tilde{x}$ for $\tilde{\mathbf{U}}$ and $x_\delta \xrightarrow[\delta \in \Delta]{} \tilde{x}T$ for $\hat{\mathbf{U}}$. Such T is uniformly continuous by Theorem 12.7. Similarly we also obtain a uniformly continuous mapping T_1 from $\hat{S}$ to $\tilde{S}$ such that $xT_1 = x$ for $x \in S$. Then the composed mapping $T_1 T$ also is uniformly continuous by Theorem 14.3 and $xT_1 T = x$ for $x \in S$. For any adding point $\hat{x} \in \hat{S} - S$ there is a convergent system $S \ni x_\delta \xrightarrow[\delta \in \Delta]{} \hat{x}$ and we have $x_\delta \xrightarrow[\delta \in \Delta]{} \hat{x}T_1 T$ by Theorem 12.1. Therefore we obtain $\hat{x}T_1 T = \hat{x}$, because $\hat{x}T_1 T \in \hat{x}I_{\hat{\mathbf{U}}}$ by Theorem 7.1 and $\hat{x}I_{\hat{\mathbf{U}}} = \{\hat{x}\}$ by 4). As $\hat{x}T_1 T = \hat{x}$ for every $\hat{x} \in \hat{S}$, T is full and T_1 is one-to-one. Considering TT_1, we also conclude that T_1 is full and T is one-to-one. Thus T is a unimorphism between $\tilde{\mathbf{U}}$ and $\hat{\mathbf{U}}$, and $T_1 = T^{-1}$. The uniqueness of such a unimorphism T is obvious, because for any unimorphism T we have by Theorem 12.1 that $S \ni x_\delta \xrightarrow[\delta \in \Delta]{} \tilde{x}$ for $\tilde{\mathbf{U}}$ implies $x_\delta \xrightarrow[\delta \in \Delta]{} \tilde{x}T$ for $\hat{\mathbf{U}}$.

As an application of completion, we can prove

Theorem 29.3. *Every directed system from a totally bounded set has a Cauchy system as a partial system.*

Proof. Let A be a totally bounded set for a uniformity $\mathbf{U}$ and let $a_\delta \in A$ $(\delta \in \Delta)$ be a directed system. We can assume by Theorem 29.1 that $\mathbf{U}$ is complete. Then A^- is totally bounded and complete, and hence compact by Theorem 9.1. Setting $A_\gamma = \{a_\delta : \delta \geqq \gamma\}$ $(\gamma \in \Delta)$, we hence obtain $\bigcap_{\gamma \in \Delta} A_\gamma^- \neq \emptyset$ by Theorem 9.6. For a point $a \in \bigcap_{\gamma \in \Delta} A_\gamma^-$, we obviously have $aU \cap A_\gamma \neq \emptyset$ for every $U \in \mathbf{U}$ and $\gamma \in \Delta$. Therefore we can find a system $\delta(\gamma, U) \in \Delta$ $(\gamma \in \Delta,\ U \in \mathbf{U})$ such that $a_{\delta(\gamma,U)} \in aU \cap A_\gamma$, $\delta(\nu, U) \geqq \gamma$. We define $(\gamma_1, U_1) \geqq (\gamma_2, U_2)$ to mean $\gamma_1 \geqq \gamma_2$ and $U_1 \geqq U_2$. Then $\delta(\gamma, U)$ $(\gamma \in \Delta,\ U \in \mathbf{U})$ is a partial system of Δ by definition, and

$$a_{\delta(\gamma,V)} \in aV \subset aU \quad \text{for } V \leqq U.$$

Therefore $a_{\delta(\gamma,U)} \xrightarrow[(\gamma,U)]{} a$ for $\mathbf{U}$ by definition. Thus $a_{\delta(\gamma,U)}$ $(\gamma \in \Delta,\ U \in \mathbf{U})$ is a Cauchy system for $\mathbf{U}$.

As a converse to Theorem 29.3, we have

Theorem 29.4. *If every sequence from a set A has a Cauchy system for* **U** *as a partial system, then A is totally bounded for* **U**.

Proof. If A is not totally bounded for **U**, then there is $U \in \mathbf{U}$ such that there is no finite system $a_\nu \in A$ $(\nu = 1, 2, \ldots, n)$ such that $A \subset \bigcup_{\nu=1}^{n} a_\nu U$. For such $U \in \mathbf{U}$ we can find a symmetric $V \in \mathbf{U}$ such that $V^2 \leqq U$, and there is a sequence $a_\nu \in A$ $(\nu = 1, 2, \ldots)$ such that $a_\nu V \cap a_\mu V = \emptyset$ for $\nu \neq \mu$, because if there is no such sequence, then we have $A \subset \bigcup_{\nu=1}^{n} a_\nu V^2$ for some finite system $a_\nu \in A$ $(\nu = 1, 2, \ldots, n)$. Such a sequence $a_\nu \in A$ $(\nu = 1, 2, \ldots)$ obviously does not have any Cauchy system for **U** as a partial system.

Referring to Theorem 20.7, we obtain immediately

Theorem 29.5. *The completions of sequential uniformities also are sequential.*

Theorem 29.6. *If* **U** *is sequential, then every sequence of points from a totally bounded set A has a Cauchy sequence as a partial sequence.*

Proof. We can assume by Theorem 29.5 that **U** is sequential and complete. For any sequence $a_\nu \in A$ $(\nu = 1, 2, \ldots)$ we can find a partial system $\nu(\delta)(\delta \in \Delta)$ by Theorem 29.3 such that $a_{\nu(\delta)}$ $(\delta \in \Delta)$ is a Cauchy system for **U**. Then there is $a \in A^-$ such that $a_{\nu(\delta)} \xrightarrow[\delta \in \Delta]{} a$ for **U**. Let $U_\mu \in \mathbf{U}$ $(\mu = 1, 2, \ldots)$ be a basis of **U**. For any U_μ we can find $\delta_\mu \in \Delta$ such that $\mu < \nu(\delta_\mu)$ and $a_{\nu(\delta_\mu)} \in aU_\mu$. Setting $\nu_\mu = \nu(\delta_\mu)$ $(\mu = 1, 2, \ldots)$, we obtain $a_{\nu_\mu} \xrightarrow[\mu \geqq 1]{} a$ for **U**, and hence a_{ν_μ} $(\mu = 1, 2, \ldots)$ is a Cauchy sequence for **U**.

Applying Theorem 29.4, we can prove a useful

Theorem 29.7. *For any directed space Δ there is a partial system $\delta_\gamma \in \Delta$ $(\gamma \in \Gamma)$ such that for any bounded function ϕ on Δ, $\phi(\delta_\gamma)$ $(\gamma \in \Gamma)$ is convergent.*

Proof. The weak-uniformity **U** on Δ by the system of all bounded functions on Δ is totally bounded by Fundamental Theorem 2 in 28. Thus Δ has a Cauchy system $\delta_\gamma \in \Delta$ $(\gamma \in \Gamma)$ for **U** as a partial system by Theorem 29.4. Then for any bounded function ϕ on Δ, $\phi(\delta_\gamma)$ $(\gamma \in \Gamma)$ also is a Cauchy system by Theorem 12.5. Therefore $\phi(\delta_\gamma)$ $(\gamma \in \Gamma)$ is convergent, because the real number space **R** is complete by the natural uniformity.

30. **Locally Compact Uniformities.** A uniformity **U** on a space S is said to be *locally compact,* if there is $U_0 \in \mathbf{U}$ such that $(xU_0)^{\mathbf{U}-}$ is compact for every $x \in S$. Since compact sets are totally bounded, every locally compact uniformity is locally totally bounded. Locally compact uniformities also are complete by Theorem 8.6, because compact sets are complete by Theorem 9.1.

Conversely, if **U** is locally totally bounded and complete, then for any totally bounded $U \in \mathbf{U}$, $(xU)^{\mathbf{U}-}$ is compact for every $x \in S$, because $(xU)^{\mathbf{U}-}$ is totally bounded by Theorem 6.2, complete by Theorem 8.2, and hence compact by Theorem 9.1. Therefore we can state

Theorem 30.1. *A uniformity* **U** *is locally compact if and only if* **U** *is locally totally bounded and complete.*

Let **U** be a locally totally bounded uniformity on S and let $\widetilde{\mathbf{U}}$ be a completion of **U** over a space $\widetilde{S}$. For a totally bounded $U \in \mathbf{U}$ there is $\widetilde{U} \in \widetilde{\mathbf{U}}$ such that $U = \widetilde{U}^S$, and we can find a symmetric $\widetilde{V} \in \widetilde{\mathbf{U}}$ such that $\widetilde{V}^2 \leqq \widetilde{U}^\circ$. Since $x\widetilde{U}^\circ \cap S \subset x\widetilde{U}^S = xU$ for every $x \in S$, $(x\widetilde{U}^\circ \cap S)^-$ is totally bounded for **U** by Theorem 6.1. Since $(x\widetilde{U}^\circ \cap S)^- \supset x\widetilde{U}^\circ \cap S^- = x\widetilde{U}^\circ$ by Theorem 3.1, $x\widetilde{U}^\circ$ also is totally bounded for **U** for every $x \in S$. For any $z \in \widetilde{S}$ we have $(z\widetilde{V} \cap S)^- \supset z\widetilde{V}^\circ \cap S^- = z\widetilde{V}^\circ \neq \emptyset$, and hence $z\widetilde{V} \cap S \neq \emptyset$. For any $x \in z\widetilde{V} \cap S$ we have then $z\widetilde{V} \subset x\widetilde{V}^2 \subset x\widetilde{U}^\circ$. Thus $z\widetilde{V}$ is totally bounded for every $z \in \widetilde{S}$. Therefore $\widetilde{\mathbf{U}}$ is totally bounded by definition. Consequently we obtain by Theorem 30.1

Theorem 30.2. *The completion of a locally totally bounded uniformity is locally compact.*

For two uniformities **U**, **V** on a space S, if both of them are locally compact, and **U** is homeomorphic to **V**, namely $\mathbf{T}(\mathbf{U}) = \mathbf{T}(\mathbf{V})$, then for a totally bounded $U \in \mathbf{U}$, $\mathbf{U}$ is compact on $(xU)^{\mathbf{U}-}$ for each $x \in S$, and hence $\mathbf{U}$ coincides with $\mathbf{V}$ on $(xU)^{\mathbf{U}-}$ for every $x \in S$ by Theorem 9.7. Therefore $\mathbf{U}$ is locally stronger than $\mathbf{V}$ by definition. We can prove similarly that $\mathbf{V}$ is locally stronger than $\mathbf{U}$. Thus we can state

Theorem 30.3. *If a locally compact uniformity* $\mathbf{U}$ *is homeomorphic to a locally compact uniformity* $\mathbf{V}$, *then* $\mathbf{U} \sim \mathbf{V}$, *that is,* $\mathbf{U}$ *is locally unimorphic to* $\mathbf{V}$.

We obviously have by Theorems 22.7 and 30.1

Theorem 30.4. *If a locally totally bounded uniformity* $\mathbf{U}$ *is locally unimorphic to a locally compact uniformity* $\mathbf{V}$, *then* $\mathbf{U}$ *is locally compact too.*

Now we suppose that $\mathbf{U} \sim \mathbf{V}$, $\tilde{\mathbf{U}}$ is a completion of $\mathbf{U}$ over $\tilde{S}$, and $\hat{\mathbf{V}}$ is a completion of $\mathbf{V}$ over $\hat{S}$. For any adding point $\tilde{x} \in \tilde{S} - S$, there is a convergent system $S \ni x_\delta \xrightarrow[\delta \in \Lambda]{} \tilde{x}$ for $\tilde{\mathbf{U}}$. Then $x_\delta \in S$ $(\delta \in \Delta)$ is a Cauchy system for $\mathbf{V}$ by Theorem 22.3, and hence there is $\hat{x} \in \hat{S}$ such that $x_\delta \xrightarrow[\delta \in \Lambda]{} \hat{x}$ for $\hat{\mathbf{V}}$, because $\hat{\mathbf{V}}$ is a completion of $\mathbf{V}$ over $\hat{S}$. Therefore there is a mapping T from $\tilde{S}$ to $\hat{S}$ such that $xT = x$ for $x \in S$, and for any $\tilde{x} \in \tilde{S}$ there is a convergent system $S \ni x_\delta \xrightarrow[\delta \in \Lambda]{} \tilde{x}$ for $\tilde{\mathbf{U}}$ such that $x_\delta \xrightarrow[\delta \in \Lambda]{} \tilde{x}T$ for $\hat{\mathbf{V}}$. Since $\mathbf{U} \sim \mathbf{V}$ by assumption, we can find $U_0 \in \mathbf{U}$ by definition such that $\mathbf{U}$ is stronger than $\mathbf{V}$ on xU_0 for every $x \in S$. Referring to Theorem 12.7, we show easily that T is uniformly continuous on $(xU_0)^{\tilde{\mathbf{U}}-}$ for every $x \in S$. For such $U_0 \in \mathbf{U}$ there is $\tilde{W} \in \tilde{\mathbf{U}}$ such that $U_0 = \tilde{W}^S$ and we can find a symmetric $\tilde{U}_1 \in \tilde{\mathbf{U}}$ such that $\tilde{U}_1{}^2 \leq \tilde{W}^\circ$. Then we have by Theorem 3.1

$$(xU_0)^{\tilde{\mathbf{U}}-} = (x\tilde{W} \cap S)^{\tilde{\mathbf{U}}-} \supset x\tilde{W}^\circ \cap S^{\tilde{\mathbf{U}}-} = x\tilde{W}^\circ$$

for every $x \in S$. On the other hand, for any $\tilde{x} \in \tilde{S}$ there is $x \in S$ such that $x \in \tilde{x}\tilde{U}_1$, and hence $\tilde{x}\tilde{U}_1 \subset x\tilde{U}_1{}^2 \subset x\tilde{W}^\circ \subset (xU_0)^{\tilde{\mathbf{U}}-}$. Therefore T is uniformly continuous on $\tilde{x}\tilde{U}_1$ for every $\tilde{x} \in \tilde{S}$.

Similarly we can find a mapping T_1 from $\hat{S}$ to $\tilde{S}$ and $\hat{V}_1 \in \hat{\mathbf{V}}$ such that $xT_1 = x$ for $x \in S$ and T_1 is uniformly continuous on $\hat{x}\hat{V}_1$ for every $\hat{x} \in \hat{S}$. Then we obviously have $xT_1T = x$ for $x \in S$. For any $\hat{x} \in \hat{S}$ there is

$\hat{V} \in \hat{\mathbf{V}}$ such that $\hat{V} \leqq \hat{V}_1$ and $\hat{x}\hat{V}T_1 \subset \hat{x}T_1\widetilde{U}_1$, because T_1 is uniformly continuous on $\hat{x}\hat{V}_1$. Thus T_1T is uniformly continuous on $\hat{x}\hat{V}$ by Theorem 14.3. Therefore we conclude by Theorem 12.1 that $S \ni x_\delta \xrightarrow[\delta\in\Lambda]{} \hat{x}$ implies $x_\delta \xrightarrow[\delta\in\Lambda]{} \hat{x}T_1T$, and hence $\hat{x} = \hat{x}T_1T$, because $\hat{x}T_1T \in \hat{x}I_{\mathbf{U}}$ by Theorem 7.1 and $\hat{x}I_{\mathbf{U}} = \{\hat{x}\}$ for any adding point $\hat{x} \in \hat{S} - S$. Consequently we obtain $\hat{x}T_1T = \hat{x}$ for every $\hat{x} \in \hat{S}$. Thus T_1 is one-to-one and T is full. We also can prove quite similarly that $\widetilde{x}TT_1 = \widetilde{x}$ for every $\widetilde{x} \in \widetilde{S}$, and hence T is one-to-one and T_1 is full. Thus T is a transformation from $\widetilde{S}$ to $\hat{S}$ and $T_1 = T^{-1}$. The weak-uniformity $T\hat{\mathbf{V}}T^{-1}$ on $\widetilde{S}$ by T is obviously a completion of $\mathbf{V}$ over $\widetilde{S}$ and $\widetilde{\mathbf{U}} \sim T\hat{\mathbf{V}}T^{-1}$. For any completion $\widetilde{\mathbf{W}}$ of $\mathbf{V}$ over $\widetilde{S}$ such that $\widetilde{\mathbf{U}} \sim \widetilde{\mathbf{W}}$, we have $\mathbf{T}(\widetilde{\mathbf{W}}) = \mathbf{T}(T\hat{\mathbf{V}}T^{-1})$ by Theorem 22.2 and $\widetilde{\mathbf{W}}^S = (T\hat{\mathbf{V}}T^{-1})^S$ by definition. Therefore $\widetilde{\mathbf{W}} = T\hat{\mathbf{V}}T^{-1}$ by Theorem 21.7. Thus we can state.

Theorem 30.5. *If* $\mathbf{U} \sim \mathbf{V}$, *then for a completion* $\widetilde{\mathbf{U}}$ *of* $\mathbf{U}$ *over* $\widetilde{S}$ *there is uniquely a completion* $\widetilde{\mathbf{V}}$ *of* $\mathbf{V}$ *over* $\widetilde{S}$ *such that* $\widetilde{\mathbf{U}} \sim \widetilde{\mathbf{V}}$.

TRANSFORMATION GROUPS
IV. GENERAL THEORY

31. Transformation Groups. Let S be a space. Transformations from S to S itself are called transformations on S. The identity on S will be denoted by E or by E_S, that is, $xE = x$ for every $x \in S$. For two transformations X, Y on S, the composed mapping XY also is a transformation on S, and the inverse transformation X^{-1} is a transformation on S too. We obviously have by definition

$$(XY)Z = X(YZ), \quad (XY)^{-1} = Y^{-1}X^{-1}$$

for transformations X, Y, Z on S.

For two systems of transformations $\mathbf{K}$, $\mathbf{L}$ on S, we make use of the notations:

$$\mathbf{KL} = \{XY\colon X \in \mathbf{K},\ Y \in \mathbf{L}\},$$

$$\mathbf{K}^{-1} = \{X^{-1}\colon X \in \mathbf{K}\}$$

and

$$A\mathbf{K} = \{xX\colon x \in A,\ X \in \mathbf{K}\} \text{ for } \emptyset \neq A \subset S.$$

With these notations we obviously have

$$(A\mathbf{K})\mathbf{L} = A(\mathbf{KL}),\ (\mathbf{KL})^{-1} = \mathbf{L}^{-1}\mathbf{K}^{-1},\ (\mathbf{K}^{-1})^{-1} = \mathbf{K},$$

$$(\bigcup_{\lambda \in \Lambda} A_\lambda)\mathbf{K} = \bigcup_{\lambda \in \Lambda} A_\lambda \mathbf{K},\ A \bigcup_{\lambda \in \Lambda} \mathbf{K}_\lambda = \bigcup_{\lambda \in \Lambda} A\mathbf{K}_\lambda,$$

$$(\bigcup_{\lambda \in \Lambda} \mathbf{K}_\lambda)(\bigcup_{\gamma \in \Gamma} \mathbf{L}_\gamma) = \bigcup_{\lambda \in \Lambda, \gamma \in \Gamma} \mathbf{K}_\lambda \mathbf{L}_\gamma,$$

$$(\bigcup_{\lambda \in \Lambda} \mathbf{K}_\lambda)^{-1} = \bigcup_{\lambda \in \Lambda} \mathbf{K}_\lambda^{-1},\ (\bigcap_{\lambda \in \Lambda} \mathbf{K}_\lambda)^{-1} = \bigcap_{\lambda \in \Lambda} \mathbf{K}_\lambda^{-1},$$

and $(\bigcap_{\lambda \in \Lambda} \mathbf{K}_\lambda)T = \bigcap_{\lambda \in \Lambda} \mathbf{K}_\lambda T$, $T(\bigcap_{\lambda \in \Lambda} \mathbf{K}_\lambda) = \bigcap_{\lambda \in \Lambda} T\mathbf{K}_\lambda$ for a transformation T on S.

A system of transformations $\mathbf{G}$ on S is called a *transformation group,* if $\mathbf{G} \ni X, Y$ implies $\mathbf{G} \ni X^{-1}Y$, that is, if $\mathbf{G}^{-1}\mathbf{G} \subset \mathbf{G}$. For any transformation group $\mathbf{G}$ on S we have $\mathbf{G} \ni E$, because $\mathbf{G} \ni X$ implies $\mathbf{G} \ni X^{-1}X = E$; $\mathbf{G} \ni X$ implies $\mathbf{G} \ni X^{-1}$, because $\mathbf{G} \ni X$ implies $\mathbf{G} \ni X^{-1}E = X^{-1}$; and $\mathbf{G} \ni X, Y$ implies $\mathbf{G} \ni XY$, because $\mathbf{G} \ni X, Y$ implies $\mathbf{G} \ni X^{-1}, Y$ and hence $\mathbf{G} \ni (X^{-1})^{-1}Y = XY$. Thus we have $\mathbf{GG} = \mathbf{G}$ and $\mathbf{G}^{-1} = \mathbf{G}$ for any transformation group $\mathbf{G}$ on S.

For a system of transformation groups $\mathbf{G}_\lambda$ $(\lambda \in \Lambda)$ on S, it is obvious by definition that $\bigcap_{\lambda\in\Lambda} \mathbf{G}_\lambda$ also is a transformation group on S. Thus we can show easily that for any system of transformations $\mathbf{K}$ on S there exists the least transformation group including $\mathbf{K}$, which will be called the transformation group *generated* by $\mathbf{K}$. For two transformation groups $\mathbf{G}, \mathbf{H}$ on S, $\mathbf{H}$ is called a *subgroup* of $\mathbf{G}$, if $\mathbf{H} \subset \mathbf{G}$.

We say that a transformation T on S *fixes* a point $x \in S$, if $xT = x$, and a system of transformations $\mathbf{K}$ *fixes* a point x, if every transformation of $\mathbf{K}$ fixes x. The system of all transformations which fix a point $x \in S$ is called the *fixer* of x and denoted by $\mathbf{F}_x$. We can show easily that the fixer $\mathbf{F}_x$ is a transformation group on S for every $x \in S$. For a transformation group $\mathbf{G}$ on S, $\mathbf{F}_x \cap \mathbf{G}$ is called the *fixer* of x in $\mathbf{G}$ and denoted by $\mathbf{F}_x^{\mathbf{G}}$. It is obvious that $\mathbf{F}_x^{\mathbf{G}}$ is a subgroup of $\mathbf{G}$.

For $\emptyset \neq A \subset S$, setting

(1) $\mathbf{F}^{\mathbf{G}}(A) = \bigcap_{x\in A} \mathbf{F}_x^{\mathbf{G}}$,

we obtain a subgroup $\mathbf{F}^{\mathbf{G}}(A)$ of $\mathbf{G}$, which will be called the *fixer* of A in $\mathbf{G}$. We obviously have $\mathbf{F}^{\mathbf{G}}(S) = \{E\}$ and

(2) $\bigcap_{\lambda\in\Lambda} \mathbf{F}^{\mathbf{G}}(A_\lambda) = \mathbf{F}^{\mathbf{G}}(\bigcup_{\lambda\in\Lambda} A_\lambda)$ for $\emptyset \neq A_\lambda \subset S$ $(\lambda \in \Lambda)$.

Thus $A \supset B \neq \emptyset$ implies $\mathbf{F}^{\mathbf{G}}(A) \subset \mathbf{F}^{\mathbf{G}}(B)$.

For a system of transformations $\mathbf{K}$ on S, $F(\mathbf{K})$ denotes the set of all points which are fixed by $\mathbf{K}$, that is,

(3) $F(\mathbf{K}) = \{x\colon xX = x \text{ for every } X \in \mathbf{K}\}$.

$F(\mathbf{K}) = \emptyset$ if there is no point fixed by $\mathbf{K}$. $F(\mathbf{K})$ is called the *fixed set* of $\mathbf{K}$. We obviously have by definition

(4) $\bigcap_{\lambda\in\Lambda} F(\mathbf{K}_\lambda) = F(\bigcup_{\lambda\in\Lambda} \mathbf{K}_\lambda)$.

Thus $\mathbf{K} \supset \mathbf{H}$ implies $F(\mathbf{K}) \subset F(\mathbf{H})$, and obviously

(5) $\mathbf{F}^{\mathbf{G}}(F(\mathbf{K})) \supset \mathbf{K}$ if $F(\mathbf{K}) \neq \emptyset$, $\mathbf{K} \subset \mathbf{G}$.

For an arbitrary set $A \neq \emptyset$ of S, $F(\mathbf{F}^{\mathbf{G}}(A))$ is called the *fix hull* of A by $\mathbf{G}$ and denoted by $A^{\mathbf{G}}$, that is,

(6) $A^{\mathbf{G}} = F(\mathbf{F}^{\mathbf{G}}(A))$ for $\emptyset \neq A \subset S$.

With this definition we obviously have

(7) $A^{\mathbf{G}} \supset A$ for $\emptyset \neq A \subset S$.

(8) $A^{\mathbf{GG}} = A^{\mathbf{G}}$ for $\emptyset \neq A \subset S$,

because $\mathbf{F}^{\mathbf{G}}(A^{\mathbf{G}}) = \mathbf{F}^{\mathbf{G}}(F(\mathbf{F}^{\mathbf{G}}(A))) \supset \mathbf{F}^{\mathbf{G}}(A)$ by (5), and hence $A^{\mathbf{GG}} \subset A^{\mathbf{G}}$. On the other hand $A^{\mathbf{GG}} \supset A^{\mathbf{G}}$ by (7).

For two transformations T, X on S we have $xTX = xT$ if and only if $xTXT^{-1} = x$. Thus $T\mathbf{F}_{xT}T^{-1} = \mathbf{F}_x$. For a transformation group $\mathbf{G}$ on S it is obvious by definition that $T^{-1}\mathbf{G}T = \mathbf{G}$ for every $T \in \mathbf{G}$. Therefore we obtain by definition

$$\mathbf{F}_{xT}{}^{\mathbf{G}} = \mathbf{F}_{xT} \cap \mathbf{G} = T^{-1}\mathbf{F}_x T \cap T^{-1}\mathbf{G}T = T^{-1}\mathbf{F}_x{}^{\mathbf{G}}T$$

for every $T \in \mathbf{G}$, that is,

(9) $\mathbf{F}_{xT}{}^{\mathbf{G}} = T^{-1}\mathbf{F}_x{}^{\mathbf{G}}T$ for $T \in \mathbf{G}$.

Thus we also obtain by (1)

(10) $\mathbf{F}^{\mathbf{G}}(AT) = T^{-1}\mathbf{F}^{\mathbf{G}}(A)T$ for $T \in \mathbf{G}$ and $\emptyset \neq A \subset S$.

32. Invariant Uniformities. Let $\mathbf{G}$ be a transformation group on a space S. For a connector U on S we define $U^{\mathbf{G}}$ by

(1) $U^{\mathbf{G}} = \bigcap_{X \in \mathbf{G}} XUX^{-1}$.

With this definition we obviously have

(2) $XU^{\mathbf{G}}X^{-1} = (XUX^{-1})^{\mathbf{G}} = U^{\mathbf{G}}$ for $X \in \mathbf{G}$,

(3) $U^{\mathbf{GG}} = U^{\mathbf{G}} \leqq U$.

Since $x(\bigcap_{\lambda \in \Lambda} U_\lambda)^{\mathbf{G}} = \bigcap_{X \in \mathbf{G}} (xX(\bigcap_{\lambda \in \Lambda} U_\lambda)X^{-1}) = \bigcap_{X \in \mathbf{G}} (\bigcap_{\lambda \in \Lambda} xXU_\lambda)X^{-1} = \bigcap_{\lambda \in \Lambda} \bigcap_{X \in \mathbf{G}} xXU_\lambda X^{-1} = x \bigcap_{\lambda \in \Lambda} U_\lambda{}^{\mathbf{G}}$, we have

(4) $(\bigcap_{\lambda \in \Lambda} U_\lambda)^{\mathbf{G}} = \bigcap_{\lambda \in \Lambda} U_\lambda{}^{\mathbf{G}}$.

We can prove easily by (13) in 11

(5) $(U^{-1})^{\mathbf{G}} = (U^{\mathbf{G}})^{-1}$.

(6) $(U^{\mathbf{G}}V^{\mathbf{G}})^{\mathbf{G}} = U^{\mathbf{G}}V^{\mathbf{G}}$,

because $\bigcap_{X \epsilon \mathbf{G}} XU^{\mathbf{G}}V^{\mathbf{G}}X^{-1} = \bigcap_{X \epsilon \mathbf{G}} XU^{\mathbf{G}}X^{-1}XV^{\mathbf{G}}X^{-1} = U^{\mathbf{G}}V^{\mathbf{G}}$ by (2).

(7) $U^{\mathbf{G}}V^{\mathbf{G}} \leqq (UV)^{\mathbf{G}}$,

because $U^{\mathbf{G}}V^{\mathbf{G}} \leqq UV$ implies

$$U^{\mathbf{G}}V^{\mathbf{G}} = XU^{\mathbf{G}}X^{-1}XV^{\mathbf{G}}X^{-1} = XU^{\mathbf{G}}V^{\mathbf{G}}X^{-1} \leqq XUVX^{-1} \quad \text{for every } X \epsilon \mathbf{G}.$$

From (2) we conclude easily

(8) $x\mathbf{K}U^{\mathbf{G}} = xU^{\mathbf{G}}\mathbf{K}$ for $x \epsilon S$ and $\mathbf{K} \subset \mathbf{G}$.

For two transformation groups $\mathbf{G}$, $\mathbf{H}$ on S we obviously have by (2)

(9) $(U^{\mathbf{G}})^{\mathbf{H}} = (U^{\mathbf{H}})^{\mathbf{G}} = U^{\mathbf{G}}$ if $\mathbf{H} \subset \mathbf{G}$,

and hence

(10) $U^{\mathbf{G}} \leqq U^{\mathbf{H}}$ for $\mathbf{H} \subset \mathbf{G}$.

A connector U on S is said to be *invariant* by $\mathbf{G}$, if $XUX^{-1} = U$ for every $X \epsilon \mathbf{G}$. $U^{\mathbf{G}}$ is invariant by $\mathbf{G}$ for any connector U on S by (2). If U is invariant by $\mathbf{G}$, then $U^{\mathbf{G}} = U$ by (1). Thus we can say that a connector U is invariant by $\mathbf{G}$ if and only if $U^{\mathbf{G}} = U$.

A uniformity $\mathbf{U}$ on S is said to be *invariant* by $\mathbf{G}$, if $\mathbf{U}$ has a basis which consists only of invariant connectors by $\mathbf{G}$. If $\mathbf{U}$ is invariant by $\mathbf{G}$, then for any $U \epsilon \mathbf{U}$ there is an invariant $V \epsilon \mathbf{U}$ by definition such that $V \leqq U$, and hence $V = V^{\mathbf{G}} \leqq U^{\mathbf{G}}$. Thus, if $\mathbf{U}$ is invariant by $\mathbf{G}$, then $\mathbf{U} \supset \mathbf{U}^{\mathbf{G}}$, making use of the notation:

$$\mathbf{U}^{\mathbf{G}} = \{U^{\mathbf{G}}: \ U \epsilon \mathbf{U}\}.$$

Conversely, if $\mathbf{U} \supset \mathbf{U}^{\mathbf{G}}$, then $\mathbf{U}^{\mathbf{G}}$ is a basis of $\mathbf{U}$ by (3), and hence $\mathbf{U}$ is invariant by $\mathbf{G}$ by definition. Therefore we can state

Theorem 32.1. *A uniformity* $\mathbf{U}$ *on* S *is invariant by* $\mathbf{G}$ *if and only if* $\mathbf{U}^{\mathbf{G}} \subset \mathbf{U}$.

For an arbitrary uniformity $\mathbf{U}$ on S we see easily by (4), (5), (7) that $\mathbf{U}^{\mathbf{G}}$ satisfies the basis conditions. Therefore there exists uniquely a uniformity on S of which $\mathbf{U}^{\mathbf{G}}$ is a basis. This uniformity is denoted by

$\mathbf{U}(\mathbf{G})$, that is, $\mathbf{U}^{\mathbf{G}}$ is a basis of $\mathbf{U}(\mathbf{G})$. With this definition we have by Theorem 26.1

Theorem 32.2. $\mathbf{U}(\mathbf{G})$ *is the single equi-uniformity by* $\mathbf{G}$ *as a system of mappings from* S *to a uniform space* S *with uniformity* $\mathbf{U}$.

It is obvious by definition that $\mathbf{U}(\mathbf{G}) \supset \mathbf{U}$. $\mathbf{U}(\mathbf{G})$ is invariant by $\mathbf{G}$, because for any $V \in \mathbf{U}(\mathbf{G})$ we can find $U \in \mathbf{U}$ such that $V \geqq U^{\mathbf{G}}$, which implies $V^{\mathbf{G}} \geqq U^{\mathbf{GG}} = U^{\mathbf{G}}$ by (3), and hence $\mathbf{U}(\mathbf{G})^{\mathbf{G}} \subset \mathbf{U}(\mathbf{G})$. For any invariant uniformity $\mathbf{V} \supset \mathbf{U}$ we have by Theorem 32.1 that $\mathbf{V} \supset \mathbf{V}^{\mathbf{G}} \supset \mathbf{U}^{\mathbf{G}}$, and hence $\mathbf{V} \supset \mathbf{U}(\mathbf{G})$. Therefore we can state

Theorem 32.3. $\mathbf{U}(\mathbf{G})$ *is the weakest among all uniformities on* S *which are invariant by* $\mathbf{G}$ *and stronger than* $\mathbf{U}$.

We suppose now that S is a uniform space with uniformity $\mathbf{U}$. A transformation group $\mathbf{G}$ on S is said to be *uniformly continuous,* if every $T \in \mathbf{G}$ is uniformly continuous for $\mathbf{U}$. If $\mathbf{G}$ is uniformly continuous, then we have $TUT^{-1} \subset \mathbf{U}$ for every $T \in \mathbf{G}$ by definition. Since $T \in \mathbf{G}$ implies $T^{-1} \in \mathbf{G}$, we also have $T^{-1}\mathbf{U}T \subset \mathbf{U}$, that is, $\mathbf{U} \subset TUT^{-1}$ for every $T \in \mathbf{G}$. Therefore we have

Theorem 32.4. $\mathbf{G}$ *is uniformly continuous for* $\mathbf{U}$ *if and only if* $TUT^{-1} = \mathbf{U}$ *for every* $T \in \mathbf{G}$. *If* $\mathbf{G}$ *is uniformly continuous for* $\mathbf{U}$ *and a connector* $U \in \mathbf{U}$ *is invariant by* $\mathbf{G}$, *then* U° *also is invariant by* $\mathbf{G}$, *that is,* $U^{\mathbf{G}} = U$ *implies* $U^{\circ\mathbf{G}} = U^{\circ}$.

Because $U^{\circ} \leqq U$ implies $xX^{-1}U^{\circ}X \subset xX^{-1}UX = xU$ for every $x \in S$ and $X \in \mathbf{G}$. Since X is continuous for $\mathbf{U}$, $xX^{-1}U^{\circ}X$ also is open by Theorem 12.2. Thus we obtain $xX^{-1}U^{\circ}X \subset xU^{\circ}$ for every $x \in S$ and $X \in \mathbf{G}$, that is, $U^{\circ} \leqq XU^{\circ}X^{-1}$ for every $X \in \mathbf{G}$. Therefore $U^{\circ} \leqq U^{\circ\mathbf{G}}$, and hence $U^{\circ\mathbf{G}} = U^{\circ}$ by (3).

$\mathbf{G}$ is said to be *equi-continuous* for $\mathbf{U}$, if $\mathbf{G}$ is equi-continuous as a system of transformations on S with uniformity $\mathbf{U}$. With this definition we obviously have by Theorems 32.1 and 32.3

Theorem 32.5. $\mathbf{G}$ *is equi-continuous for* $\mathbf{U}$ *if and only if* $\mathbf{U}$ *is invariant by* $\mathbf{G}$, *that is, if and only if* $\mathbf{U}^{\mathbf{G}} \subset \mathbf{U}$.

$\mathbf{G}$ is said to be *locally equi-continuous* for $\mathbf{U}$, if there is $U \in \mathbf{U}$ such that $\mathbf{G}$ is equi-continuous on xU for $\mathbf{U}$ for every $x \in S$.

Theorem 32.6. **G** *is locally equi-continuous for* **U** *if and only if* **U**$\sim$**U**(**G**).

Proof. If **G** is locally equi-continuous for **U**, then **U** is locally stronger than **U**(**G**). Because, if **G** is equi-continuous on xU for **U**, then **U** is stronger than **U**(**G**) on xU by Theorems 32.2 and 26.5. On the other hand, we have **U**(**G**) $\supset$ **U** by definition. Thus we obtain **U**$\sim$**U**(**G**).

Conversely, if **U**$\sim$**U**(**G**), then there is $U \in$ **U** such that **U** is stronger than **U**(**G**) on xU for every $x \in S$ by definition, and hence **G** is equi-continuous on xU for **U**, because **U**(**G**) is the single equi-uniformity on S by **G** by Theorem 32.2. Thus **G** is locally equi-continuous by definition.

Theorem 32.7. *If* **U**$\sim$ **U**(**G**) *and* **U** *is locally totally bounded, then* **U**(**G**) *also is locally totally bounded. If* **U** $\sim$ **U**(**G**) *and* **U** *is totally bounded, then* **U** = **U**(**G**).

Proof. We suppose that **U**$\sim$**U**(**G**). If **U** is locally totally bounded, then there is $U \in$ **U** such that xU is totally bounded for **U** for every $x \in S$, and hence xU is totally bounded for **U**(**G**) for every $x \in S$ by Theorem 22.1. Since **U** $\subset$ **U**(**G**), we have $U \in$ **U**(**G**). Thus **U**(**G**) is locally totally bounded. If **U** is totally bounded, then it is obvious by Theorem 22.1 that **U**(**G**) also is totally bounded and **U** = **U**(**G**).

Theorem 32.8. *If* **G** *is uniformly continuous for a pure uniformity* **U** *on* S *and* $A^{\mathbf{U}-} = S$, *then* $\bigcap_{x \in A} \mathbf{F}_x{}^{\mathbf{G}} = \{E\}$.

Proof. For any $X \in \bigcap_{x \in A} \mathbf{F}_x{}^{\mathbf{G}}$ we have $xX = x$ for every $x \in A$. For any $a \in S$ we can find a convergent system $A \ni x_\delta \xrightarrow[\delta \in \Lambda]{} a$, and hence $x_\delta = x_\delta X \xrightarrow[\delta \in \Lambda]{} aX$, because X is uniformly continuous by assumption. Thus we obtain $a = aX$ by Theorem 7.1, because **U** is pure by assumption. Therefore $X = E$.

33. **Point Mappings.** Let **A** be the system of all transformations on S. **A** is obviously a transformation group on S. Setting $(x, T) = xT \in S$ for

$x \in S$, $T \in \mathbf{A}$, we obtain a binary mapping xT $(x \in S, T \in \mathbf{A})$. For this binary mapping, setting

$$TM_x = xT \quad \text{for } x \in S,\ T \in \mathbf{A}$$

we obtain a mapping M_x from $\mathbf{A}$ to S. M_x is called the *point mapping* at $x \in S$. With this definition we obviously have

$$\mathbf{K}M_{xT} = T\mathbf{K}M_x,\quad \mathbf{K}M_x T = \mathbf{K}TM_x \quad (x \in S,\ T \in \mathbf{A})$$

for any system of transformations $\mathbf{K}$.

Let $\mathbf{G}$ be a transformation group on S. In the sequel, we use the notation M_x as the relative mapping of M_x on $\mathbf{G}$, instead of $M_x^{\mathbf{G}}$, because our consideration will be restricted in $\mathbf{G}$. We also use the notation $\mathbf{F}_x$ instead of $\mathbf{F}_x^{\mathbf{G}}$ for the fixer in $\mathbf{G}$ for the same reason.

Concerning point mappings on $\mathbf{G}$, we have

(1) $ATM_x^{-1} = AM_x^{-1}T$ for $A \subset S$, $T \in \mathbf{G}$,

because $ATM_x^{-1} = \{X\colon xX \in AT\} = \{YT\colon xY \in A\} = AM_x^{-1}T$.

(2) $AM_{xT}^{-1} = T^{-1}(AM_x^{-1})$ for $A \subset S$, $T \in \mathbf{G}$,

because $AM_{xT}^{-1} = \{X\colon xTX \in A\} = \{T^{-1}Y\colon xY \in A\} = T^{-1}(AM_x^{-1})$.

(3) $AM_x^{-1} = \mathbf{F}_x(AM_x^{-1})$ for $A \subset S$,

because $x\mathbf{F}_x = \{x\}$ by definition, and hence we have $xX \in A$ if and only if $x\mathbf{F}_x X \subset A$.

From (1) we conclude immediately

(4) $A\mathbf{K}M_x^{-1} = AM_x^{-1}\mathbf{K}$ for $A \subset S$, $\mathbf{K} \subset \mathbf{G}$.

Since $xM_x^{-1} = \mathbf{F}_x$ by definition, we obtain by (4)

(5) $x\mathbf{K}M_x^{-1} = \mathbf{F}_x\mathbf{K}$ for $\mathbf{K} \subset \mathbf{G}$.

For a connector U on S we have

(6) $(xU^{\mathbf{G}}M_x^{-1})^{-1} = x(U^{\mathbf{G}})^{-1}M_x^{-1} = x(U^{-1})^{\mathbf{G}}M_x^{-1}$,

because, as $xX^{-1}U^{\mathbf{G}} = xU^{\mathbf{G}}X^{-1}$ for every $X \in \mathbf{G}$ by (2) in 32, we have by (5) in 32

$$\begin{aligned}(xU^{\mathbf{G}}M_x^{-1})^{-1} &= \{X^{-1}\colon xX \in xU^{\mathbf{G}}\} = \{X^{-1}\colon x \in xX^{-1}U^{\mathbf{G}}\} \\ &= \{Y\colon xY \in x(U^{\mathbf{G}})^{-1}\} = x(U^{\mathbf{G}})^{-1}M_x^{-1} = x(U^{-1})^{\mathbf{G}}M_x^{-1}.\end{aligned}$$

From (2) and (5) we also conclude

(7) $x\mathbf{K}M_{xT}^{-1} = T^{-1}\mathbf{F}_x\mathbf{K}$ for $\mathbf{K} \subset \mathbf{G}$, $T \in \mathbf{G}$.

Theorem 33.1. *If a connector U on S is invariant by* $\mathbf{G}$, *then*

$$X(M_{xT}UM_{xT}^{-1}) = T^{-1}(xUM_x^{-1})TX \quad \textit{for } T, X \in \mathbf{G}$$

and $y \in xU$ implies $AM_x^{-1} \subset AUM_y^{-1}$ for $A \subset S$.

Proof. Since $XUX^{-1} = U$ for every $X \in \mathbf{G}$ by assumption, we obtain by (1) and (2)

$$X(M_{xT}UM_{xT}^{-1}) = xTXUM_{xT}^{-1} = T^{-1}(xUM_x^{-1})TX.$$

If $y \in xU$, then $X \in AM_x^{-1}$ implies $yX \in xUX = xXU \subset AU$ and hence $X \in AUM_y^{-1}$.

For a uniformity $\mathbf{U}$ on S, the weak-uniformity on $\mathbf{G}$ by M_x is denoted by $\mathbf{W}(\mathbf{U}, x)$, and we make use of the notation

$$\mathbf{W}(\mathbf{U}, A) = \bigvee_{x \in A} \mathbf{W}(\mathbf{U}, x) \quad \text{for } \emptyset \neq A \subset S,$$

that is, $\mathbf{W}(\mathbf{U}, A)$ is the weak-uniformity on $\mathbf{G}$ by the system of mappings M_x $(x \in A)$. We obviously have by definition

$$\mathbf{W}(\mathbf{U}, A) \subset \mathbf{W}(\mathbf{U}, B) \quad \text{for } A \subset B.$$

$\mathbf{W}(\mathbf{U}, S)$ is denoted by $\mathbf{W}(\mathbf{U})$.

Theorem 33.2. *When* $\mathbf{U}$ *is invariant by* $\mathbf{G}$, *we have* $W \in \mathbf{W}(\mathbf{U}, A)$ *if and only if we can find an invariant $U \in \mathbf{U}$ and a finite system $a_\nu \in A$ $(\nu = 1, 2, \ldots, n)$ such that*

$$XW \supset \Big(\bigcap_{\nu=1}^{n} a_\nu UM_{a_\nu}^{-1}\Big)X \quad \textit{for every } X \in \mathbf{G}.$$

Proof. It is obvious by Theorem 23.6 that we have $W \in \mathbf{W}(\mathbf{U}, A)$ if and only if we can find an invariant $U \in \mathbf{U}$ and a finite system $a_\nu \in A$ $(\nu = 1, 2, \ldots, n)$ such that $W \geqq \bigcap_{\nu=1}^{n} M_{a_\nu}UM_{a_\nu}^{-1}$. On the other hand, for any $X \in \mathbf{G}$ we have by (1)

$$X \bigcap_{\nu=1}^{n} M_{a_\nu}UM_{a_\nu}^{-1} = \bigcap_{\nu=1}^{n} a_\nu XUM_{a_\nu}^{-1} = \Big(\bigcap_{\nu=1}^{n} a_\nu UM_{a_\nu}^{-1}\Big)X,$$

because $XU = XUX^{-1}X = UX$.

We obviously have by Theorem 16.3

Theorem 33.3. *If* **G** *is equi-continuous on a totally bounded set* A *for* **U**, *then* M_x $(x \in A)$ *is equi-continuous on* **G** *for* **W**(**U**, A).

For a uniformity **U** and a connector W on S, the multiple equi-uniformity on **G** by a double system M_z $(z \in xW, x \in S)$ is denoted by **E**(**U**, W). We obviously have by definition

$$\mathbf{E}(\mathbf{U}, W) \geqq \mathbf{E}(\mathbf{U}, V) \quad \text{for} \quad W \geqq V.$$

We also use the notation

$$\mathbf{E}(\mathbf{U}) = \bigwedge_{U \in \mathbf{U}} \mathbf{E}(\mathbf{U}, U).$$

Theorem 33.4. *If* **U** *is locally totally bounded, then* **E**(**U**) = **E**(**U**, U) *for any totally bounded* $U \in$ **U**.

Proof. Let U_0 be a totally bounded connector of **U**. For $U_0 \geqq U \in$ **U** and $x \in S$, we can find a finite system $a_\nu \in xU_0$ $(\nu = 1, 2, \ldots, n)$ such that $xU_0 \subset \bigcup_{\nu=1}^{n} a_\nu U$. Since M_z $(z \in a_\nu U)$ is equi-continuous on **G** for **E**(**U**, U) for every $\nu = 1, 2, \ldots, n$, we see easily by definition that M_z $(z \in xU_0)$ also is equi-continuous for **E**(**U**, U). Thus we obtain **E**(**U**, U) $\supset$ **E**(**U**, U_0) by definition. On the other hand, $U_0 \geqq U$ implies **E**(**U**, U) $\subset$ **E**(**U**, U_0). Therefore **E**(**U**, U) = **E**(**U**, U_0) for $U_0 \geqq U \in$ **U**. Consequently **E**(**U**) = **E**(**U**, U) for every totally bounded $U \in$ **U**.

Theorem 33.5. *If* **U** *is locally totally bounded and* **G** *is locally equi-continuous for* **U**, *then* **E**(**U**) $\subset$ **W**(**U**(**G**)), *and if* **W**(**U**) *is locally totally bounded in addition, then* **W**(**U**) $\sim$ **E**(**U**) $\sim$ **W**(**U**(**G**)).

Proof. Since **G** is equi-continuous for **U**(**G**) by Theorem 32.5 and **W**(**U**(**G**)) $\supset$ **W**(**U**(**G**), A) by definition, for any totally bounded set $A \neq \emptyset$ for **U**(**G**), we see easily by Theorem 33.3 that M_x $(x \in A)$ is equi-con-continuous on **G** with uniformity **W**(**U**(**G**)) for **U**(**G**) on S. Since **U**(**G**) $\sim$ **U** by Theorem 32.6 and **U** $\subset$ **U**(**G**) by definition, we conclude that for any totally bounded set $A \neq \emptyset$ for **U**, M_x $(x \in A)$ is equi-continuous on **G** with **W**(**U**(**G**)) for **U** on S. Therefore **E**(**U**, U) $\subset$ **W**(**U**(**G**)) for any totally bounded $U \in$ **U**, and hence **E**(**U**) $\subset$ **W**(**U**(**G**)). If **W**(**U**) is locally totally bounded in addition, then for any totally bounded $W \in \mathbf{W}(\mathbf{U})$, TWM_x is totally bounded for $\mathbf{U}$ for every $T \in \mathbf{G}$ and $x \in S$ by Theorem 23.8, and hence $\mathbf{U}(\mathbf{G})$ coincides with $\mathbf{U}$ on TWM_x by Theorem 22.1, because $\mathbf{U}(\mathbf{G}) \sim \mathbf{U}$. Therefore

$$\mathbf{W}(\mathbf{U}(\mathbf{G}), x)^{TW} = \mathbf{W}(\mathbf{U}, x)^{TW} \quad \text{for every } x \in S.$$

Consequently we obtain $\mathbf{W}(\mathbf{U}(\mathbf{G}))^{TW} = \mathbf{W}(\mathbf{U})^{TW}$ for every $T \in \mathbf{G}$ by Theorem 21.3. Since $\mathbf{W}(\mathbf{U}) \subset \mathbf{E}(\mathbf{U}) \subset \mathbf{W}(\mathbf{U}(\mathbf{G}))$, we hence conclude

$$\mathbf{W}(\mathbf{U})^{TW} = \mathbf{E}(\mathbf{U})^{TW} = \mathbf{W}(\mathbf{U}(\mathbf{G}))^{TW} \quad \text{for every } T \in \mathbf{G}.$$

Therefore we see easily that $\mathbf{W}(\mathbf{U}) \sim \mathbf{E}(\mathbf{U}) \sim \mathbf{W}(\mathbf{U}(\mathbf{G}))$.

Theorem 33.6. *If* $\mathbf{G}$ *is locally equi-continuous, then* $S \ni x_\delta \xrightarrow[\delta \in \Delta]{} x$ *implies* $M_{x_\delta} \underset{\delta \in \Delta}{\Longrightarrow} M_x$, *and* M_{x_δ} $(\delta \in \Delta)$ *is a uniform Cauchy system for any Cauchy system* $x_\delta \in S$ $(\delta \in \Delta)$ *for* $\mathbf{U}$.

Proof. If $\mathbf{G}$ is locally equi-continuous for $\mathbf{U}$, then there is $U_0 \in \mathbf{U}$ by definition such that $\mathbf{G}$ is equi-continuous on xU_0 for every $x \in S$. If $S \ni x_\delta \xrightarrow[\delta \in \Delta]{} x$, then we can find $\delta_0 \in \Delta$ such that $x_\delta \in xU_0$ for $\delta \leqq \delta_0$. Since $\mathbf{G}$ is equi-continuous on xU_0, we obtain $M_{x_\delta} \underset{\delta \in \Delta}{\Longrightarrow} M_x$ by Theorem 17.6. If $x_\delta \in S$ $(\delta \in \Delta)$ is a Cauchy system for $\mathbf{U}$, then we conclude similarly by Theorem 17.6 that M_{x_δ} $(\delta \in \Delta)$ is a uniform Cauchy system.

Theorem 33.7. *If* $\mathbf{U}$ *is invariant by* $\mathbf{G}$ *and pure on a set* $A \subset S$ *such that* $A^{\mathbf{U}-} = S$, *then* $\mathbf{W}(\mathbf{U})$ *on* $\mathbf{G}$ *is pure.*

Proof. If $X \neq Y \in \mathbf{G}$, then there is $a \in A$ such that $aX \neq aY$. Because, if $xX = xY$ for every $x \in A$, then $X = Y$. If $aX \neq aY$ and $a \in A$, then $aXY^{-1} \neq a$. Since $\mathbf{U}$ is pure at a, there is an invariant $U \in \mathbf{U}$ such that $aXY^{-1} \bar{\in} aU$, that is, $aX \bar{\in} aUY = aYU$. Thus $X \bar{\in} aYUM_a^{-1} = YM_aUM_a^{-1}$. Therefore $X \neq Y$ implies $X \bar{\in} YI_{\mathbf{W}(\mathbf{U})}$, that is, $\mathbf{W}(\mathbf{U})$ is pure by definition.

Theorem 33.8. *If* $\mathbf{U}$ *is pure, then the fixer* $\mathbf{F}_a$ *is closed for* $\mathbf{W}(\mathbf{U})$ *for every* $a \in S$.

Proof. If $\mathbf{F}_a \ni X_\delta \xrightarrow[\delta \in \Delta]{} X$ for $\mathbf{W}(\mathbf{U})$, then $a = aX_\delta \xrightarrow[\delta \in \Delta]{} aX$ by Theorem 12.1, and hence $aX \in aI_{\mathbf{U}}$ by Theorem 7.1. Since $\mathbf{U}$ is pure by assumption, we hence obtain $\mathbf{F}_a \ni X$. Therefore $\mathbf{F}_a$ is closed for $\mathbf{W}(\mathbf{U})$ by Theorem 7.3.

34. Adjoint Uniformities. Let $\mathbf{G}$ be a transformation group on a space S. For a connector U on S, setting

$$(1)\ xU(a_1, \ldots, a_n) = \Big(\bigcap_{\nu=1}^{n} a_\nu U^{\mathbf{G}} M_{a_\nu}^{-1}\Big) M_x \quad \text{for } x, a_\nu \in S\ (\nu = 1, 2, \ldots,$$

$n)$ we obtain a connector $U(a_1, \ldots, a_n)$ on S, because $a_\nu \in a_\nu U^{\mathbf{G}}$ implies $E \in a_\nu U^{\mathbf{G}} M_{a_\nu}^{-1}$ for every $\nu = 1, 2, \ldots, n$, and hence $x \in \big(\bigcap_{\nu=1}^{n} a_\nu U^{\mathbf{G}} M_{a_\nu}^{-1}\big) M_x$. When we need to indicate $\mathbf{G}$, we use the notation $U(a_1, \ldots, a_n, \mathbf{G})$.

From the definition (1) we conclude immediately

$$(2)\ U(a_1, \ldots, a_n) \leqq U(a_1, \ldots, a_m) \quad \text{for } n \geqq m,$$

$$(3)\ AU(a_1, \ldots, a_n) = A \bigcap_{\nu=1}^{n} a_\nu U^{\mathbf{G}} M_{a_\nu}^{-1} \quad \text{for } A \subset S,$$

$$(4)\ U^{\mathbf{G}}(a_1, \ldots, a_n) = U(a_1, \ldots, a_n),$$

$$(5)\ \Big(\bigcap_{\lambda \in \Lambda} U_\lambda\Big)(a_1, \ldots, a_n) \leqq \bigcap_{\lambda \in \Lambda} U_\lambda(a_1, \ldots, a_n).$$

$$(6)\ U(a_1, \ldots, a_n) \leqq V(a_1, \ldots, a_n) \quad \text{for } U \leqq V.$$

Since $(TUT^{-1})^{\mathbf{G}} = U^{\mathbf{G}}$ for $T \in \mathbf{G}$ by (2) in 32, we obtain

$$(7)\ (TUT^{-1})(a_1, \ldots, a_n) = U(a_1, \ldots, a_n) \quad \text{for } T \in \mathbf{G}.$$

Since $T^{-1}(aU^{\mathbf{G}} M_a^{-1})T = aTU^{\mathbf{G}} M_{aT}^{-1}$ by (1) and (2) in 33, we have

$$(8)\ T^{-1}U(a_1, \ldots, a_n)T = U(a_1 T, \ldots, a_n T) \quad \text{for } T \in \mathbf{G}.$$

$$(9)\ U(a_1, \ldots, a_n)V(a_1, \ldots, a_n) \leqq (VU)(a_1, \ldots, a_n),$$

because we have by (3) in 34, (4) in 33, (7) in 32, and (9) in 11

$$xU(a_1, \ldots, a_n)V(a_1, \ldots, a_n) = \Big(\bigcap_{\nu=1}^{n} a_\nu U^{\mathbf{G}} M_{a_\nu}^{-1}\Big) M_x \Big(\bigcap_{\mu=1}^{n} a_\mu V^{\mathbf{G}} M_{a_\mu}^{-1}\Big)$$

$$= \Big(\bigcap_{\nu=1}^{n} a_\nu \Big(\bigcap_{\mu=1}^{n} a_\mu V^{\mathbf{G}} M_{a_\mu}^{-1}\Big) U^{\mathbf{G}} M_{a_\nu}^{-1}\Big) M_x \subset \Big(\bigcap_{\nu=1}^{n} a_\nu (a_\nu V^{\mathbf{G}} M_{a_\nu}^{-1}) U^{\mathbf{G}} M_{a_\nu}^{-1}\Big) M_x$$

$$\subset \Big(\bigcap_{\nu=1}^{n} a_\nu V^{\mathbf{G}} U^{\mathbf{G}} M_{a_\nu}^{-1}\Big) M_x \subset \Big(\bigcap_{\nu=1}^{n} a_\nu (VU)^{\mathbf{G}} M_{a_\nu}^{-1}\Big) M_x.$$

Since $x \in y\mathbf{K}$ if and only if $y \in x\mathbf{K}^{-1}$ for $\mathbf{K} \subset \mathbf{G}$, we obtain by (6) in 33

$$xU(a_1, \ldots, a_n)^{-1} = x(\bigcap_{\nu=1}^{n} a_\nu U^{\mathbf{G}} M_{a_\nu}{}^{-1})^{-1} = x \bigcap_{\nu=1}^{n} (a_\nu U^{\mathbf{G}} M_{a_\nu}{}^{-1})^{-1}$$

$$= x \bigcap_{\nu=1}^{n} (a_\nu (U^{-1})^{\mathbf{G}} M_{a_\nu}{}^{-1}) = xU^{-1}(a_1, \ldots, a_n).$$

Thus we obtain

(10) $U(a_1, \ldots, a_n)^{-1} = U^{-1}(a_1, \ldots, a_n)$.

We obviously have by the definition

(11) $U(a_1, \ldots, a_n) \leqq \bigcap_{\nu=1}^{n} U(a_\nu)$.

(12) $a(U^{\mathbf{G}})^\nu U(a) \subset a(U^{\mathbf{G}})^{\nu+1}$ for $\nu = 0, 1, 2, \ldots,$

because we have by (3) in 34, (8) in 32, and (9) in 11

$$a(U^{\mathbf{G}})^\nu U(a) = a(U^{\mathbf{G}})^\nu (aU^{\mathbf{G}} M_a{}^{-1}) = a(aU^{\mathbf{G}} M_a{}^{-1})(U^{\mathbf{G}})^\nu$$

$$= aU^{\mathbf{G}} M_a{}^{-1} M_a (U^{\mathbf{G}})^\nu \subset a(U^{\mathbf{G}})^{\nu+1}.$$

Theorem 34.1. *If* $xV(a_1, \ldots, a_n) \subset xU^{\mathbf{G}}$ *for* $x \in A$, *then* $V(a_1, \ldots, a_n) \leqq U(b_1, \ldots, b_m)$ *for any* $b_\mu \in A$ $(\mu = 1, 2, \ldots, m)$.

Proof. If $xV(a_1, \ldots, a_n) \subset xU^{\mathbf{G}}$, then we have by (1) in 34, and (7) in 11

$$\bigcap_{\nu=1}^{n} (a_\nu V^{\mathbf{G}} M_{a_\nu}{}^{-1}) \subset (\bigcap_{\nu=1}^{n} a_\nu V^{\mathbf{G}} M_{a_\nu}{}^{-1}) M_x M_x{}^{-1} \subset xU^{\mathbf{G}} M_x{}^{-1}.$$

Thus $\bigcap_{\nu=1}^{n} a_\nu V^{\mathbf{G}} M_{a_\nu}{}^{-1} \subset \bigcap_{\mu=1}^{m} b_\mu U^{\mathbf{G}} M_{b_\mu}{}^{-1}$ for any $b_\mu \in A$ $(\mu = 1, 2, \ldots, m)$.

Theorem 34.2. *If* $a_\nu X \in a_\nu Y U^{\mathbf{G}}$ $(\nu = 1, 2, \ldots, n)$, $X, Y, \in \mathbf{G}$, *then* $xY^{-1} \in xX^{-1}U(a_1, \ldots, a_n)$ *for every* $x \in S$.

Proof. If $a_\nu X \in a_\nu Y U^{\mathbf{G}}$ $(\nu = 1, 2, \ldots, n)$ then we have by (8) in 32

$$XY^{-1} M_{a_\nu} = a_\nu XY^{-1} \in a_\nu U^{\mathbf{G}}$$

and hence $XY^{-1} \in a_\nu U^{\mathbf{G}} M_{a_\nu}{}^{-1}$, that is, $Y^{-1} \in X^{-1} (a_\nu U^{\mathbf{G}} M_{a_\nu}{}^{-1})$ for every

$\nu = 1, 2, \ldots, n$. Thus we obtain $Y^{-1} \epsilon X^{-1} \bigcap_{\nu=1}^{n} a_\nu U^{\mathbf{G}} M_{a_\nu}^{-1}$, and consequently we have $xY^{-1} \epsilon xX^{-1}U(a_1, \ldots, a_n)$ for every $x \epsilon S$.

Theorem 34.3. *If* $b_\nu \epsilon a_\nu V^{\mathbf{G}}$ $(\nu = 1, 2, \ldots, n)$, *then*

$$U(a_1, \ldots, a_n) \leqq (V^{-1}UV)(b_1, \ldots, b_n).$$

Proof. Since $b_\nu \epsilon a_\nu V^{\mathbf{G}}$ implies $a_\nu \epsilon b_\nu (V^{\mathbf{G}})^{-1}$, we have by Theorem 33.1 and (5), (7) in 32

$$a_\nu U^{\mathbf{G}} M_{a_\nu}^{-1} \subset b_\nu (V^{\mathbf{G}})^{-1} U^{\mathbf{G}} M_{a_\nu}^{-1} \subset b_\nu (V^{\mathbf{G}})^{-1} U^{\mathbf{G}} V^{\mathbf{G}} M_{b_\nu}^{-1} \subset b_\nu (V^{-1}UV)^{\mathbf{G}} M_{b_\nu}^{-1}$$

for every $\nu = 1, 2, \ldots, n$. Thus we obtain

$$\bigcap_{\nu=1}^{n} a_\nu U^{\mathbf{G}} M_{a_\nu}^{-1} \subset \bigcap_{\nu=1}^{n} b_\nu (V^{-1}UV)^{\mathbf{G}} M_{b_\nu}^{-1}.$$

Theorem 34.4. *For two transformation groups* $\mathbf{G} \supset \mathbf{H}$ *on* S

$$U^{\mathbf{G}}(a_1, \ldots, a_n, \mathbf{H}) \leqq U(a_1, \ldots, a_n, \mathbf{G}).$$

Proof. We have by (9) in 32

$$xU^{\mathbf{G}}(a_1, \ldots, a_n, \mathbf{H}) = x \bigcap_{\nu=1}^{n} (a_\nu U^{\mathbf{G}} M_{a_\nu}^{-1} \cap \mathbf{H}) \subset xU(a_1, \ldots, a_n, \mathbf{G}).$$

Let $\mathbf{U}$ be a uniformity on S.

Theorem 34.5. *If a set* $A \neq \emptyset$ *is totally bounded for* $\mathbf{U}(\mathbf{G})$, *then for any* $U \epsilon \mathbf{U}$ *we can find* $V \epsilon \mathbf{U}$ *and a finite system* $a_\nu \epsilon A$ $(\nu = 1, 2, \ldots, n)$ *such that* $xV(a_1, \ldots, a_n) \subset xU^{\mathbf{G}}$ *for every* $x \epsilon A$.

Proof. Since $\mathbf{G}$ is equi-continuous for $\mathbf{U}(\mathbf{G})$ by Theorem 32.2, M_x $(x \epsilon A)$ is equi-continuous on $\mathbf{G}$ for $\mathbf{W}(\mathbf{U}(\mathbf{G}), A)$ by Theorem 33.3. Therefore for any $U \epsilon \mathbf{U}$ there is $W \epsilon \mathbf{W}(\mathbf{U}(\mathbf{G}), A)$ such that $W \leqq M_x U^{\mathbf{G}} M_x^{-1}$ for every $x \epsilon A$. For such W we can find $V \epsilon \mathbf{U}$ and a finite system $a_\nu \epsilon A$ $(\nu = 1, 2, \ldots, n)$ by Theorem 33.2 such that $XW \supset (\bigcap_{\nu=1}^{n} a_\nu V^{\mathbf{G}} M_{a_\nu}^{-1})X$ for every $X \epsilon \mathbf{G}$. Thus we have

$$\bigcap_{\nu=1}^{n} a_\nu V^{\mathbf{G}} M_{a_\nu}^{-1} \subset EM_x U^{\mathbf{G}} M_x^{-1} = xU^{\mathbf{G}} M_x^{-1} \quad \text{for every } x \epsilon A.$$

Therefore we obtain by definition (1)

$$xV(a_1, \ldots, a_n) \subset xU^{\mathbf{G}}M_x \subset xU^{\mathbf{G}} \text{ for every } x \in A.$$

For a uniformity $\mathbf{U}$ on S, the system of connectors

$$\{U(a_1, \ldots, a_n): U \in \mathbf{U}, a_\nu \in S\ (\nu = 1, 2, \ldots, n), n = 1, 2, \ldots\}$$

satisfies the basis conditions, as we can show easily by (2), (5), (9), (10). Thus there exists uniquely a uniformity on S, of which the system $U(a_1, \ldots, a_n)$ is a basis. This uniformity is called the *adjoint uniformity* of $\mathbf{U}$ and denoted by $\mathbf{U}^*$. With this definition we obviously have

$$\mathbf{U}^* = \mathbf{U}(\mathbf{G})^*.$$

Referring to Theorem 21.1, we can show easily

Theorem 34.6. *We have* $W \in \mathbf{U}^*$ *if and only if we can find* $U \in \mathbf{U}$ and *a finite system* $a_\nu \in S\ (\nu = 1, 2, \ldots, n)$ *such that* $W \geqq U(a_1, \ldots, a_n)$.

Since $aU(a) \subset aU^{\mathbf{G}}$ for every $a \in S$ by (12), we have

Theorem 34.7. $\mathbf{T}(\mathbf{U}^*) \supset \mathbf{T}(\mathbf{U}(\mathbf{G})) \supset \mathbf{T}(\mathbf{U})$ *for the adjoint uniformity* $\mathbf{U}^*$ *of* $\mathbf{U}$.

We also conclude by (8)

Theorem 34.8. $\mathbf{G}$ *is uniformly continuous for* $\mathbf{U}^*$ *on* S.

A uniformity $\mathbf{U}$ on S is said to be *normal* for $\mathbf{G}$, if there is $U \in \mathbf{U}$ such that both xU and $xU(a)$ are totally bounded for $\mathbf{U}$ for every $x, a \in S$. Such U is called a *normal connector* of $\mathbf{U}$ for $\mathbf{G}$. It is obvious by definition that if $U \in \mathbf{U}$ is a normal connector for $\mathbf{G}$ and $U \geqq V \in \mathbf{U}$, then V also is a normal connector for $\mathbf{G}$.

Theorem 34.9. If $\mathbf{U}$ *is locally totally bounded and* $\mathbf{U}(\mathbf{G})$ *is connected, then* $\mathbf{U}$ *is normal for* $\mathbf{G}$.

Proof. Let $U \in \mathbf{U}$ be totally bounded. For any $x, a \in S$ we can find $\sigma = 1, 2, \ldots$ such that $x \in a(U^{\mathbf{G}})^\sigma$, because $\mathbf{U}(\mathbf{G})$ is connected by assumption. Then we have by (12)

$$xU(a) \subset a(U^{\mathbf{G}})^\sigma U(a) \subset a(U^{\mathbf{G}})^{\sigma+1} \subset aU^{\sigma+1}.$$

Since $aU^{\sigma+1}$ is totally bounded, $xU(a)$ also is totally bounded for $\mathbf{U}$ for every $x, a \in S$.

Theorem 34.10. *If* $\mathbf{U} \sim \mathbf{U}(\mathbf{G})$ *and* $\mathbf{U}$ *is normal for* $\mathbf{G}$, *then* $\mathbf{U}(\mathbf{G})$ *also is normal for* $\mathbf{G}$.

Proof. For a normal $U \in \mathbf{U}$, both xU and $xU(a)$ are totally bounded for $\mathbf{U}$ by definition, and hence so for $\mathbf{U}(\mathbf{G})$ for every $x, a \in S$ by Theorem 22.1, because $\mathbf{U} \sim \mathbf{U}(\mathbf{G})$ by assumption. Since $\mathbf{U}(\mathbf{G}) \ni U^{\mathbf{G}} \leqq U$ and $U^{\mathbf{G}}(a) = U(a)$ by (4), both $xU^{\mathbf{G}}$ and $xU^{\mathbf{G}}(a)$ are totally bounded for $\mathbf{U}(\mathbf{G})$, and consequently $\mathbf{U}(\mathbf{G})$ also is normal for $\mathbf{G}$ by definition.

Theorem 34.11. *If* $\mathbf{U}(\mathbf{G})$ *is normal for* $\mathbf{G}$, *then* $\mathbf{W}(\mathbf{U}(\mathbf{G}))$ *on* $\mathbf{G}$ *is locally totally bounded.*

Proof. Let $U \in \mathbf{U}(\mathbf{G})$ be a normal connector for $\mathbf{G}$. We have by (8) in 32 and (1) in 33

$$(XM_a U^{\mathbf{G}} M_a^{-1})M_x = (aXU^{\mathbf{G}} M_a^{-1})M_x = (aU^{\mathbf{G}} M_a^{-1})M_x X = xU(a)X$$

for every $x, a \in S$, $X \in \mathbf{G}$. Since $U^{\mathbf{G}} \in \mathbf{U}(\mathbf{G})$, we have $M_a U^{\mathbf{G}} M_a^{-1} \in \mathbf{W}(\mathbf{U}(\mathbf{G}))$ and $xU(a)X$ is totally bounded for $\mathbf{U}(\mathbf{G})$, because every $X \in \mathbf{G}$ is uniformly continuous for $\mathbf{U}(\mathbf{G})$ by Theorem 32.4. Therefore $XM_a U^{\mathbf{G}} M_a^{-1}$ is totally bounded for $\mathbf{W}(\mathbf{U}(\mathbf{G}))$ for every $X \in \mathbf{G}$ by Theorem 23.8. Thus $\mathbf{W}(\mathbf{U}(\mathbf{G}))$ is locally totally bounded by definition.

35. **Sharp Uniformities.** Let $\mathbf{U}$ be a uniformity on S and let $\mathbf{U}^*$ be the adjoint uniformity of $\mathbf{U}$ for $\mathbf{G}$. For a set $A \neq \emptyset$ of S, $\mathbf{U}$ is said to be *sharp* on A for $\mathbf{G}$, if for any $U \in \mathbf{U}$ there is $V \in \mathbf{U}^*$ such that $xV \subset xU^{\mathbf{G}}$ for every $x \in A$. With this definition it is obvious that $\mathbf{U}$ is sharp on A for $\mathbf{G}$ if and only if $\mathbf{U}(\mathbf{G})$ is sharp on A for $\mathbf{G}$. If $\mathbf{U}$ is sharp on S for $\mathbf{G}$, that is, if $\mathbf{U}^* \subset \mathbf{U}(\mathbf{G})$, then $\mathbf{U}$ is said to be *sharp* for $\mathbf{G}$. If there is an invariant $U \in \mathbf{U}$ such that $\mathbf{U}$ is sharp on xU for $\mathbf{G}$ for every $x \in S$, then $\mathbf{U}$ is said to be *locally sharp* for $\mathbf{G}$.

Referring to Theorem 34.5, we obviously have by definition

Theorem 35.1. *If a set* $A \neq \emptyset$ *of* S *is totally bounded for* $\mathbf{U}(\mathbf{G})$, *then* $\mathbf{U}$ *is sharp on* A *for* $\mathbf{G}$.

Theorem 35.2. *Let* $\mathbf{U}$ *be invariant by* $\mathbf{G}$. $\mathbf{U}$ *is sharp on* A *for* $\mathbf{G}$ *if and only if* M_x $(x \in A)$ *is equi-continuous for* $\mathbf{W}(\mathbf{U})$ *on* $\mathbf{G}$.

Proof. If $\mathbf{U}$ is sharp on A for $\mathbf{G}$, then for any $U \in \mathbf{U}$ there is $V \in \mathbf{U}^*$ by definition such that $xV \subset xU^{\mathbf{G}}$ for every $x \in A$. For such $V \in \mathbf{U}^*$ we can find $W \in \mathbf{U}$ and a finite system $a_\nu \in S$ $(\nu = 1, 2, \ldots, n)$ by Theorem 34.6 such that $V \geqq W(a_1, \ldots, a_n)$. Then we have $xU^{\mathbf{G}} \supset xW(a_1, \ldots, a_n)$ for every $x \in A$. Therefore for any $x \in A$ and $X \in \mathbf{G}$ we have by (3), (8) in 32, (1) in 33

$$XM_x UM_x^{-1} = xXUM_x^{-1} \supset xXU^{\mathbf{G}}M_x^{-1}$$
$$= xU^{\mathbf{G}}M_x^{-1}X \supset xW(a_1, \ldots, a_n)M_x^{-1}X$$
$$= (\bigcap_{\nu=1}^{n} a_\nu W^{\mathbf{G}}M_{a_\nu}^{-1})M_x M_x^{-1}X \supset \bigcap_{\nu=1}^{n} (a_\nu W^{\mathbf{G}}M_{a_\nu}^{-1})X = \bigcap_{\nu=1}^{n} a_\nu XW^{\mathbf{G}}M_{a_\nu}^{-1}$$
$$= X \bigcap_{\nu=1}^{n} M_{a_\nu} W^{\mathbf{G}}M_{a_\nu}^{-1},$$

and hence $X \bigcap_{x \in A} M_x UM_x^{-1} \supset X \bigcap_{\nu=1}^{n} M_{a_\nu} W^{\mathbf{G}}M_{a_\nu}^{-1}$ for every $X \in \mathbf{G}$. Thus the system M_x $(x \in A)$ is equi-continuous for $\mathbf{W}(\mathbf{U})$ by Theorems 15.1 and 23.6.

Conversely, if M_x $(x \in A)$ is equi-continuous for $\mathbf{W}(\mathbf{U})$ on $\mathbf{G}$, then for any $U \in \mathbf{U}$ we can find $V \in \mathbf{U}$ and a finite system $a_\nu \in S$ $(\nu = 1, 2, \ldots, n)$ such that $XM_x U^{\mathbf{G}}M_x^{-1} \supset X \bigcap_{\nu=1}^{n} a_\nu V^{\mathbf{G}}M_{a_\nu}^{-1}$ for every $x \in A$ and $X \in \mathbf{G}$.

Then we obtain by (9) in 11.

$$xU^{\mathbf{G}} \supset EM_x U^{\mathbf{G}}M_x^{-1}M_x \supset x \bigcap_{\nu=1}^{n} a_\nu V^{\mathbf{G}}M_{a_\nu}^{-1} = xV(a_1, \ldots, a_n)$$

for every $x \in A$. Therefore $\mathbf{U}$ is sharp on A for $\mathbf{G}$ by definition

From Theorem 35.2 we immediately conclude the following two theorems.

Theorem 35.3. *If* $\mathbf{U}$ *is invariant and sharp for* $\mathbf{G}$, *then* $\mathbf{W}(\mathbf{U})$ *on* $\mathbf{G}$ *is the single equi-uniformity on* $\mathbf{G}$ *by the system* M_x $(x \in S)$.

Theorem 35.4. *If* $\mathbf{U}$ *is invariant and locally sharp for* $\mathbf{G}$, *then there is* $U_0 \in \mathbf{U}$ *such that* $\mathbf{W}(\mathbf{U}) = \mathbf{E}(\mathbf{U}) = \mathbf{E}(\mathbf{U}, U)$ *for* $\mathbf{U} \ni U \leqq U_0$.

Concerning fixers in $\mathbf{G}$, we obviously have $\mathbf{F}(S) = \{E\}$, that is,

$$\bigcap_{x \in S} \mathbf{F}_x = \{E\}.$$

If there is a finite system $x_\nu \in S$ $(\nu = 1, 2, \ldots, n)$ such that

$$\bigcap_{\nu=1}^{n} \mathbf{F}_{x_\nu} = \{E\},$$

then **G** is said to be of *finite character,* and the minimum of such n is called the *character* of **G**.

A connector U on S is said to be *proper* to **G**, if U is invariant by **G** and for any $E \neq T \in \mathbf{G}$ we can find $x \in S$ and $\sigma = \pm 1, \pm 2, \ldots$ such that $xT^\sigma \bar{\in} xU$, that is, $xT^\sigma \in xU$ for every $x \in S$ and $\sigma = \pm 1, \pm 2, \ldots$ implies $T = E$.

Theorem 35.5. *If* **U** *is sharp for* **G** *and contains a connector proper to* **G**, *then* **G** *is of finite character.*

Proof. Let $U \in \mathbf{U}$ be proper to **G**. Since **U** is sharp by assumption, we can find $V \in \mathbf{U}$ and a finite system $a_\nu \in S$ $(\nu = 1, 2, \ldots, n)$ by definition such that $V(a_1, \ldots, a_n) \leqq U^{\mathbf{G}} = U$. For such $a_\nu \in S$ $(\nu = 1, 2, \ldots, n)$, if $X \in \bigcap_{\nu=1}^{n} \mathbf{F}_{a_\nu}$, then $X^\sigma \in \bigcap_{\nu=1}^{n} \mathbf{F}_{a_\nu}$ for every $\sigma = \pm 1, \pm 2, \ldots$, because $\mathbf{F}_{a_\nu}$ is a subgroup of **G** for every $\nu = 1, 2, \ldots, n$. Thus we have by (1) in 34 and (3) in 33

$$xX^\sigma \in xX^\sigma V(a_1, \ldots, a_n) = x \bigcap_{\nu=1}^{n} X^\sigma(a_\nu V^{\mathbf{G}} M_{a_\nu}^{-1})$$

$$\subset x \bigcap_{\nu=1}^{n} \mathbf{F}_{a_\nu}(a_\nu V^{\mathbf{G}} M_{a_\nu}^{-1}) = x \bigcap_{\nu=1}^{n} (a_\nu V^{\mathbf{G}} M_{a_\nu}^{-1}) = xV(a_1, \ldots, a_n) \subset xU$$

for every $x \in S$ and $\sigma = \pm 1, \pm 2, \ldots$, and hence $X = E$.

A point $a \in S$ is said to be *proper* to **G** for **U**, if for any $U \in \mathbf{U}$ there is $V \in \mathbf{U}$ such that $T \in \mathbf{G}$, $xT^\sigma \in xV$ for every $x \in aU$ and $\sigma = \pm 1, \pm 2, \ldots$ implies $T = E$.

Theorem 35.6. *If we can find a point* $a \in S$ *proper to* **G** *for* **U** *and* $U_0 \in \mathbf{U}$ *such that* **U** *is sharp on* aU_0 *for* **G**, *then* **G** *is of finite character.*

Proof. For such $U_0 \in \mathbf{U}$ there is $V \in \mathbf{U}$ such that $xT^\sigma \in xV$ for every $x \in aU_0$ and $\sigma = \pm 1, \pm 2, \ldots$ implies $T = E$, since a is proper to **G** for **U** by assumption. For such $V \in \mathbf{U}$ we can find $W \in \mathbf{U}$ and a finite system $a_\nu \in S$ $(\nu = 1, 2, \ldots, n)$ such that $xW(a_1, \ldots, a_n) \subset xV^{\mathbf{G}}$ for every $x \in aU_0$, because **U** is sharp on aU_0 for **G** by assumption. Then for any

$X \in \bigcap_{\nu=1}^{n} \mathbf{F}_{a_\nu}$ we have by (1) in 34 and (3) in 33

$$xX^\sigma \in xX^\sigma W(a_1, \ldots, a_n) \subset x \bigcap_{\nu=1}^{n} \mathbf{F}_{a_\nu}(a_\nu W^{\mathbf{G}} M_{a_\nu}{}^{-1}) = x \bigcap_{\nu=1}^{n} a_\nu W^{\mathbf{G}} M_{a_\nu}{}^{-1}$$

$$= xW(a_1, \ldots, a_n) \subset xV^{\mathbf{G}} \subset xV$$

for every $x \in aU_0$ and $\sigma = \pm 1, \pm 2, \ldots$, and hence $X = E$.

36. **Invariant Sets.** Let $\mathbf{G}$ be a transformation group on a space S. A set $A \neq \emptyset$ of S is said to be *invariant* by $\mathbf{G}$, if $A\mathbf{G} \subset A$. If a set A is invariant by $\mathbf{G}$, then every $X \in \mathbf{G}$ is a transformation on A, because $AX \subset A$, $AX^{-1} \subset A$ implies $AX = A$ for every $X \in \mathbf{G}$. We can also show easily that for a system of invariant sets A_λ $(\lambda \in \Lambda)$, both $\bigcup_{\lambda \in \Lambda} A_\lambda$ and $\bigcap_{\lambda \in \Lambda} A_\lambda$ are invariant by $\mathbf{G}$, if $\bigcap_{\lambda \in \Lambda} A_\lambda \neq \emptyset$.

Theorem 36.1. *$x\mathbf{G}$ is invariant by $\mathbf{G}$ for every $x \in S$ and the system $x\mathbf{G}$ $(x \in S)$ gives a partition of S.*

Proof. If $z \in x\mathbf{G} \cap y\mathbf{G}$, then we can find $X, Y \in \mathbf{G}$ such that $z = xX$, $z = yY$, and then $x\mathbf{G} = zX^{-1}\mathbf{G} = z\mathbf{G} = zY^{-1}\mathbf{G} = y\mathbf{G}$.

For any invariant set A, we have $A \supset A\mathbf{G} \supset x\mathbf{G}$ for $x \in A$. Therefore we obtain $A = \bigcup_{x \in A} x\mathbf{G}$ for any invariant set A by $\mathbf{G}$.

Let $\mathbf{U}$ be a uniformity on S.

Theorem 36.2. *If $\mathbf{G}$ is uniformly continuous for $\mathbf{U}$, then for any invariant set A by $\mathbf{G}$, $A^{\mathbf{U}-}$ also is invariant by $\mathbf{G}$.*

Proof. For any $x \in A^{\mathbf{U}-}$ we can find a convergent system $A \ni a_\delta \xrightarrow[\delta \in \Delta]{} x$ by Theorem 7.3, and $A \ni a_\delta X \xrightarrow[\delta \in \Delta]{} xX$ for every $X \in \mathbf{G}$, because $\mathbf{G}$ is uniformly continuous by assumption. Therefore $x \in A^{\mathbf{U}-}$ implies $x\mathbf{G} \subset A^{\mathbf{U}-}$, and hence $A^{\mathbf{U}-}\mathbf{G} \subset A^{\mathbf{U}-}$. Thus $A^{\mathbf{U}-}$ is invariant by definition.

Theorem 36.3. *If $\mathbf{G}$ is equi-continuous for $\mathbf{U}$, then the system $(x\mathbf{G})^{\mathbf{U}-}$ $(x \in S)$ gives a partition of S.*

Proof. Since $(x\mathbf{G})^{\mathbf{U}-}$ is invariant by Theorem 36.2, $y \in (x\mathbf{G})^{\mathbf{U}-}$ implies $y\mathbf{G} \subset (x\mathbf{G})^{\mathbf{U}-}$, and hence $(y\mathbf{G})^{\mathbf{U}-} \subset (x\mathbf{G})^{\mathbf{U}-}$. On the other hand, for any invariant $U \in \mathbf{U}$ we can find $T \in \mathbf{G}$ such that $y \in xTU$, and hence $x \in yT^{-1}U^{-1}$. Thus we obtain $x\mathbf{G} \subset y\mathbf{G}U$ for every $U \in \mathbf{U}$, because $\mathbf{U}$ is invariant by $\mathbf{G}$ by Theorem 32.5. Therefore $x\mathbf{G} \subset (y\mathbf{G})^{\mathbf{U}-}$, and hence $(x\mathbf{G})^{\mathbf{U}-} \subset (y\mathbf{G})^{\mathbf{U}-}$. Consequently $y \in (x\mathbf{G})^{\mathbf{U}-}$ implies $(y\mathbf{G})^{\mathbf{U}-} = (x\mathbf{G})^{\mathbf{U}-}$. Therefore $(x\mathbf{G})^{\mathbf{U}-} \cap (y\mathbf{G})^{\mathbf{U}-} \neq \emptyset$ implies $(x\mathbf{G})^{\mathbf{U}-} = (y\mathbf{G})^{\mathbf{U}-}$.

Let A be an invariant set by $\mathbf{G}$. For a connector U on S we have

(1) $X^A U^A (X^A)^{-1} = (XUX^{-1})^A$ for $X \in \mathbf{G}$,

because for any $x \in A$ we have

$$xX^A U^A (X^{-1})^A = (xXU \cap A)X^{-1} = xXUX^{-1} \cap AX^{-1} = xXUX^{-1} \cap A$$
$$= x(XUX^{-1})^A.$$

Referring to (2) in 5, we obtain by (1)

(2) $(U^A)^{\mathbf{G}} = (U^{\mathbf{G}})^A$.

For any $a \in A$, as $AM_a^{-1} = \mathbf{G}$, we have

$$aU^A M_a^{-1} = (aU \cap A)M_a^{-1} = aUM_a^{-1} \cap AM_a^{-1} = aUM_a^{-1}.$$

Thus we obtain by (2)

(3) $xU^A(a_1, \ldots, a_n) = xU(a_1, \ldots, a_n)$ for $x, a_\nu \in A$ ($\nu = 1, 2, \ldots, n$).

We also obtain by (2)

(4) $(\mathbf{U}^A)^{\mathbf{G}} = (\mathbf{U}^{\mathbf{G}})^A$

and by (3)

(5) $(\mathbf{U}^A)^* = (\mathbf{U}^*)^A$.

We obviously have by (1)

Theorem 36.4. *If* $\mathbf{G}$ *is equi-continuous or locally equi-continuous for* $\mathbf{U}$, *then* $\mathbf{G}$ *also is so on any set* A *invariant by* $\mathbf{G}$.

$\mathbf{G}$ is said to be *semi-transitive* for $\mathbf{U}$, if there is $U \in \mathbf{U}$ such that $xU \subset x\mathbf{G}$ for every $x \in S$. Since $y \in x\mathbf{G}$ implies $y\mathbf{G} = x\mathbf{G}$, if $\mathbf{G}$ is semi-transitive, then $x\mathbf{G}$ is open for $\mathbf{T}(\mathbf{U})$ for every $x \in S$. For an invariant set A by $\mathbf{G}$, we obviously have $A = \bigcup_{x \in A} x\mathbf{G}$. Thus every invariant set is open for **T**(**U**). If A is invariant by **G**, then A' also is invariant by **G**, and hence A' is open for **T**(**U**) too. Therefore we have

Theorem 36.5. *If* **G** *is semi-transitive for* **U**, *then every invariant set by* **G** *is open and closed for* **T**(**U**).

Since $xU(a_1, \ldots, a_n) \subset x\mathbf{G}$ for every x, $a_\nu \in S$ $(\nu = 1, 2, \ldots, n)$ and for any connector U on S by definition, we can state

Theorem 36.6. *For any uniformity* **U** *on* S, **G** *is semi-transitive for the adjoint uniformity* **U*** *of* **U**.

V. TRANSITIVE GROUPS

37. **Regular Uniformities.** A transformation group $\mathbf{G}$ on a space S is said to be *transitive,* if $x\mathbf{G} = S$ for some $x \in S$. Referring to Theorem 36.1, we see that if $x\mathbf{G} = S$ for some $x \in S$, then $x\mathbf{G} = S$ for every $x \in S$. If $\mathbf{G}$ is transitive, then the point mapping M_x is full for every $x \in S$ by definition. We also see easily that $\mathbf{G}$ is transitive if and only if the point mapping M_x is full for some $x \in S$.

In the sequel, $\mathbf{G}$ is a transitive group on S. For any $a, x \in S$ we can find $X \in \mathbf{G}$ such that $x = aX$, and we have $\mathbf{F}_x = X^{-1}\mathbf{F}_a X$ by (9) in 31. Thus we obtain

$$\bigcap_{X \in \mathbf{G}} X\mathbf{F}_a X^{-1} = \{E\} \text{ for every } a \in S.$$

Theorem 37.1. *If a transitive group* $\mathbf{G}$ *is of character 1, then* $\mathbf{F}_x = \{E\}$ *for every* $x \in S$, $x \bigcap_{\lambda \in \Lambda} \mathbf{K}_\lambda = \bigcap_{\lambda \in \Lambda} x\mathbf{K}_\lambda$ *for* $\mathbf{K}_\lambda \subset \mathbf{G}$ $(\lambda \in \Lambda)$, *and* $U(a_1, \ldots, a_n) = \bigcap_{\nu=1}^{n} U(a_\nu)$ *for any connector* U *on* S *and* $a_\nu \in S$ $(\nu = 1, 2, \ldots, n)$.

Proof. If $\mathbf{F}_a = \{E\}$ for some $a \in S$, then $\mathbf{F}_{aT} = T^{-1}\mathbf{F}_a T = \{E\}$ for every $T \in \mathbf{G}$ by (9) in 31, and hence $\mathbf{F}_x = \{E\}$ for every $x \in S$. If $xT \in x\mathbf{K}$, then there is $X \in \mathbf{K}$ such that $xT = xX$, and hence $T = X$, because $\mathbf{F}_x = \{E\}$, as proved just above. Thus $xT \in x\mathbf{K}$ implies $T \in \mathbf{K}$. Therefore $x \bigcap_{\lambda \in \Lambda} \mathbf{K}_\lambda = \bigcap_{\lambda \in \Lambda} x\mathbf{K}_\lambda$, and hence $U(a_1, \ldots, a_n) = \bigcap_{\nu=1}^{n} U(a_\nu)$ by definition (1) in 34.

A transformation group $\mathbf{G}$ is said to be *commutative,* if $XY = YX$ for every $X, Y \in \mathbf{G}$. If $\mathbf{G}$ is commutative, then $X\mathbf{F}_a X^{-1} = \mathbf{F}_a$ for every $a \in S$ and $X \in \mathbf{G}$. Thus we can state

Theorem 37.2. *If a transitive group* **G** *is commutative, then* **G** *is of character* 1.

If **G** is commutative, then for any connector U on S we have

$$aXU(a) = aX(aU^{\mathbf{G}}M_a^{-1}) = a(aU^{\mathbf{G}}M_a^{-1})X = aU^{\mathbf{G}}X = aXU^{\mathbf{G}}$$

for every $X \epsilon \mathbf{G}$, because $\mathbf{F}_a = \{E\}$ by Theorem 37.1. Thus we obtain $U(a) = U^{\mathbf{G}}$ for every $a \epsilon S$. Therefore we obtain by Theorem 37.1

Theorem 37.3. *If a transitive group* **G** *is commutative, then* $U(a_1, \ldots, a_n) = U^{\mathbf{G}}$ *for every connector* U *on* S *and* $a_\nu \epsilon S$ $(\nu = 1, 2, \ldots, n)$.

Theorem 37.4. *If* **G** *includes a subgroup* **H** *which is transitive and commutative, then* $U(a_1, \ldots, a_n, \mathbf{G}) \geqq U^{\mathbf{G}}$ *for any connector* U *on* S *and* $a_\nu \epsilon S$ $(\nu = 1, 2, \ldots, n)$.

Proof. We have $U^{\mathbf{G}}(a_1, \ldots, a_n, \mathbf{H}) = (U^{\mathbf{G}})^{\mathbf{H}}$ by Theorem 37.3. Thus we obtain by Theorem 34.4 and (9) in 32

$$U(a_1, \ldots, a_n, \mathbf{G}) \geqq U^{\mathbf{G}}(a_1, \ldots, a_n, \mathbf{H}) = (U^{\mathbf{G}})^{\mathbf{H}} = U^{\mathbf{G}}.$$

A uniformity **U** on S is said to be *regular* for **G**, if **U** is invariant by **G** and $\mathbf{T}(\mathbf{U}) \supset \mathbf{T}(\mathbf{U}^*)$. According to Theorem 34.7, we have always $\mathbf{T}(\mathbf{U}^*) \supset \mathbf{T}(\mathbf{U}(\mathbf{G})) \supset \mathbf{T}(\mathbf{U})$. Thus, if **U** is regular for **G**, then we have $\mathbf{T}(\mathbf{U}) = \mathbf{T}(\mathbf{U}^*)$.

A uniformity **U** on S is said to be *uniformly regular* for **G**, if **U** is invariant by **G** and $\mathbf{U} \supset \mathbf{U}^*$. Since $\mathbf{U} \supset \mathbf{U}^*$ implies $\mathbf{T}(\mathbf{U}) \supset \mathbf{T}(\mathbf{U}^*)$ by Theorem 20.1, it is obvious by definition that if **U** is uniformly regular for **G**, then **U** is regular for **G**.

Theorem 37.5. *If* **G** *includes a subgroup which is transitive and commutative, then every invariant uniformity on* S *by* **G** *is uniformly regular for* **G**.

Proof. If **G** includes a transitive, commutative subgroup, then $U(a_1, \ldots, a_n) \geqq U^{\mathbf{G}}$ for any connector U on S and $a_\nu \epsilon S$ $(\nu = 1, 2, \ldots, n)$ by Theorem 37.4. Thus, if **U** is invariant by **G**, we have $U(a_1, \ldots, a_n) \epsilon \mathbf{U}$ for every $U \epsilon \mathbf{U}$ and $a_\nu \epsilon S$ $(\nu = 1, 2, \ldots, n)$, and hence $\mathbf{U} \supset \mathbf{U}^*$.

U is said to be *locally uniformly regular* for **G**, if **U** is invariant by **G** and locally stronger than $\mathbf{U}^*$. If **U** is uniformly regular, then **U** is obviously locally uniformly regular by definition. If **U** is locally uniformly regular, then **U** is regular by Theorem 22.2.

We obviously have by definition

Theorem 37.6. *If* **U** *is locally uniformly regular and locally sharp, then* $\mathbf{U} \sim \mathbf{U}^*$.

If **U** is normal for **G**, then **U** is locally totally bounded by definition, but $\mathbf{U}^*$ is not always so.

Theorem 37.7. *If* **U** *is normal and locally uniformly regular, then* $\mathbf{U}^*$ *is locally totally bounded.*

Proof. If **U** is normal, then there is $U \in \mathbf{U}$ by definition such that xU and $xU(a)$ are totally bounded for **U** for every $x,\ a \in S$. If **U** is locally uniformly regular in addition, then $xU(a)$ also is totally bounded for $\mathbf{U}^*$ by Theorem 22.1, and hence $\mathbf{U}^*$ is locally totally bounded by definition.

Referring to Theorem 9.7, we conclude easily

Theorem 37.8. *If* **U** *is locally compact and regular for* **G**, *then* **U** *is locally uniformly regular for* **G**. *If* **U** *is compact and regular for* **G**, *then* **U** *is uniformly regular and sharp, namely* $\mathbf{U} = \mathbf{U}^*$.

Theorem 37.9. *An invariant uniformity* **U** *on* S *by* **G** *is regular for* **G** *if and only if the point mapping* M_x *is uniformly open for* **W**(**U**) *on* **G** *for every* $x \in S$.

Proof. For any $W \in \mathbf{W}(\mathbf{U})$ we can find an invariant $U \in \mathbf{U}$ and $a_\nu \in S$ $(\nu = 1, 2, \ldots, n)$ by Theorem 33.2 such that $XW \supset (\bigcap_{\nu=1}^{n} a_\nu U M_{a_\nu}^{-1})X$ for every $X \in \mathbf{G}$, since **U** is invariant by **G** by assumption. If **U** is regular for **G**, then for any $x, a_\nu \in S$ $(\nu = 1, 2, \ldots, n)$ there is an invariant $V \in \mathbf{U}$ such that $xU(a_1, \ldots, a_n) \supset xV$, and we have

$$XWM_x = x(XW) \supset x(\bigcap_{\nu=1}^{n} a_\nu U M_{a_\nu}^{-1})X = xU(a_1, \ldots, a_n)X \supset xVX$$
$$= xXV = XM_x V$$

for every $X \in \mathbf{G}$. Thus M_x is uniformly open for every $x \in S$ by definition.

Conversely, if M_x is uniformly open, then for any $W \in \mathbf{W}(\mathbf{U})$ we can find an invariant $V \in \mathbf{U}$ such that $XWM_x \supset XM_xV$ for every $X \in \mathbf{G}$ by definition. For any $a_\nu \in S$ $(\nu = 1, 2, \ldots, n)$ setting $XW = (\bigcap_{\nu=1}^{n} a_\nu U^{\mathbf{G}} M_{a_\nu}^{-1})X$ for $X \in \mathbf{G}$, $U \in \mathbf{U}$, we have $W \in \mathbf{W}(\mathbf{U})$ by Theorem 33.2 and

$$x(\bigcap_{\nu=1}^{n} a_\nu U^{\mathbf{G}} M_{a_\nu}^{-1})X \supset xXV = xVX$$

and hence $xU(a_1, \ldots, a_n) \supset xV$. Therefore $\mathbf{U}$ is regular, if M_x is uniformly open for every $x \in S$.

Theorem 37.10. *If* $\mathbf{U}$ *is regular and sharp for* $\mathbf{G}$, *then* $\mathbf{U}$ *is uniformly regular for* $\mathbf{G}$.

Proof. For any invariant $U \in \mathbf{U}$ we can find an invariant $V \in \mathbf{U}$ and $a_\nu \in S$ $(\nu = 1, 2, \ldots, n)$ such that $V(a_1, \ldots, a_n) \leqq U$, because $\mathbf{U}$ is sharp by assumption. Then we have by Theorem 34.1

$$U(b_1, \ldots, b_m) \geqq V(a_1, \ldots, a_n) \quad \text{for any } b_\mu \in S \ (\mu = 1, 2, \ldots, m).$$

We also can find an invariant $W \in \mathbf{U}$ and $a \in S$ such that $aV(a_1, \ldots, a_n) \supset aW$, because $\mathbf{U}$ is regular by assumption. Then we have by (8) in 34

$$aXU(b_1, \ldots, b_m) = aU(b_1X^{-1}, \ldots, b_mX^{-1})X \supset aV(a_1, \ldots, a_n)X \supset aWX$$
$$= aXW$$

for every $X \in \mathbf{G}$ and $b_\mu \in S$ $(\mu = 1, 2, \ldots, m)$. Therefore $\mathbf{U}$ is uniformly regular for $\mathbf{G}$ by definition.

Theorem 37.11. *If* $\mathbf{U}$ *is invariant and normal for* $\mathbf{G}$, *then for any totally bounded set* $A \subset S$ *for* $\mathbf{U}$, AM_a^{-1} *also is totally bounded for* $\mathbf{W}(\mathbf{U})$ *for every* $a \in S$.

Proof. Let $U_0 \in \mathbf{U}$ be a normal connector for $\mathbf{G}$. If A is totally bounded for $\mathbf{U}$, then we can find $X_\nu \in \mathbf{G}$ $(\nu = 1, 2, \ldots, n)$ such that $A \subset \bigcup_{\nu=1}^{n} aX_\nu U_0^{\mathbf{G}}$, because $\mathbf{G}$ is transitive. Thus we have by (1) in 33

$$AM_a^{-1}M_x \subset \bigcup_{\nu=1}^{n} aX_\nu U_0^{\mathbf{G}} M_a^{-1} M_x = \bigcup_{\nu=1}^{n} aU_0^{\mathbf{G}} M_a^{-1} M_x X_\nu = \bigcup_{\nu=1}^{n} xU_0(a)X_\nu$$

for every $x \in S$. Since $xU_0(a)$ is totally bounded and X_ν is uniformly continuous, we conclude that $AM_a^{-1}M_x$ is totally bounded for every $x \in S$. Therefore AM_a^{-1} is totally bounded for $\mathbf{W}(\mathbf{U})$ by Theorem 23.8.

Theorem 37.12. *If* $\mathbf{U}$ *is invariant and normal for* $\mathbf{G}$, *then for any totally bounded sets* $A, B \neq \emptyset$ *of* S *for* $\mathbf{U}$, $\bigcup_{x \in B} AM_x^{-1}$ *is totally bounded for* $\mathbf{W}(\mathbf{U})$.

Proof. Let $U \in \mathbf{U}$ be a totally bounded symmetric connector. Since B is totally bounded by assumption, we can find a finite system $x_\nu \in B$ $(\nu = 1, 2, \ldots, n)$ such that $B \subset \bigcup_{\nu=1}^{n} x_\nu U^{\mathbf{G}}$. Then, since $AM_x^{-1} \subset AU^{\mathbf{G}}M_{x_\nu}^{-1}$ for $x \in x_\nu U^{\mathbf{G}}$ by Theorem 33.1, we have

$$\bigcup_{x \in B} AM_x^{-1} \subset \bigcup_{\nu=1}^{n} AU^{\mathbf{G}}M_{x_\nu}^{-1}.$$

On the other hand, since $AU^{\mathbf{G}}$ is totally bounded, $AU^{\mathbf{G}}M_{x_\nu}^{-1}$ is totally bounded for $\mathbf{W}(\mathbf{U})$ for every $\nu = 1, 2, \ldots, n$ by Theorem 37.11. Consequently $\bigcup_{x \in B} AM_x^{-1}$ is totally bounded for $\mathbf{W}(\mathbf{U})$.

38. **Abstract Groups.** A space G is called a *group,* if for any $a, b \in$ G we have $ab \in$ G such that

1) $(ab)c = a(bc)$
2) for any $a, b \in$ G we can find $x, y \in$ G such that $a = xb = by$.

If G is a group, then there is $e' \in$ G such that $a = e'a$ for every $a \in$ G. Because for an element $a \in$ G there is $e' \in$ G by 2) such that $a = e'a$. For any $b \in$ G there is $y \in$ G by 2) such that $b = ay$, and we have $b = ay = (e'a)y = e'(ay) = e'b$. We also can show similarly that there is $e'' \in$ G such that $a = ae''$ for every $a \in$ G. Then we have $e'' = e'e'' = e'$. Thus such e'', e' are determined uniquely and $e' = e''$. This element is called the *unit* of G and denoted by e.

For any $a \in$ G we can find $a', a'' \in$ G by 2) such that $e = a'a = aa''$. Then we have

$$a' = a'e = a'(aa'') = (a'a)a'' = ea'' = a''.$$

Thus such a', a'' are determined uniquely and $a' = a''$. This element is called the *inverse* of a, and denoted by a^{-1}. For the inverse a^{-1} we obviously have

$$a^{-1}a = aa^{-1} = e, \quad (a^{-1})^{-1} = a.$$

For a group G, setting

$$xR_a = xa \quad \text{for } a, x \in G,$$

we obtain a system of transformations R_a $(a \in G)$ on G, and we can show easily

$$R_e = E, \quad R_a R_b = R_{ab}, \quad R_a^{-1} = R_{a^{-1}} \quad (a, b \in G).$$

Thus R_a $(a \in G)$ is a transformation group on G. Furthermore this transformation group is transitive and of character 1. Because $xR_a = x$ implies $xa = x$, that is, $a = x^{-1}x = e$, and hence $R_a = E$. This transformation group is called the *right transformation group* of G, and denoted by R_G.

If a connector U on G is invariant by R_G, then $aR_x U R_x^{-1} = aU$ for every $a, x \in G$. Thus, setting $a = e$, we obtain $xU = eUx$. Conversely, setting

(1) $xU(\mathbf{n}) = \mathbf{n}x \quad (e \in \mathbf{n} \subset G)$

we obtain a connector $U(\mathbf{n})$ on G, which is invariant by R_G. Because

$$xR_a U(\mathbf{n}) R_a^{-1} = \mathbf{n}(xa)a^{-1} = \mathbf{n}x \quad \text{for } x, a \in G.$$

Thus every invariant connector on G by R_G can be represented by $U(\mathbf{n})$ $(e \in \mathbf{n} \subset G)$.

Concerning the connectors $U(\mathbf{n})$ $(e \in \mathbf{n} \subset G)$, we obviously have by definition (1)

(2) $AU(\mathbf{n}) = \mathbf{n}A \quad \text{for } A \subset G,$

(3) $\bigcap_{\lambda \in \Lambda} U(\mathbf{n}_\lambda) = U(\bigcap_{\lambda \in \Lambda} \mathbf{n}_\lambda),$

(4) $U(\mathbf{n}) \leqq U(\mathbf{m})$ if and only if $\mathbf{n} \subset \mathbf{m}$.

(5) $U(\mathbf{m})U(\mathbf{n}) = U(\mathbf{nm}),$

because $xU(\mathbf{m})U(\mathbf{n}) = \mathbf{m}xU(\mathbf{n}) = \mathbf{nm}x = xU(\mathbf{nm})$ by (2).

(6) $U(\mathbf{n})^{-1} = U(\mathbf{n}^{-1}),$

because $x \in \mathbf{n}y$ if and only if $\mathbf{n}^{-1}x \ni y$, that is, $x \in yU(\mathbf{n})$ if and only if $xU(\mathbf{n}^{-1}) \ni y$, making use of the notation $\mathbf{n}^{-1} = \{x^{-1}: x \in \mathbf{n}\}$.

Concerning the point mappings, we have by definition

(7) $R_x M_a = aR_x = ax$ for $a, x \in G$.

Making use of the notation $R_A = \{R_x: x \in A\}$ for $A \subset G$, we obviously have

$$\bigcap_{\lambda \in \Lambda} R_{A_\lambda} = R_{\bigcap_\lambda A_\lambda}, \quad AR_B = AB.$$

Thus we obtain by (7)

(8) $R_A M_a = aA$ for $\emptyset \neq A \subset G$.

Since $AM_a^{-1} = \{R_x: ax \in A\} = \{R_x: x \in a^{-1}A\}$, we have

(9) $AM_a^{-1} = R_{a^{-1}A}$ for $\emptyset \neq A \subset G$.

Since $R_x M_a U(\mathbf{n}) M_a^{-1} = axU(\mathbf{n})M_a^{-1} = \mathbf{n}axM_a^{-1}$, we obtain by (9)

(10) $R_x M_a U(\mathbf{n}) M_a^{-1} = R_{a^{-1}\mathbf{n}ax}$.

(11) $xU(\mathbf{n})(a_1, \ldots, a_n) = \bigcap_{\nu=1}^{n} xa_\nu^{-1}\mathbf{n}a_\nu$,

because we have by (8), (9)

$$xU(\mathbf{n})(a) = (aU(\mathbf{n})M_a^{-1})M_x = x(\mathbf{n}aM_a^{-1}) = xa^{-1}\mathbf{n}a,$$

and hence we obtain (11) by Theorem 37.1.

A set $\mathbf{n} \subset G$ is said to be *symmetric,* if $\mathbf{n}^{-1} = \mathbf{n}$, that is, if $x \in \mathbf{n}$ implies $x^{-1} \in \mathbf{n}$.

Let $\mathbf{U}$ be an invariant uniformity on G by R_G. Setting

(12) $\mathbf{N} = \{\mathbf{n}: U(\mathbf{n}) \in \mathbf{U}\}$,

we can show easily by (3), (5), (6) that $\mathbf{N}$ satisfies the *neighbourhood conditions:*

1) $\mathbf{N} \ni \mathbf{n} \subset \mathbf{m}$ implies $\mathbf{N} \ni \mathbf{m}$,

2) $\mathbf{N} \ni \mathbf{n}, \mathbf{m}$ implies $\mathbf{N} \ni \mathbf{n} \cap \mathbf{m}$,

3) for any $\mathbf{n} \in \mathbf{N}$ there is $\mathbf{m} \in \mathbf{N}$ such that $\mathbf{m}^{-1}\mathbf{m} \subset \mathbf{n}$.

A system $\mathbf{N}$ of sets which contain e, is called a *neighbourhood* on G, if $\mathbf{N}$ satisfies the neighbourhood conditions 1), 2), 3). If $\mathbf{N}$ is a neighbourhood, then $\mathbf{n} \in \mathbf{N}$ implies $\mathbf{n}^{-1} \in \mathbf{N}$. Because we can find $\mathbf{m} \in \mathbf{N}$ by 3) such that $\mathbf{m}^{-1}\mathbf{m} \subset \mathbf{n}$. Then we have $\mathbf{m}^{-1} \subset \mathbf{n}$, since $\mathbf{m} \ni e$, and hence $\mathbf{m} \subset \mathbf{n}^{-1}$, which implies $\mathbf{n}^{-1} \in \mathbf{N}$ by 1). Since

$$(\mathbf{m}^{-1} \cap \mathbf{m})(\mathbf{m}^{-1} \cap \mathbf{m}) \subset \mathbf{m}^{-1}\mathbf{m} \subset \mathbf{n}, \quad (\mathbf{m}^{-1} \cap \mathbf{m})^{-1} = \mathbf{m}^{-1} \cap \mathbf{m},$$

we can also state for any $\mathbf{n} \in \mathbf{N}$ there is a symmetric $\mathbf{m} \in \mathbf{N}$ such that $\mathbf{mm} \subset \mathbf{n}$.

For any neighbourhood $\mathbf{N}$ on G, we can show easily by (3), (5), (6) that $\{U(\mathbf{n}) : \mathbf{n} \in \mathbf{N}\}$ satisfies the basis conditions. Thus there exists uniquely an invariant uniformity $\mathbf{U}$ on G by R_G, such that the relation (12) holds. This uniformity $\mathbf{U}$ is called the *induced uniformity* of $\mathbf{N}$, and denoted by $\mathbf{U}(\mathbf{N})$. Therefore we can consider neighbourhoods on G instead of invariant uniformities on G by R_G. We say that a system of mappings on G is continuous, uniformly continuous or equi-continuous for a neighbourhood $\mathbf{N}$, if it is so for the induced uniformity $\mathbf{U}(\mathbf{N})$.

For two neighbourhoods $\mathbf{M}$, $\mathbf{N}$ on G, $\mathbf{N}$ is said to be *stronger* than $\mathbf{M}$, or $\mathbf{M}$ is said to be *weaker* than $\mathbf{N}$, if $\mathbf{N} \supset \mathbf{M}$. With this definition we obviously have

Theorem 38.1. $\mathbf{N} \supset \mathbf{M}$ *if and only if* $\mathbf{U}(\mathbf{N}) \supset \mathbf{U}(\mathbf{M})$.

For a system of neighbourhoods $\mathbf{N}_\lambda$ $(\lambda \in \Lambda)$, setting

$$\mathbf{U} = \bigvee_{\lambda \in \Lambda} \mathbf{U}(\mathbf{N}_\lambda),$$

we obtain a uniformity $\mathbf{U}$. Referring to (4) in 32 and Theorem 21.1, we can show easily that $\mathbf{U}$ is invariant by R_G. Therefore there exists uniquely a neighbourhood $\mathbf{N}$ such that $\mathbf{U} = \mathbf{U}(\mathbf{N})$. Then we see easily by Theorem 38.1 that $\mathbf{N}$ is the weakest among all neighbourhoods which are stronger than every $\mathbf{N}_\lambda$ $(\lambda \in \Lambda)$. Thus this neighbourhood $\mathbf{N}$ is called the *weakest stronger neighbourhood of* $\mathbf{N}_\lambda$ $(\lambda \in \Lambda)$, and denoted by $\bigvee_{\lambda \in \Lambda} \mathbf{N}_\lambda$. With this definition, we hence have

Theorem 38.2. $\mathbf{U}(\bigvee_{\lambda \in \Lambda} \mathbf{N}_\lambda) = \bigvee_{\lambda \in \Lambda} \mathbf{U}(\mathbf{N}_\lambda)$.

Referring to Theorem 21.1, we can prove easily

Theorem 38.3. $\mathbf{n} \in \bigvee_{\lambda \in \Lambda} \mathbf{N}_\lambda$ *if and only if we can find a finite system* $\mathbf{n}_\nu \in \mathbf{N}_{\lambda_\nu}$, $\lambda_\nu \in \Lambda$ $(\nu = 1, 2, \ldots, n)$ *such that* $\mathbf{n} \supset \bigcap_{\nu=1}^{n} \mathbf{n}_\nu$.

For a neighbourhood $\mathbf{N}$ on G, a subset $\mathbf{B} \subset \mathbf{N}$ is called a *basis* of $\mathbf{N}$, if for any $\mathbf{n} \in \mathbf{N}$ there is $\mathbf{m} \in \mathbf{B}$ such that $\mathbf{n} \supset \mathbf{m}$. With this definition, we see easily that every basis $\mathbf{B}$ of $\mathbf{N}$ satisfies the *basis conditions:*

1) for any $\mathbf{n}_1, \mathbf{n}_2 \in \mathbf{B}$ there is $\mathbf{m} \in \mathbf{B}$ such that $\mathbf{n}_1 \cap \mathbf{n}_2 \supset \mathbf{m}$,

2) for any $\mathbf{n} \in \mathbf{B}$ there is $\mathbf{m} \in \mathbf{B}$ such that $\mathbf{m}^{-1}\mathbf{m} \subset \mathbf{n}$.

Conversely we can prove easily

Theorem 38.4. *If a system of sets* $\mathbf{B}$ *of* G *which contain* e*, satisfies the basis condition, then there exists uniquely a neighbourhood on* G *of which* $\mathbf{B}$ *is a basis.*

39. **Regular Neighbourhoods.** Let $\mathbf{N}$ be a neighbourhood on a group G. $\mathbf{N}$ is said to be *regular,* if $x\mathbf{N}x^{-1} \subset \mathbf{N}$ for every $x \in G$, that is, if $\mathbf{n} \in \mathbf{N}$ implies $x\mathbf{n}x^{-1} \in \mathbf{N}$ for every $x \in G$.

Theorem 39.1. $\mathbf{N}$ *is regular if and only if* $U(\mathbf{N})$ *is regular for* R_G.

Proof. Since $xU(\mathbf{n})(a_1, \ldots, a_n) = \bigcap_{\nu=1}^{n} xa_\nu{}^{-1}\mathbf{n}a_\nu = (\bigcap_{\nu=1}^{n} xa_\nu{}^{-1}\mathbf{n}(xa_\nu{}^{-1})^{-1})x$ by (11) in 38, we have by definition (1) in 38

$$(1)\ xU(\mathbf{n})(a_1, \ldots, a_n) = xU(\bigcap_{\nu=1}^{n} xa_\nu{}^{-1}\mathbf{n}(xa_\nu{}^{-1})^{-1}) = x \bigcap_{\nu=1}^{n} a_\nu{}^{-1}\mathbf{n}a_\nu$$

for any $x, a_\nu \in G$ $(\nu = 1, 2, \ldots, n)$. If $\mathbf{N}$ is regular, then we have $\bigcap_{\nu=1}^{n} xa_\nu{}^{-1}\mathbf{n}(xa_\nu{}^{-1})^{-1} \in \mathbf{N}$ for $\mathbf{n} \in \mathbf{N}$ by definition, and hence $U(\mathbf{N})$ is regular for R_G by Theorems 34.6 and 4.4.

Conversely, if $U(\mathbf{N})$ is regular for R_G, then for any $a, x \in G$ and $\mathbf{n} \in \mathbf{N}$ there is $\mathbf{m} \in \mathbf{N}$ by Theorem 4.4 such that $aU(\mathbf{m}) \subset aU(\mathbf{n})(xa)$. Since we have by (11) in 38

$$aU(\mathbf{n})(xa) = a(xa)^{-1}\mathbf{n}xa = aa^{-1}x^{-1}\mathbf{n}xa = x^{-1}\mathbf{n}xa,$$

we obtain $\mathbf{m}a \subset x^{-1}\mathbf{n}xa$, and hence $\mathbf{m} \subset x^{-1}\mathbf{n}x$. Thus $\mathbf{n} \in \mathbf{N}$ implies $x^{-1}\mathbf{n}x \in \mathbf{N}$ for every $x \in G$.

Setting

$$xL_a = ax \quad \text{for } x, a \in G,$$

we obtain a system of transformations L_a $(a \in G)$ on G. These transformations are called *left transformations* of G. About left transformations we can show easily

$$L_e = E, \quad L_a L_b = L_{ba}, \quad L_a^{-1} = L_{a^{-1}}.$$

Thus the system of all left transformations of G forms a transitive group on G, which will be called the *left transformation group* of G, and denoted by L_G.

Since $xL_a U(\mathbf{n}) L_a^{-1} = axU(\mathbf{n})L_{a^{-1}} = a^{-1}\mathbf{n}ax = xU(a^{-1}\mathbf{n}a)$, we have

(2) $L_a U(\mathbf{n}) L_a^{-1} = U(a^{-1}\mathbf{n}a)$ for $a \in G$, $e \in \mathbf{n} \subset G$.

Thus we obtain by (3) in 38

(3) $\bigcap_{x \in A} L_x U(\mathbf{n}) L_x^{-1} = U(\bigcap_{x \in A} x^{-1}\mathbf{n}x)$ for $\emptyset \neq A \subset G$, $e \in \mathbf{n} \subset G$.

From this (3) we conclude immediately

Theorem 39.2. *The system* L_x $(x \in A)$ *is equi-continuous for* $\mathbf{N}$ *if and only if* $\bigcap_{x \in A} x^{-1}\mathbf{n}x \in \mathbf{N}$ *for every* $\mathbf{n} \in \mathbf{N}$.

Theorem 39.3. *The left transformations* L_x $(x \in G)$ *are uniformly continuous for* $\mathbf{N}$ *if and only if* $\mathbf{N}$ *is regular.*

Proof. It is obvious by (2) that L_a is uniformly continuous for $\mathbf{N}$, if $\mathbf{N}$ is regular. Conversely, if L_a is uniformly continuous for $\mathbf{N}$, then for any $\mathbf{n} \in \mathbf{N}$ there is $\mathbf{m} \in \mathbf{N}$ by definition such that $L_a U(\mathbf{n}) L_a^{-1} \geqq U(\mathbf{m})$, that is, $U(a^{-1}\mathbf{n}a) \geqq U(\mathbf{m})$ by (2), and hence $a^{-1}\mathbf{n}a \in \mathbf{N}$ by (4) in 38. Thus $\mathbf{N}$ is regular, if L_a is uniformly continuous for every $a \in G$.

$\mathbf{N}$ is said to be *uniformly regular,* if $\bigcap_{x \in G} x\mathbf{N}x^{-1} \subset \mathbf{N}$, that is, if $\mathbf{n} \in \mathbf{N}$ implies $\bigcap_{x \in G} x\mathbf{n}x^{-1} \in \mathbf{N}$.

Theorem 39.4. $\mathbf{N}$ *is uniformly regular if and only if* $\mathbf{U}(\mathbf{N})$ *is uniformly regular for* R_G.

Proof. Since $xU(\mathbf{n})(a_1, \ldots, a_n) \supset xU(\bigcap_{z \in G} \mathbf{z}\mathbf{n}z^{-1})$ by (1), if $\mathbf{N}$ is uniformly regular, then $\mathbf{U}(\mathbf{N})$ is uniformly regular for R_G by definition. Conversely, if $\mathbf{U}(\mathbf{N})$ is uniformly regular for R_G, then for any $\mathbf{n} \in \mathbf{N}$ and $a \in G$ there is $\mathbf{m} \in \mathbf{N}$ by definition such that

$$xU(\mathbf{n})(a) \supset xU(\mathbf{m}) = \mathbf{m}x \quad \text{for every } x \in G.$$

Then we have by (1)

$$\mathbf{m}x \subset xU(xa^{-1}\mathbf{n}(xa^{-1})^{-1}) = (xa^{-1}\mathbf{n}(xa^{-1})^{-1})x$$

for every $x \in G$. Thus we have

$$\mathbf{m} \subset \bigcap_{x \in G} (xa^{-1})\mathbf{n}(xa^{-1})^{-1} = \bigcap_{x \in G} x\mathbf{n}x^{-1}.$$

Therefore $\mathbf{N}$ is uniformly regular by definition.

Theorem 39.5. *The system L_x $(x \in G)$ is equi-continuous for* $\mathbf{N}$ *if and only if* $\mathbf{N}$ *is uniformly regular.*

Proof. If $\mathbf{N}$ is uniformly regular, then L_x $(x \in G)$ is equi-continuous for $\mathbf{N}$ by (3). Conversely, if L_x $(x \in G)$ is equi-continuous for $\mathbf{N}$, then for any $\mathbf{n} \in \mathbf{N}$ we can find $\mathbf{m} \in \mathbf{N}$ by definition such that

$$U(\mathbf{m}) \leqq \bigcap_{x \in G} L_x U(\mathbf{n}) L_x^{-1}.$$

Thus we obtain $\mathbf{m} \subset x^{-1}\mathbf{n}x$ for every $x \in G$ by (2) in 39 and (4) in 38. Therefore $\mathbf{N}$ is uniformly regular by definition.

$\mathbf{N}$ is said to be *locally uniformly regular,* if $\mathbf{N}$ is regular and there is $\mathbf{m} \in \mathbf{N}$ such that $\bigcap_{x \in \mathbf{m}} x\mathbf{N}x^{-1} \subset \mathbf{N}$, that is, $\mathbf{n} \in \mathbf{N}$ implies $\bigcap_{x \in \mathbf{m}} x\mathbf{n}x^{-1} \in \mathbf{N}$.

Theorem 39.6. $\mathbf{N}$ *is locally uniformly regular if and only if* $\mathbf{U}(\mathbf{N})$ *is locally uniformly regular for* R_G.

Proof. If $\mathbf{N}$ is locally uniformly regular, then $\mathbf{N}$ is regular by definition and hence

$$\bigcap_{\nu=1}^{n} ya_\nu^{-1}\mathbf{n}(ya_\nu^{-1})^{-1} \in \mathbf{N} \quad \text{for any } \mathbf{n} \in \mathbf{N} \text{ and } y, a_\nu \in G \ (\nu = 1, 2, \ldots, n).$$

We also can find $\mathbf{m} \in \mathbf{N}$ such that $\bigcap_{z \in \mathbf{m}} z(\bigcap_{\nu=1}^{n} ya_\nu^{-1}\mathbf{n}(ya_\nu^{-1})^{-1})z^{-1} \in \mathbf{N}$.

Since we obtain by (1)

$$xU(\mathbf{n})(a_1, \ldots, a_n) \supset xU(\bigcap_{z \in \mathbf{m}} \bigcap_{\nu=1}^{n} zya_\nu^{-1}\mathbf{n}(zya_\nu^{-1})^{-1}) \quad \text{for } x \in \mathbf{m}y = yU(\mathbf{m}),$$

we hence conclude that $\mathbf{U}(\mathbf{N})$ is locally uniformly regular for R_G.

Conversely, if $\mathbf{U}(\mathbf{N})$ is locally uniformly regular for R_G, then we can find $\mathbf{m}_0 \in \mathbf{N}$ by definition such that for any $\mathbf{n} \in \mathbf{N}$ and y, $a \in G$ there is $\mathbf{m} \in \mathbf{N}$ such that

$$xU((ya^{-1})^{-1}\mathbf{n}ya^{-1})(a) \cap yU(\mathbf{m}_0) \supset xU(\mathbf{m}) \cap yU(\mathbf{m}_0) \quad \text{for } x \in yU(\mathbf{m}_0),$$

because $\mathbf{N}$ is regular by Theorem 39.1 and hence $(ya^{-1})^{-1}\mathbf{n}ya^{-1} \in \mathbf{N}$. Since we have by (1)

$$xU((ya^{-1})^{-1}\mathbf{n}ya^{-1})(a) = xa^{-1}(ya^{-1})^{-1}\mathbf{n}ya^{-1}a = xy^{-1}\mathbf{n}y,$$

we obtain $xy^{-1}\mathbf{n}y \supset \mathbf{m}x \cap \mathbf{m}_0 y$ for $x \in \mathbf{m}_0 y$. Setting $x = zy$ $(z \in \mathbf{m}_0)$, we conclude

$$z\mathbf{n} \supset \mathbf{m}z \cap \mathbf{m}_0 \quad \text{for } z \in \mathbf{m}_0.$$

Since we can find a symmetric $\mathbf{m}_1 \in \mathbf{N}$ such that $\mathbf{m}_1\mathbf{m}_1 \subset \mathbf{m}_0$, for such $\mathbf{m}_1 \in \mathbf{N}$ we thus have $z\mathbf{n} \supset \mathbf{m}z \cap \mathbf{m}_1 z$ for $z \in \mathbf{m}_1$. Therefore

$$\bigcap_{z \in \mathbf{m}_1} z\mathbf{n}z^{-1} \supset \mathbf{m} \cap \mathbf{m}_1 \in \mathbf{N}.$$

Consequently $\mathbf{N}$ is locally uniformly regular by definition.

Theorem 39.7. *A regular neighbourhood* $\mathbf{N}$ *is uniformly regular if and only if* $\mathbf{U}(\mathbf{N})$ *is sharp for* R_G.

Proof. If $\mathbf{N}$ is uniformly regular, then for any $\mathbf{n} \in \mathbf{N}$, setting $\mathbf{m} = \bigcap_{x \in G} x\mathbf{n}x^{-1}$, we have $\mathbf{m} \in \mathbf{N}$ by definition and we obtain by (1)

$$xU(\mathbf{m})(a) = xU(xa^{-1}\mathbf{m}(xa^{-1})^{-1}) \subset xU(\mathbf{n}) \quad \text{for every } x, a \in G,$$

because $xa^{-1}\mathbf{m}(xa^{-1})^{-1} \subset \mathbf{n}$. Therefore $\mathbf{U}(\mathbf{N})$ is sharp for R_G by definition.

Conversely, if $\mathbf{U}(\mathbf{N})$ is sharp for R_G, then for any $\mathbf{n} \in \mathbf{N}$ we can find $\mathbf{m} \in \mathbf{N}$ and $a_\nu \in G$ $(\nu = 1, 2, \ldots, n)$ by definition such that $U(\mathbf{m})(a_1, \ldots, a_n) \leqq U(\mathbf{n})$. Then we have by (11) in 38

$$\bigcap_{\nu=1}^{n} xa_\nu^{-1}\mathbf{m}a_\nu = xU(\mathbf{m})(a_1, \ldots, a_n) \subset \mathbf{n}x \text{ for every } x \in G.$$

Since **N** is regular by assumption, we hence obtain

$$\mathbf{N} \ni \bigcap_{\nu=1}^{n} a_\nu^{-1}\mathbf{m}a_\nu \subset x^{-1}\mathbf{n}x \text{ for every } x \in G.$$

Therefore **N** is uniformly regular by definition.

Theorem 39.8. *A regular neighbourhood* **N** *is locally uniformly regular if and only if* U(**N**) *is locally sharp for* R_G.

Proof. If **N** is locally uniformly regular, then there is $\mathbf{m}_0 \in \mathbf{N}$ by definition such that $\bigcap_{x\in\mathbf{m}_0} x\mathbf{N}x^{-1} \subset \mathbf{N}$. Since **N** is regular by assumption, for any $\mathbf{n} \in \mathbf{N}$ and $y, a \in G$ we have $(ya^{-1})^{-1}\mathbf{n}ya^{-1} \in \mathbf{N}$. Thus, setting $\mathbf{m} = \bigcap_{z\in\mathbf{m}_0} z(ya^{-1})^{-1}\mathbf{n}(ya^{-1})z^{-1}$, we have $\mathbf{m} \in \mathbf{N}$ and $x \in yU(\mathbf{m}_0) = \mathbf{m}_0 y$ implies by (1)

$$xU(\mathbf{m})(a) = xU(xy^{-1}(ya^{-1})\mathbf{m}(ya^{-1})^{-1}(xy^{-1})^{-1}) \subset xU(\mathbf{n}).$$

Thus U(**N**) is locally sharp for R_G by definition.

Conversely, if U(**N**) is locally sharp, then there is $\mathbf{m}_0 \in \mathbf{N}$ by definition such that for any $\mathbf{n} \in \mathbf{N}$ and $y \in G$ we can find $\mathbf{m} \in \mathbf{N}$ and $a_\nu \in G$ $(\nu = 1, 2, \ldots, n)$ such that

$$xU(\mathbf{m})(a_1, \ldots, a_n) \cap yU(\mathbf{m}_0) \subset xU(\mathbf{n}) \cap yU(\mathbf{m}_0) \text{ for } x \in yU(\mathbf{m}_0).$$

Thus we obtain by (11) in 38

$$\bigcap_{\nu=1}^{n} xa_\nu^{-1}\mathbf{m}a_\nu \cap \mathbf{m}_0 y \subset \mathbf{n}x \text{ for } x \in \mathbf{m}_0 y.$$

Setting $x = zy$ $(z \in \mathbf{m}_0)$, we hence have

$$z \bigcap_{\nu=1}^{n} ya_\nu^{-1}\mathbf{m}a_\nu y^{-1} \cap \mathbf{m}_0 \subset \mathbf{n}z \text{ for } z \in \mathbf{m}_0.$$

Since there is a symmetric $\mathbf{m}_1 \in \mathbf{N}$ such that $\mathbf{m}_1\mathbf{m}_1 \subset \mathbf{m}_0$, for such $\mathbf{m}_1 \in \mathbf{N}$ we have $z\mathbf{m}_1 \subset \mathbf{m}_0$ for $z \in \mathbf{m}_1$ and hence

$$\mathbf{N} \ni \bigcap_{\nu=1}^{n} ya_\nu^{-1}\mathbf{m}a_\nu y^{-1} \cap \mathbf{m}_1 \subset z^{-1}\mathbf{n}z \text{ for } z \in \mathbf{m}_1,$$

because **N** is regular by assumption. Thus we obtain $\bigcap_{z \in m_1} znz^{-1} \in \mathbf{N}$.

Therefore **N** is locally uniformly regular by definition.

Theorem 39.9. *If* **N** *is regular, then* $(AB)^{\mathbf{U}(\mathbf{N})-} \supset A^{\mathbf{U}(\mathbf{N})-}B^{\mathbf{U}(\mathbf{N})-}$ *for* $\emptyset \neq A, B \subset G$.

Proof. If **N** is regular, then both R_x and L_x are uniformly continuous for U(N) for every $x \in G$ by Theorem 39.3. Thus for any $x \in A$ we have by Theorem 12.2

$$(AB)^- \supset (xB)^- = (BL_x)^- \supset B^- L_x = xB^-.$$

Therefore $(AB)^- \supset AB^-$. From this we conclude similarly that $(AB)^- \supset A^- B^-$.

Theorem 39.10. *If a transformation group* **G**, *not necessarily transitive, on* S *is equi-continuous for a uniformity* **U**, *then* **W(U)** *on* **G** *is invariant by the right transformation group of* **G**, *and the neighbourhood* **N** *such that* **U(N)** = **W(U**, *is regular.*

Proof. Since **U** is invariant by **G** by Theorem 32.5, we see by Theorem 33.2 that the system

$$\{\bigcap_{\nu=1}^{n} a_\nu U^{\mathbf{G}} M_{a_\nu}^{-1} : U \in \mathbf{U},\ a_\nu \in S\ (\nu = 1, 2, \ldots, n),\ n = 1, 2, \ldots\}$$

forms a basis of a neighbourhood **N** such that **U(N)** = **W(U)**, and we conclude by Theorem 33.1 that **N** is regular.

40. Totally Bounded Neighbourhoods.

A set $A \subset G$ is said to be *right totally bounded* for a neighbourhood **N**, if for any $\mathbf{n} \in \mathbf{N}$ we can find a finite system $a_\nu \in G$ $(\nu = 1, 2, \ldots, n)$ such that $A \subset \bigcup_{\nu=1}^{n} \mathbf{n}a_\nu$. A is said to be *left totally bounded* for **N**, if for any $\mathbf{n} \in \mathbf{N}$ we can find a finite system $a_\nu \in G$ $(\nu = 1, 2, \ldots, n)$ such that $A \subset \bigcup_{\nu=1}^{n} a_\nu\mathbf{n}$. If A is right or left totally bounded for **N**, then we can find such a system a_ν $(\nu = 1, 2, \ldots, n)$ in A. Because for any $\mathbf{n} \in \mathbf{N}$ there is a symmetric $\mathbf{m} \in \mathbf{N}$ such that $\mathbf{m}\mathbf{m}^{-1} \subset \mathbf{n}$, and $x \in \mathbf{m}a$ implies $\mathbf{m}a \subset \mathbf{m}\mathbf{m}^{-1}x \subset \mathbf{n}x$; and $x \in a\mathbf{m}$ implies $a\mathbf{m} \subset x\mathbf{m}^{-1}\mathbf{m} \subset x\mathbf{n}$. It is obvious by definition that if A is right totally bounded, then Ax also is right totally bounded for every $x \in G$, and if

A is left totally bounded, then xA also is left totally bounded for every $x \in G$. A is said to be *totally bounded* for **N**, if A is right and left totally bounded for **N** at the same time.

We have obviously by (1) in 38

Theorem 40.1. *A is right totally bounded for* **N** *if and only if A is totally bounded for* **U(N)**.

Theorem 40.2. *If* **N** *is uniformly regular, then every right or left totally bounded set is totally bounded for* **N**.

Proof. For any $\mathbf{n} \in \mathbf{N}$, setting $\mathbf{m} = \bigcap_{x \in G} x\mathbf{n}x^{-1}$, we have $\mathbf{m} \in \mathbf{N}$, because **N** is uniformly regular by assumption. If A is right totally bounded for **N**, then we can find $a_\nu \in G$ $(\nu = 1, 2, \ldots, n)$ such that $A \subset \bigcup_{\nu=1}^{n} \mathbf{m}a_\nu$. Since $\mathbf{m}a_\nu \subset a_\nu\mathbf{n}$ $(\nu = 1, 2, \ldots, n)$, we hence obtain $A \subset \bigcup_{\nu=1}^{n} a_\nu\mathbf{n}$. Thus A is left totally bounded for **N**. We also can prove similarly that if A is left totally bounded, then A is right totally bounded.

N is said to be *right* or *left totally bounded,* if there is $\mathbf{m} \in \mathbf{N}$ such that **m** is right or left totally bounded for **N** respectively. **N** is said to be *totally bounded,* if there is $\mathbf{m} \in \mathbf{N}$ such that **m** is totally bounded for **N**.

Referring to (1) in 38, we conclude immediately

Theorem 40.3. **N** *is right totally bounded if and only if* **U(N)** *is locally totally bounded.*

Theorem 40.4. *If* **N** *is regular and right totally bounded, then* **N** *is locally uniformly regular and totally bounded, and every right or left totally bounded set for* **N** *is totally bounded for* **N**.

Proof. Since $yL_x = xR_y = xy$, R_y $(y \in G)$ is equi-continuous for **N** by Theorem 32.5, and L_x $(x \in G)$ is uniformly continuous by Theorem 39.3, we see by Theorem 16.3 that L_x $(x \in A)$ is equi-continuous for **N**, if A is right totally bounded for **N**. Let $\mathbf{m}_0 \in \mathbf{N}$ be right totally bounded for N. Since L_x $(x \in \mathbf{m}_0)$ is equi-continuous for N, for any $\mathbf{n} \in \mathbf{N}$ we can find $\mathbf{m} \in \mathbf{N}$ such that $\bigcap_{x \in \mathbf{m}_0} L_x U(\mathbf{n}) L_x^{-1} \geqq U(\mathbf{m})$. Then we obtain by (3) in 39 and (4) in 38

$$\bigcap_{x \in \mathbf{m}_0} x^{-1}\mathbf{n}x \supset \mathbf{m}.$$

For a symmetric $\mathbf{m}_1 \in \mathbf{N}$ such that $\mathbf{m}_1 \subset \mathbf{m}_0$, $\mathbf{m}_1$ also is right totally bounded for $\mathbf{N}$ and

$$\bigcap_{x \in \mathbf{m}_1} x\mathbf{n}x^{-1} \supset \mathbf{m}.$$

Thus $\mathbf{N}$ is locally uniformly regular by definition. Furthermore, for a symmetric $\mathbf{n}_1 \in \mathbf{N}$ such that $\mathbf{n}_1\mathbf{n}_1 \subset \mathbf{m}$, we can find $a_\nu \in G$ $(\nu = 1, 2, \ldots, n)$ such that $\mathbf{m}_1 \subset \bigcup_{\nu=1}^{n} \mathbf{n}_1 a_\nu$. Then for $y_\nu \in \mathbf{m}_1 \cap \mathbf{n}_1 a_\nu$ $(\nu = 1, 2, \ldots, n)$ we have $\mathbf{n}_1 y_\nu \ni a_\nu$, and hence

$$\mathbf{m}_1 \subset \bigcup_{\nu=1}^{n} \mathbf{n}_1\mathbf{n}_1 y_\nu \subset \bigcup_{\nu=1}^{n} \mathbf{m}y_\nu \subset \bigcup_{\nu=1}^{n} y_\nu\mathbf{n},$$

because $y_\nu \in \mathbf{m}_1$ $(\nu = 1, 2, \ldots, n)$. Therefore $\mathbf{m}_1 \in \mathbf{N}$ is left totally bounded for $\mathbf{N}$. Consequently $\mathbf{N}$ is totally bounded by definition.

Let $\mathbf{m}_0 \in \mathbf{N}$ be totally bounded for $\mathbf{N}$. If A is left totally bounded for $\mathbf{N}$, then we can find $a_\nu \in G$ $(\nu = 1, 2, \ldots, n)$ such that $A \subset \bigcup_{\nu=1}^{n} a_\nu\mathbf{m}_0$. Since $\mathbf{N}$ is regular by assumption, for any $\mathbf{n} \in \mathbf{N}$ there is $\mathbf{n}_0 \in \mathbf{N}$ such that $\mathbf{n}_0 \subset \bigcap_{\nu=1}^{n} a_\nu^{-1}\mathbf{n}a_\nu$. For such $\mathbf{n}_0 \in \mathbf{N}$ we can find $b_\mu \in G$ $(\mu = 1, 2, \ldots, m)$ such that $\mathbf{m}_0 \subset \bigcup_{\mu=1}^{m} \mathbf{n}_0 b_\mu$. Then we have

$$A \subset \bigcup_{\nu=1}^{n} \bigcup_{\mu=1}^{m} a_\nu\mathbf{n}_0 b_\mu \subset \bigcup_{\nu=1}^{n} \bigcup_{\mu=1}^{m} \mathbf{n}a_\nu b_\mu.$$

Therefore A is right totally bounded for $\mathbf{N}$. We also can prove similarly that if A is right totally bounded for $\mathbf{N}$, then A is left totally bounded for $\mathbf{N}$.

Theorem 40.5. *If* $\mathbf{U}(\mathbf{N})$ *is locally totally bounded and regular for* R_G, *then* $\mathbf{U}(\mathbf{N})$ *is normal, locally uniformly regular, and locally sharp.*

Proof. Under the assumptions on $\mathbf{U}(\mathbf{N})$, $\mathbf{N}$ is right totally bounded by Theorem 40.3 and regular by Theorem 39.1. Therefore $\mathbf{N}$ is locally uniformly regular by Theorem 40.4. Referring to Theorems 39.6 and 39.8 we can hence conclude that $\mathbf{U}(\mathbf{N})$ is locally uniformly regular and locally sharp. $\mathbf{N}$ also is totally bounded by Theorem 40.4. Let $\mathbf{m}_0 \in \mathbf{N}$ be totally bounded for $\mathbf{N}$. Since we have by (11) in 38

$$xU(\mathbf{m}_0)(a) = xa^{-1}\mathbf{m}_0 a \quad \text{for } x,\ a \in G,$$

we also conclude by Theorem 40.4 that $xU(\mathbf{m}_0)(a)$ is totally bounded for $\mathbf{N}$ for every $x,\ a \in G$. Therefore $\mathbf{U}(\mathbf{N})$ is normal by definition.

Theorem 40.6. *If* $\mathbf{N}$ *is regular, then* AB *is right totally bounded for any right totally bounded sets* $A,\ B \subset G$ *for* $\mathbf{N}$.

Proof. For the binary mapping $(x,\ y) = xy \in G\ (x \in G,\ y \in G)$, $xN_y = yM_x = xy$, we obviously have $N_y = R_y$, $M_x = L_x$. If $\mathbf{N}$ is regular, then $L_x\ (x \in G)$ is uniformly continuous for $\mathbf{U}(\mathbf{N})$ by Theorem 39.3, and the system $R_y\ (y \in G)$ is equi-continuous for $\mathbf{U}(\mathbf{N})$ by Theorem 32.5. Therefore, if $A,\ B \subset G$ are totally bounded for $\mathbf{U}(\mathbf{N})$, then $AB = (A,\ B)$ also is totally bounded for $\mathbf{U}(\mathbf{N})$ by Theorem 16.4. Thus we obtain Theorem 40.6 by Theorem 40.1.

41. **Products of Elements.** Let G be a group. For a finite system $a_\nu \in G\ (\nu = 1, 2, \ldots, n)$ we define the *product* $\prod_{\nu=1}^{n} a_\nu$ by

$$\prod_{\nu=1}^{\mu} a_\nu = \Big(\prod_{\nu=1}^{\mu-1} a_\mu\Big)a \quad (\mu = 2, 3, \ldots, n), \quad \prod_{\nu=1}^{1} a_\nu = a_1$$

and the *n power* a^n by $a^n = \prod_{\nu=1}^{n} a_\nu$ for $a_\nu = a\ (\nu = 1, 2, \ldots, n)$.

We make use of the notation

$$\prod_{\nu=1}^{n} K_\nu = \Big\{ \prod_{\nu=1}^{n} x_\nu \colon x_\nu \in K_\nu\ (\nu = 1, 2, \ldots, n)\Big\}$$

for $\emptyset \neq K_\nu \subset G\ (\nu = 1, 2, \ldots, n)$ and

$$K^n = \Big\{ \prod_{\nu=1}^{n} x_\nu \colon x_\nu \in K\ (\nu = 1, 2, \ldots, n)\Big\}$$

for $\emptyset \neq K \subset G$.

Let $\mathbf{N}$ be a neighbourhood on G. If $\mathbf{N}$ is regular, then for any $\mathbf{n} \in \mathbf{N}$

and $x \in G$ we can find $\mathbf{m}_1, \mathbf{m}_2 \in \mathbf{N}$ such that $\mathbf{m}_1\mathbf{m}_1 \subset \mathbf{n}$ and $\mathbf{m}_2 \subset x^{-1}\mathbf{m}_1 x$. Then, setting $\mathbf{m} = \mathbf{m}_1 \cap \mathbf{m}_2$, we have $\mathbf{m} \in \mathbf{N}$ and

$$\mathbf{n}xy \supset \mathbf{m}_1\mathbf{m}_1 xy \supset (\mathbf{m}x)(\mathbf{m}y) \quad \text{for any } y \in G.$$

We can prove generally by induction

Theorem 41.1. *If* $\mathbf{N}$ *is regular, then for any* $\mathbf{n} \in \mathbf{N}$ *and* $a_\nu \in G$ $(\nu = 1, 2, \ldots, n)$ *we can find* $\mathbf{m} \in \mathbf{N}$ *such that*

$$\prod_{\nu=1}^{n} \mathbf{m}a_\nu \subset \mathbf{n} \prod_{\nu=1}^{n} a_\nu.$$

As an immediate consequence of Theorem 41.1, we obtain

Theorem 41.2. *If* $\mathbf{N}$ *is regular, then* $x_\delta \xrightarrow[\delta\in\Lambda]{} x$, $y_\gamma \xrightarrow[\gamma\in\Gamma]{} y$ *for* $\mathbf{U}(\mathbf{N})$ *implies* $x_\delta y_\gamma \xrightarrow[(\delta,\gamma)\in\Lambda\times\Gamma]{} xy$ *for* $\mathbf{U}(\mathbf{N})$.

Thus we also obtain by Theorem 7.2

Theorem 41.3. *If* $\mathbf{N}$ *is regular, then* $x_\delta \xrightarrow[\delta\in\Lambda]{} x$, $y_\delta \xrightarrow[\delta\in\Lambda]{} y$ *for* $\mathbf{U}(\mathbf{N})$ *implies* $x_\delta y_\delta \xrightarrow[\delta\in\Lambda]{} xy$ *for* $\mathbf{U}(\mathbf{N})$.

If $\mathbf{N}$ is uniformly regular, then for any $\mathbf{n} \in \mathbf{N}$ we can find $\mathbf{m}_1, \mathbf{m}_2 \in \mathbf{N}$ such that $\mathbf{m}_1\mathbf{m}_1 \subset \mathbf{n}$, $\mathbf{m}_2 \subset \bigcap_{z\in G} z^{-1}\mathbf{m}_1 z$. Then, setting $\mathbf{m} = \mathbf{m}_1 \cap \mathbf{m}_2$, we have $\mathbf{m} \in \mathbf{N}$ and

$$\mathbf{n}xy \supset \mathbf{m}_1\mathbf{m}_1 xy \supset \mathbf{m}_1 x\mathbf{m}_2 y \supset (\mathbf{m}x)(\mathbf{m}y) \quad \text{for every } x, y \in G.$$

We can prove generally by induction

Theorem 41.4. *If* $\mathbf{N}$ *is uniformly regular, then for any* $\mathbf{n} \in \mathbf{N}$ *and* $n = 1, 2, \ldots$ *we can find* $\mathbf{m} \in \mathbf{N}$ *such that*

$$\mathbf{n} \prod_{\nu=1}^{n} x_\nu \supset \prod_{\nu=1}^{n} (\mathbf{m}x_\nu) \quad \text{for any } x_\nu \in G \ (\nu = 1, 2, \ldots, n).$$

Theorem 41.5. *If* $\mathbf{N}$ *is locally uniformly regular, then there is* $\mathbf{m}_0 \in \mathbf{N}$ *such that for any* $\mathbf{n} \in \mathbf{N}$ *and* $a_\nu \in G$ $(\nu = 1, 2, \ldots, n)$ *we can find* $\mathbf{m} \in \mathbf{N}$ *such that*

$$\mathbf{n} \prod_{\nu=1}^{n} x_\nu \supset \Big(\prod_{\nu=1}^{n} \mathbf{m}x_\nu\Big)\mathbf{m} \quad \text{for any } x_\nu \in \mathbf{m}_0 a_\nu \ (\nu = 1, 2, \ldots, n).$$

Proof. Since $\mathbf{N}$ is locally uniformly regular by assumption, there is a symmetric $\mathbf{m}_0 \in \mathbf{N}$ by definition such that $\bigcap_{z \in \mathbf{m}_0} z\mathbf{n}z^{-1} \in \mathbf{N}$ for every $\mathbf{n} \in \mathbf{N}$. For any $\mathbf{n} \in \mathbf{N}$ there is $\mathbf{n}_1 \in \mathbf{N}$ by definition such that $\mathbf{n}_1\mathbf{n}_1 \subset \mathbf{n}$. For such $\mathbf{n}_1 \in \mathbf{N}$, setting $\mathbf{m}_1 = \bigcap_{z \in \mathbf{m}_0} z^{-1}\mathbf{n}_1 z$, we have $\mathbf{m}_1 \in \mathbf{N}$, and there is $\mathbf{m}_2 \in \mathbf{N}$ such that $\mathbf{m}_2 \subset a^{-1}\mathbf{m}_1 a$ for an element $a \in G$, because $\mathbf{N}$ is regular by assumption. Then $x = za$, $z \in \mathbf{m}_0$ implies

$$\mathbf{n}_1 x = \mathbf{n}_1 za \supset z\mathbf{m}_1 a \supset za\mathbf{m}_2 = x\mathbf{m}_2.$$

Thus, setting $\mathbf{m} = \mathbf{n}_1 \cap \mathbf{m}_2 \in \mathbf{N}$, we obtain

$$\mathbf{n}x \supset \mathbf{n}_1\mathbf{n}_1 x \supset \mathbf{n}_1 x\mathbf{m}_2 \supset \mathbf{m}x\mathbf{m} \quad \text{for every } x \in \mathbf{m}_0 a.$$

Therefore for any $\mathbf{n} \in \mathbf{N}$ and $a \in G$, there is $\mathbf{m} \in \mathbf{N}$ such that $\mathbf{n}x \supset \mathbf{m}x\mathbf{m}$ for every $x \in \mathbf{m}_0 a$.

If for any $\mathbf{n} \in \mathbf{N}$ and $a_\nu \in G$ $(\nu = 1, 2, \ldots, n)$ there is $\mathbf{m}_1 \in \mathbf{N}$ such that $\mathbf{n} \prod_{\nu=1}^{n} x_\nu \supset (\prod_{\nu=1}^{n} \mathbf{m}_1 x_\nu)\mathbf{m}_1$ for $x_\nu \in \mathbf{m}_0 a$ $(\nu = 1, 2, \ldots, n)$, then for any $a \in G$ there is $\mathbf{m} \in \mathbf{N}$ such that $\mathbf{m}_1 x \supset \mathbf{m}x\mathbf{m}$ for $x \in \mathbf{m}_0 a$, as proved just above. Thus we obtain

$$\mathbf{n}(\prod_{\nu=1}^{n} x_\nu)x \supset (\prod_{\nu=1}^{n} \mathbf{m}x_\nu)\mathbf{m}x\mathbf{m} \quad \text{for } x \in \mathbf{m}_0 a,\ x_\nu \in \mathbf{m}_0 a \ (\nu = 1, 2, \ldots, n).$$

Therefore we conclude Theorem 41.5 by induction.

Theorem 41.6. *If $\mathbf{N}$ is locally uniformly regular, then $x_\delta y_\gamma \in G$ $((\delta, \gamma) \in \Delta \times \Gamma)$ is a Cauchy system for any Cauchy systems $x_\delta \in G$ $(\delta \in \Delta)$ and $y_\gamma \in G$ $(\gamma \in \Gamma)$ for $\mathbf{U}(\mathbf{N})$.*

Proof. If $\mathbf{N}$ is locally uniformly regular, then there is $\mathbf{m}_0 \in \mathbf{N}$ by Theorem 41.5 such that for any $\mathbf{n} \in \mathbf{N}$ and $a, b \in G$ we can find $\mathbf{m} \in \mathbf{N}$ such that

$$\mathbf{n}xy \supset (\mathbf{m}x)(\mathbf{m}y) \quad \text{for every } x \in \mathbf{m}_0 a,\ y \in \mathbf{m}_0 b.$$

If $x_\delta \in G$ $(\delta \in \Delta)$ and $y_\gamma \in G$ $(\gamma \in \Gamma)$ are Cauchy systems for $\mathbf{U}(\mathbf{N})$, then we can find $\delta_0 \in \Delta$ and $\gamma_0 \in \Gamma$ such that $x_\delta \in \mathbf{m}_0 x_{\delta_0}$ for $\delta \leqq \delta_0$ and $y_\gamma \in \mathbf{m}_0 y_{\gamma_0}$ for $\gamma \leqq \gamma_0$. Thus for any $\mathbf{n} \in \mathbf{N}$ there is $\mathbf{m} \in \mathbf{N}$ such that

$$\mathbf{n}x_\delta y_\gamma \supset (\mathbf{m}x_\delta)(\mathbf{m}y_\gamma) \quad \text{for } \delta \leqq \delta_0,\ \gamma \leqq \gamma_0.$$

We also can find $\delta_1 \leqq \delta_0$ and $\gamma_1 \leqq \gamma_0$ such that $x_\delta \in \mathbf{m}x_{\delta_1}$ for $\delta \leqq \delta_1$ and $y_\gamma \in \mathbf{m}y_\gamma$ for $\gamma \leqq \gamma_1$. Then we have $\mathbf{n}x_{\delta_1}y_{\gamma_1} \ni x_\delta y_\gamma$ for $\delta \leqq \delta_1$, $\gamma \leqq \gamma_1$. Therefore $x_\delta y_\gamma$ $((\delta, \gamma) \in \Delta \times \Gamma)$ is a Cauchy system for $\mathbf{U}(\mathbf{N})$.

We consider now mappings from G to G. For a finite system of mappings M_ν $(\nu = 1, 2, \ldots, n)$ from G to G, we define the *product* $\prod_{\nu=1}^{n} \otimes M_\nu$ by

$$x \prod_{\nu=1}^{n} \otimes M_\nu = \prod_{\nu=1}^{n} xM_\nu \quad \text{for every } x \in G,$$

and the *n power* $M^{\otimes n}$ by $xM^{\otimes n} = (xM)^n$ for every $x \in G$. The product of two mappings M, N is denoted by $M \otimes N$.

With this definition we obviously have by Theorem 41.1

Theorem 41.7. *If* $\mathbf{N}$ *is regular, then the product* $\prod_{\nu=1}^{n} \otimes M_\nu$ *is continuous for* $\mathbf{U}(\mathbf{N})$, *if every* M_ν $(\nu = 1, 2, \ldots, n)$ *is continuous for* $\mathbf{U}(\mathbf{N})$.

As an immediate consequence of Theorem 41.4, we have

Theorem 41.8. *If* $\mathbf{N}$ *is uniformly regular, then the product* $\prod_{\nu=1}^{n} \otimes M_\nu$ *is uniformly continuous for* $\mathbf{U}(\mathbf{N})$, *if every* M_ν $(\nu = 1, 2, \ldots, n)$ *is uniformly continuous for* $\mathbf{U}(\mathbf{N})$.

Theorem 41.9. *If* $\mathbf{N}$ *is locally uniformly regular, then the product* $(\prod_{\nu=1}^{n} \otimes M_\nu) \otimes N$ *is locally uniformly continuous for* $\mathbf{U}(\mathbf{N})$, *if every* M_ν $(\nu = 1, 2, \ldots, n)$ *is uniformly continuous and* N *is locally uniformly continuous for* $\mathbf{U}(\mathbf{N})$.

Proof. If $\mathbf{N}$ is locally uniformly regular, then there is $\mathbf{m}_0 \in \mathbf{N}$ by Theorem 41.5 such that for any $\mathbf{n} \in \mathbf{N}$ and $a_\nu \in G$ $(\nu = 1, 2, \ldots, n)$ we can find $\mathbf{m} \in \mathbf{N}$ such that

$$\mathbf{n} \prod_{\nu=1}^{n} x_\nu \supset \left(\prod_{\nu=1}^{n} \mathbf{m}x_\nu\right)\mathbf{m} \quad \text{for } x_\nu \in \mathbf{m}_0 a_\nu \ (\nu = 1, 2, \ldots, n).$$

If M_ν is uniformly continuous for $\mathbf{U(N)}$ for every $\nu = 1, 2, \ldots, n$, then we can find $\mathbf{m}_1 \in \mathbf{N}$ such that $\mathbf{m}_1 xM_\nu \subset \mathbf{m}_0(xM\ )$ for every $x \in G$ and $\nu = 1, 2, \ldots, n$. If N is locally uniformly continuous for $\mathbf{U(N)}$, then there is $\mathbf{m}_2 \in \mathbf{N}$ such that N is uniformly continuous on $\mathbf{m}_2\mathbf{m}_2 a$ for every $a \in G$. We also can find $\mathbf{m}_3 \in \mathbf{N}$ such that $\mathbf{m}_3 \subset \mathbf{m}_1 \cap \mathbf{m}_2$, $\mathbf{m}_3 xM_\nu \subset \mathbf{m}(xM_\nu)$ for every $x \in G$, $\nu = 1, 2, \ldots, n$, and $\mathbf{m}_3 xN \subset \mathbf{m}(xN)$ for every $x \in \mathbf{m}_2 a$. Then we have

$$\mathbf{n}(\prod_{\nu=1}^{n} xM_\nu)(xN) \supset (\prod_{\nu=1}^{n} \mathbf{m}_3 xM_\nu)(\mathbf{m}_3 xN) \quad \text{for every } x \in (\mathbf{m}_1 \cap \mathbf{m}_2)a.$$

Therefore $(\prod_{\nu=1}^{n} \otimes M_\nu) \otimes N$ is locally uniformly continuous for $\mathbf{U(N)}$.

Setting $xP_n = x^n$ $(x \in G)$, we obtain a mapping P_n from G to G. This mapping P_n is called the *n power mapping* on G. Concerning the n power mapping P_n, we obviously have by Theorems 41.7, 41.8 and 41.9

Theorem 41.10. *The n power mapping P_n on G is continuous for* $\mathbf{U(N)}$, *if* $\mathbf{N}$ *is regular; P_n is uniformly continuous for* $\mathbf{U(N)}$, *if* $\mathbf{N}$ *is uniformly regular; and P_n is locally uniformly continuous for* $\mathbf{U(N)}$, *if* $\mathbf{N}$ *is locally uniformly regular.*

Setting $x\mathrm{Iv} = x^{-1}$ $(x \in G)$, we obtain a transformation Iv from G to G. This transformation Iv is called the *inversion* on G. For the inversion Iv on G, we obviously have by definition

$$\mathrm{IvIv} = E, \quad \mathrm{IvIv}^{-1} = \mathrm{Iv}.$$

Theorem 41.11. *The inversion* Iv *is continuous for* $\mathbf{U(N)}$, *if* $\mathbf{N}$ *is regular;* Iv *is uniformly continuous for* $\mathbf{U(N)}$, *if* $\mathbf{N}$ *is uniformly regular; and* Iv *is locally uniformly continuous for* $\mathbf{U(N)}$, *if* $\mathbf{N}$ *is locally uniformly regular.*

Proof. If $\mathbf{N}$ is regular, then $a\mathbf{n}^{-1}a^{-1} \in \mathbf{N}$ for every $\mathbf{n} \in \mathbf{N}$ and $a \in G$, and we have

$$(a\mathbf{n}^{-1}a^{-1})a\mathrm{Iv} = (a\mathbf{n}^{-1})\mathrm{Iv} = (a\mathbf{n}^{-1})^{-1} = \mathbf{n}a^{-1} = \mathbf{n}(a\mathrm{Iv}).$$

Therefore Iv is continuous for $\mathbf{U(N)}$ by definition. If $\mathbf{N}$ is uniformly regular, then for any $\mathbf{n} \in \mathbf{N}$, setting $\mathbf{m} = \bigcap_{x \in G} x\mathbf{n}^{-1}x^{-1}$, we have $\mathbf{m} \in \mathbf{N}$ and

$$\mathbf{m}x\mathrm{Iv} = (\mathbf{m}x)^{-1} \subset (x\mathbf{n}^{-1}x^{-1}x)^{-1} = \mathbf{n}x^{-1} = \mathbf{n}(x\mathrm{Iv}) \quad \text{for every } x \in G.$$

Therefore Iv is uniformly continuous for $\mathbf{U(N)}$ by definition.

If $\mathbf{N}$ is locally uniformly regular, then there is $\mathbf{m}_0 \in \mathbf{N}$ such that $\bigcap_{z \in \mathbf{m}_0} z\mathbf{n}z^{-1} \in \mathbf{N}$ for $\mathbf{n} \in \mathbf{N}$. For any $\mathbf{n} \in \mathbf{N}$ and $a \in G$, setting

$$\mathbf{m} = \bigcap_{z \in \mathbf{m}_0} z(a\mathbf{n}^{-1}a^{-1})z^{-1}$$

we have $\mathbf{m} \in \mathbf{N}$ and

$$\mathbf{m}za\mathrm{Iv} \subset za\mathbf{n}^{-1}a^{-1}z^{-1}za\mathrm{Iv} = za\mathbf{n}^{-1}\mathrm{Iv} = \mathbf{n}(za)^{-1} = \mathbf{n}(za\mathrm{Iv})$$

for every $z \in \mathbf{m}_0$. Thus $\mathbf{m}x\mathrm{Iv} \subset \mathbf{n}(x\mathrm{Iv})$ for every $x \in \mathbf{m}_0 a$. Therefore Iv is locally uniformly continuous for $\mathbf{U(N)}$ by definition.

Referring to Theorem 12.12, we conclude from Theorem 41.11

Theorem 41.12. *If* $\mathbf{N}$ *is regular, then* $G \ni x_\delta \xrightarrow[\delta \in \Delta]{} x$ *implies* $x_\delta^{-1} \xrightarrow[\delta \in \Delta]{} x^{-1}$. *If* $\mathbf{N}$ *is locally uniformly regular, then* x_δ^{-1} $(\delta \in \Delta)$ *is a Cauchy system for any Cauchy system* $x_\delta \in G$ $(\delta \in \Delta)$ *for* $\mathbf{U(N)}$.

Referring to Theorem 7.3, we obtain by Theorem 41.12

Theorem 41.13. *If* $\mathbf{N}$ *is regular, then for* $\emptyset \neq A \subset G$ *we have*

$$(A^{-1})^{\mathbf{U(N)}-} = (A^{\mathbf{U(N)}-})^{-1}.$$

Theorem 41.14. *If* $\mathbf{N}$ *is regular and if* $\bigcap_{x \in A} x^{-1}\mathbf{n}x \in \mathbf{N}$ *for every* $\mathbf{n} \in \mathbf{N}$, *then* $\bigcap_{x \in A^-} x^{-1}\mathbf{n}x \in \mathbf{N}$ *for every* $\mathbf{n} \in \mathbf{N}$.

Proof. For any $\mathbf{n} \in \mathbf{N}$ there is a symmetric $\mathbf{n}_1 \in \mathbf{N}$ such that $\mathbf{n}_1\mathbf{n}_1\mathbf{n}_1 \subset \mathbf{n}$. For such $\mathbf{n}_1 \in \mathbf{N}$ we can find $\mathbf{m} \in \mathbf{N}$ by assumption such that $\bigcap_{x \in A} x^{-1}\mathbf{n}_1 x \supset \mathbf{m}$. Then for any $y \in A^-$ we can find $x \in A$ by Theorem 7.3 such that $x \in \mathbf{n}_1 y$. Thus we have $y^{-1}\mathbf{n}_1 = (\mathbf{n}_1 y)^{-1} \ni x^{-1}$ and hence

$$y^{-1}\mathbf{n}y \supset y^{-1}\mathbf{n}_1\mathbf{n}_1\mathbf{n}_1 y \supset x^{-1}\mathbf{n}_1 x \supset \mathbf{m}.$$

Therefore $\bigcap_{y \in A^-} y^{-1}\mathbf{n}y \in \mathbf{N}$.

42. **Adjusted Neighbourhoods.** Let $\mathbf{G}$ be a transitive group on a space S. For the fixer $\mathbf{F}_a$ in $\mathbf{G}$ at $a \in S$, setting

(1) $aTU_a(\mathbf{n}) = a\mathbf{n}\mathbf{F}_a T$ for $E \in \mathbf{n} \subset \mathbf{G}$, $T \in \mathbf{G}$,

we obtain a connector $U_a(\mathbf{n})$ on S. Because, if $aX = aY$ for $X, Y \in \mathbf{G}$, then we have $a = aYX^{-1}$, and hence $\mathbf{F}_a = \mathbf{F}_a YX^{-1}$, that is, $\mathbf{F}_a X = \mathbf{F}_a Y$, which implies $aXU_a(\mathbf{n}) = aYU_a(\mathbf{n})$. Since $a\mathbf{G} = S$, $aT \in aTU_a(\mathbf{n})$, we see by definition that $U_a(\mathbf{n})$ is a connector on S. Furthermore $U_a(\mathbf{n})$ is invariant by $\mathbf{G}$, because

$$aTXU_a(\mathbf{n}) = a\mathbf{n}\mathbf{F}_a TX = aTU_a(\mathbf{n})X \quad \text{for every } X, T \in \mathbf{G}.$$

With definition (1) we obtain by (3) in 33

(2) $AU_a(\mathbf{n}) = a\mathbf{n}(AM_a^{-1}) = \mathbf{n}(AM_a^{-1})M_a \quad \text{for } \emptyset \neq A \subset S.$

Here M_a is the point mapping from $\mathbf{G}$ to S. We also have by definition

(3) $\bigcap_{\lambda\in\Lambda} U_a(\mathbf{n}_\lambda) \geqq U_a(\bigcap_{\lambda\in\Lambda} \mathbf{n}_\lambda).$

Thus $\mathbf{n} \supset \mathbf{m}$ implies $U_a(\mathbf{n}) \geqq U_a(\mathbf{m})$.

(4) $U_a(\mathbf{n})U_a(\mathbf{m}) = U_a(\mathbf{m}\mathbf{F}_a\mathbf{n}),$

because we have by (2) in 42 and (5) in 33

$$aTU_a(\mathbf{n})U_a(\mathbf{m}) = a\mathbf{n}\mathbf{F}_a TU_a(\mathbf{m}) = a\mathbf{m}((a\mathbf{n}\mathbf{F}_a T)M_a^{-1})$$
$$= a\mathbf{m}\mathbf{F}_a\mathbf{n}\mathbf{F}_a T = aTU_a(\mathbf{m}\mathbf{F}_a\mathbf{n}).$$

(5) $U_a(\mathbf{n})^{-1} = U_a(\mathbf{n}^{-1}),$

because, if $aX \in aYU_a(\mathbf{n}) = a\mathbf{n}\mathbf{F}_a Y$, then we can find $T_1, T_2 \in \mathbf{F}_a$ such that $T_1 X \in \mathbf{n}T_2 Y$, and hence

$$aY = aT_2 Y \in a\mathbf{n}^{-1}T_1 X \subset a\mathbf{n}^{-1}\mathbf{F}_a X = aXU_a(\mathbf{n}^{-1}).$$

Referring to (5) in 33, we conclude from definition (1)

(6) $XM_aU_a(\mathbf{n})M_a^{-1} = \mathbf{F}_a\mathbf{n}\mathbf{F}_a X \quad \text{for every } X \in \mathbf{G}.$

For a connector U on S we have by (8) in 32

$$aXU_a(aU^{\mathbf{G}}M_a^{-1}) = a(aU^{\mathbf{G}}M_a^{-1})\mathbf{F}_a X = aU^{\mathbf{G}}\mathbf{F}_a X = aXU^{\mathbf{G}}.$$

Thus we obtain

(7) $U_a(aU^{\mathbf{G}}M_a^{-1}) = U^{\mathbf{G}}.$

Since $T\mathbf{F}_{aT}T^{-1} = \mathbf{F}_a$ by (9) in 31, we have

$$aTXU_{aT}(T^{-1}\mathbf{n}T) = aT(T^{-1}\mathbf{n}T)\mathbf{F}_{aT}X = a\mathbf{n}\mathbf{F}_aTX = aTXU_a(\mathbf{n}).$$

Thus we obtain

(8) $U_{aT}(T^{-1}\mathbf{n}T) = U_a(\mathbf{n})$.

A neighbourhood $\mathbf{N}$ on $\mathbf{G}$ is said to be *adjusted* to a point $a \in S$, if $\mathbf{F}_a\mathbf{N}\mathbf{F}_a$ is a basis of $\mathbf{N}$, that is, if for any $\mathbf{n} \in \mathbf{N}$ there is $\mathbf{m} \in \mathbf{N}$ such that $\mathbf{F}_a\mathbf{m}\mathbf{F}_a \subset \mathbf{n}$.

If $\mathbf{N}$ is adjusted to $a \in S$, then the system of connectors

$$\{U_a(\mathbf{n}): \mathbf{n} \in \mathbf{N}\}$$

satisfies the basis conditions. Indeed, the basis condition 1) is satisfied obviously by (3). For any $\mathbf{n} \in \mathbf{N}$ there is $\mathbf{m} \in \mathbf{N}$ such that $\mathbf{m}\mathbf{m}^{-1} \subset \mathbf{n}$, and we can find $\mathbf{m}_0 \in \mathbf{N}$ such that $\mathbf{F}_a\mathbf{m}_0\mathbf{F}_a \subset \mathbf{m}$. Then we have by (4) and (5)

$$U_a(\mathbf{m}_0)^{-1}U_a(\mathbf{m}_0) = U_a(\mathbf{m}_0\mathbf{F}_a\mathbf{m}_0^{-1}) \subset U_a(\mathbf{m}\mathbf{m}^{-1}) \subset U_a(\mathbf{n}).$$

Thus the basis condition 2) also is satisfied. Therefore there exists uniquely a uniformity $\mathbf{U}$ on S such that $\{U_a(\mathbf{n}): \mathbf{n} \in \mathbf{N}\}$ is a basis of $\mathbf{U}$. This uniformity $\mathbf{U}$ on S is called the *induced uniformity* of $\mathbf{N}$ at $a \in S$, and denoted by $\mathbf{U}_a(\mathbf{N})$ or $\mathbf{U}_a(\mathbf{N}, \mathbf{G})$ when we need to indicate $\mathbf{G}$. It is obvious by (1) that $\mathbf{U}_a(\mathbf{N})$ is invariant by $\mathbf{G}$.

Conversely for a uniformity $\mathbf{U}$ on S, the system of sets on $\mathbf{G}$

$$\{aU^{\mathbf{G}}M_a^{-1}: U \in \mathbf{U}\}$$

satisfies the basis conditions of neighbourhoods. Indeed the basis condition 1) is obviously satisfied by (4) in 32. If $VV^{-1} \leqq U$, then we have by (5), (7), (8) in 32 and (4), (6) in 33

$$(aV^{\mathbf{G}}M_a^{-1})^{-1}(aV^{\mathbf{G}}M_a^{-1}) = a(V^{-1})^{\mathbf{G}}M_a^{-1}(aV^{\mathbf{G}}M_a^{-1})$$

$$= a(aV^{\mathbf{G}}M_a^{-1})(V^{-1})^{\mathbf{G}}M_a^{-1} = aV^{\mathbf{G}}(V^{-1})^{\mathbf{G}}M_a^{-1} \subset a(VV^{-1})^{\mathbf{G}}M_a^{-1} \subset aU^{\mathbf{G}}M_a^{-1}.$$

Thus the basis condition 2) also is satisfied. Therefore there exists uniquely a neighbourhood $\mathbf{N}$ on $\mathbf{G}$ such that the system $\{aU^{\mathbf{G}}M_a^{-1}: U \in \mathbf{U}\}$ is a basis of $\mathbf{N}$. This neighbourhood $\mathbf{N}$ is called the *induced neighbourhood* of $\mathbf{U}$ at $a \in S$, and denoted by $\mathbf{N}_a(\mathbf{U})$ or $\mathbf{N}_a(\mathbf{U}, \mathbf{G})$ when we need to indicate $\mathbf{G}$. $\mathbf{N}_a(\mathbf{U})$ is adjusted to a, because we have by (8) in 32 and (3), (4) in 33

$$\mathbf{F}_a(aU^{\mathbf{G}}M_a{}^{-1})\mathbf{F}_a = a\mathbf{F}_aU^{\mathbf{G}}M_a{}^{-1} = aU^{\mathbf{G}}M_a{}^{-1}.$$

It is obvious by definition that $\mathbf{N}_a(\mathbf{U}(\mathbf{G})) = \mathbf{N}_a(\mathbf{U})$.

We can state now by (1) and (7)

Theorem 42.1. *If* $\mathbf{N}$ *is adjusted to* $a \in S$, *then* $\mathbf{U}_a(\mathbf{N})$ *is invariant by* $\mathbf{G}$ *and* $\mathbf{N}_a(\mathbf{U}_a(\mathbf{N})) = \mathbf{N}$. *If* $\mathbf{U}$ *is invariant by* $\mathbf{G}$, *then* $\mathbf{N}_a(\mathbf{U})$ *is adjusted to* a *and* $\mathbf{U}_a(\mathbf{N}_a(\mathbf{U})) = \mathbf{U}$.

We obviously have by Theorem 33.2 and (1) in 38

Theorem 42.2. $\mathbf{W}(\mathbf{U}(\mathbf{G}), a)$ *on* $\mathbf{G}$ *is the induced uniformity of* $\mathbf{N}_a(\mathbf{U})$ *on* $\mathbf{G}$.

Theorem 42.3. *If* $\mathbf{N}$ *is adjusted to* $a \in S$, *then* $T^{-1}\mathbf{N}T$ *is adjusted to* aT *for every* $T \in \mathbf{G}$ *and* $\mathbf{U}_{aT}(T^{-1}\mathbf{N}T) = \mathbf{U}_a(\mathbf{N})$.

Proof. If $\mathbf{n} \supset \mathbf{F}_a\mathbf{m}\mathbf{F}_a$, then we have by (9) in 31

$$T^{-1}\mathbf{n}T \supset (T^{-1}\mathbf{F}_aT)T^{-1}\mathbf{m}T(T^{-1}\mathbf{F}_aT) = \mathbf{F}_{aT}(T^{-1}\mathbf{m}T)\mathbf{F}_{aT}.$$

Thus, if $\mathbf{N}$ is adjusted to a, then $T^{-1}\mathbf{N}T$ is adjusted to aT. Furthermore we see by (8) that $\mathbf{U}_{aT}(T^{-1}\mathbf{N}T) = \mathbf{U}_a(\mathbf{N})$.

A neighbourhood $\mathbf{N}$ on $\mathbf{G}$ is said to be *adjusted,* if there is a neighbourhood $\mathbf{N}_a$ on $\mathbf{G}$ such that $\mathbf{N}_a$ is adjusted to $a \in S$ and

$$\mathbf{N} = \bigvee_{X \in \mathbf{G}} X\mathbf{N}_aX^{-1}.$$

Referring to Theorem 38.3, we conclude from this definition

$$T\mathbf{N}T^{-1} = \bigvee_{X \in \mathbf{G}} TX\mathbf{N}_a(TX)^{-1} = \mathbf{N}.$$

Thus we can state

Theorem 42.4. *Every adjusted neighbourhood on* $\mathbf{G}$ *is regular.*

For a uniformity $\mathbf{U}$ on S, setting

$$\mathbf{N}(\mathbf{U}) = \bigvee_{X \in \mathbf{G}} X\mathbf{N}_a(\mathbf{U})X^{-1} \quad (a \in S),$$

we obtain an adjusted neighbourhood $\mathbf{N}(\mathbf{U})$ on $\mathbf{G}$. $\mathbf{N}(\mathbf{U})$ is called the *induced neighbourhood* of $\mathbf{U}$ on $\mathbf{G}$. $\mathbf{N}(\mathbf{U})$ will be denoted by $\mathbf{N}(\mathbf{U}, \mathbf{G})$ when we need to indicate $\mathbf{G}$. Referring to Theorem 42.3, we obtain

$$\mathbf{N}(\mathbf{U}) = \bigvee_{x \in S} \mathbf{N}_x(\mathbf{U}).$$

Thus we have by Theorem 38.3

Theorem 42.5. *We have* $\mathbf{n} \in \mathbf{N}(\mathbf{U})$ *if and only if we can find* $U \in \mathbf{U}$ *and* $a_\nu \in S$ $(\nu = 1, 2, \ldots, n)$ *such that* $\mathbf{n} \supset \bigcap_{\nu=1}^{n} (a_\nu U^{\mathbf{G}} M_{a_\nu}^{-1})$. Furthermore we obtain by Theorems 38.2 and 42.2

Theorem 42.6. *The weak-uniformity* $\mathbf{W}(\mathbf{U}(\mathbf{G}))$ *on* $\mathbf{G}$ *is the induced uniformity of the induced neighbourhood* $\mathbf{N}(\mathbf{U})$ *on* $\mathbf{G}$.

Let $\mathbf{N}$ be an adjusted neighbourhood on $\mathbf{G}$ and $\mathbf{N} = \bigvee_{X \in \mathbf{G}} X\mathbf{N}_a X^{-1}$ for a neighbourhood $\mathbf{N}_a$ adjusted to $a \in S$. Let $\mathbf{C}_a$ be the weakest stronger neighbourhood of all neighbourhoods which are weaker than $\mathbf{N}$ and adjusted to a. Then we obviously have $\mathbf{C}_a \subset \mathbf{N}$ and we see easily by Theorem 38.3 that $\mathbf{C}_a$ also is adjusted to a. Thus $\mathbf{C}_a$ is the strongest among all neighbourhoods which are weaker than $\mathbf{N}$ and adjusted to a. Such $\mathbf{C}_a$ is called the *component* of $\mathbf{N}$ at a. With this definition, we obviously have by Theorem 42.3

Theorem 42.7. *For an adjusted neighbourhood* $\mathbf{N}$ *on* $\mathbf{G}$, *if* $\mathbf{C}_a$ *is the component of* $\mathbf{N}$ *at* $a \in S$, *then* $T^{-1}\mathbf{C}_a T$ *is the component of* $\mathbf{N}$ *at* aT *for every* $T \in \mathbf{G}$ *and* $\mathbf{N} = \bigvee_{X \in \mathbf{G}} X\mathbf{C}_a X^{-1}$.

A uniformity $\mathbf{U}$ on S is said to be *reflexive,* if there is an adjusted neighbourhood $\mathbf{N}$ on $\mathbf{G}$ such that $\mathbf{U} = \mathbf{U}_a(\mathbf{C}_a)$ for the component $\mathbf{C}_a$ of $\mathbf{N}$ at a point $a \in S$. With this definition we obviously have by Theorem 42.1

Theorem 42.8. *A uniformity* $\mathbf{U}$ *on* S *is reflexive if and only if* $\mathbf{U}$ *is invariant by* $\mathbf{G}$ *and* $\mathbf{N}_a(\mathbf{U})$ *is the component of* $\mathbf{N}(\mathbf{U})$ *at* a *for every* $a \in S$.

Theorem 42.9. *A uniformity* $\mathbf{U}$ *on* S *is reflexive if and only if* $\mathbf{W}(\mathbf{U}(\mathbf{G})) = \mathbf{W}(\mathbf{V}(\mathbf{G}))$ *implies* $\mathbf{U} \supset \mathbf{V}(\mathbf{G})$.

Proof. If $\mathbf{U}$ is reflexive and $\mathbf{W}(\mathbf{U}(\mathbf{G})) = \mathbf{W}(\mathbf{V}(\mathbf{G}))$ on $\mathbf{G}$, then we have $\mathbf{N}(\mathbf{U}) = \mathbf{N}(\mathbf{V})$ by Theorem 42.6. Thus we obtain $\mathbf{N}_a(\mathbf{U}) \supset \mathbf{N}_a(\mathbf{V})$, because $\mathbf{N}_a(\mathbf{U})$ is the component of $\mathbf{N}(\mathbf{U})$ at a by Theorem 42.8. Therefore we obtain by Theorem 42.1

$$\mathbf{U} = \mathbf{U}_a(\mathbf{N}_a(\mathbf{U})) \supset \mathbf{U}_a(\mathbf{N}_a(\mathbf{V})) = \mathbf{U}_a(\mathbf{N}_a(\mathbf{V}(\mathbf{G}))) = \mathbf{V}(\mathbf{G}).$$

Conversely, if $\mathbf{W}(\mathbf{U}(\mathbf{G})) = \mathbf{W}(\mathbf{V}(\mathbf{G}))$ implies $\mathbf{U} \supset \mathbf{V}(\mathbf{G})$, then for the component $\mathbf{C}_a$ of $\mathbf{N}(\mathbf{U})$ at a we have $\mathbf{N}(\mathbf{U}) = \bigvee_{X \in \mathbf{G}} X\mathbf{C}_a X^{-1}$ by definition and hence $\mathbf{N}(\mathbf{U}) = \mathbf{N}(\mathbf{U}_a(\mathbf{C}_a))$ by Theorem 42.1. Thus we obtain $\mathbf{W}(\mathbf{U}(\mathbf{G})) = \mathbf{W}(\mathbf{U}_a(\mathbf{C}_a))$ by Theorem 42.6, and hence $\mathbf{U} \supset \mathbf{U}_a(\mathbf{C}_a)$ by assumption. Therefore we obtain by Theorem 42.1

$$\mathbf{N}_a(\mathbf{U}) \supset \mathbf{N}_a(\mathbf{U}_a(\mathbf{C}_a)) = \mathbf{C}_a .$$

Since $\mathbf{C}_a$ is the component of $\mathbf{N}(\mathbf{U})$, we hence conclude $\mathbf{N}_a(\mathbf{U}) = \mathbf{C}_a$. On the other hand, we have $\mathbf{W}(\mathbf{U}(\mathbf{G})) = \mathbf{W}((\mathbf{U}(\mathbf{G}))(\mathbf{G}))$, and hence $\mathbf{U} \supset \mathbf{U}(\mathbf{G})$ by assumption, that is, $\mathbf{U}$ is invariant by $\mathbf{G}$. Thus we have by Theorem 42.1

$$\mathbf{U} = \mathbf{U}_a(\mathbf{N}_a(\mathbf{U})) = \mathbf{U}_a(\mathbf{C}_a).$$

Therefore $\mathbf{U}$ is reflexive by definition.

43. Strongly Adjusted Neighbourhoods. Let $\mathbf{G}$ be a transitive group on S. An adjusted neighbourhood $\mathbf{N}$ on $\mathbf{G}$ is said to be *strongly adjusted,* if for any $\mathbf{n} \in \mathbf{N}$ and $a \in S$ we can find $\mathbf{m} \in \mathbf{N}$ such that

$$\mathbf{F}_a\mathbf{n}\mathbf{F}_a \supset \mathbf{m}\mathbf{F}_a\mathbf{m}.$$

If for a point $a \in S$ there is such $\mathbf{m} \in \mathbf{N}$, then for any $X \in \mathbf{G}$ there is $\mathbf{m} \in \mathbf{N}$ such that $\mathbf{F}_a X\mathbf{n}X^{-1}\mathbf{F}_a \supset \mathbf{m}\mathbf{F}_a\mathbf{m}$, because $\mathbf{n} \in \mathbf{N}$ implies $X\mathbf{n}X^{-1} \in \mathbf{N}$ by Theorem 42.4. Thus we have by (9) in 31

$$\mathbf{F}_{aX}\mathbf{n}\mathbf{F}_{aX} = X^{-1}\mathbf{F}_a X\mathbf{n}X^{-1}\mathbf{F}_a X \supset X^{-1}\mathbf{m}\mathbf{F}_a\mathbf{m}X = X^{-1}\mathbf{m}X(X^{-1}\mathbf{F}_a X)X^{-1}\mathbf{m}X$$

$$= (X^{-1}\mathbf{m}X)\mathbf{F}_{aX}(X^{-1}\mathbf{m}X)$$

and $X^{-1}\mathbf{m}X \in \mathbf{N}$. Therefore for any $\mathbf{n} \in \mathbf{N}$ and for any $a \in S$ there is such $\mathbf{m} \in \mathbf{N}$, if there is such $\mathbf{m} \in \mathbf{N}$ for a single point of S.

Theorem 43.1. *An adjusted neighbourhood* $\mathbf{N}$ *is strongly adjusted if and only if* $\mathbf{F}_a\mathbf{N}\mathbf{F}_a$ *satisfies the basis conditions of neighbourhood for* $a \in S$.

Proof. $\mathbf{F}_a\mathbf{N}\mathbf{F}_a$ obviously satisfies the basis condition 1). If $\mathbf{N}$ is strongly adjusted, then for any $\mathbf{n} \in \mathbf{N}$ there is a symmetric $\mathbf{m} \in \mathbf{N}$ such that $\mathbf{F}_a\mathbf{n}\mathbf{F}_a \supset \mathbf{m}\mathbf{F}_a\mathbf{m}$. Then we have

$$\mathbf{F}_a\mathbf{n}\mathbf{F}_a \supset \mathbf{F}_a\mathbf{m}\mathbf{F}_a\mathbf{m}\mathbf{F}_a = (\mathbf{F}_a\mathbf{m}\mathbf{F}_a)^{-1}(\mathbf{F}_a\mathbf{m}\mathbf{F}_a)$$

because $\mathbf{F}_a\mathbf{F}_a = \mathbf{F}_a$, $\mathbf{F}_a^{-1} = \mathbf{F}_a$ and $\mathbf{m}^{-1} = \mathbf{m}$. Therefore $\mathbf{F}_a\mathbf{N}\mathbf{F}_a$ satisfies the basis condition 2). Conversely, if $\mathbf{F}_a\mathbf{N}\mathbf{F}_a$ satisfies the basis condition 2), then for any $\mathbf{n} \in \mathbf{N}$ we can find a symmetric $\mathbf{m} \in \mathbf{N}$ such that

$$\mathbf{F}_a\mathbf{n}\mathbf{F}_a \supset (\mathbf{F}_a\mathbf{m}\mathbf{F}_a)^{-1}(\mathbf{F}_a\mathbf{m}\mathbf{F}_a) \supset \mathbf{m}\mathbf{F}_a\mathbf{m}.$$

Thus $\mathbf{N}$ is strongly adjusted.

Theorem 43.2. *An adjusted neighbourhood* $\mathbf{N}$ *is strongly adjusted if and only if* $\mathbf{F}_a\mathbf{N}\mathbf{F}_a$ *is included in the component* $\mathbf{C}_a$ *of* $\mathbf{N}$ *at* $a \in S$.

Proof. If $\mathbf{F}_a\mathbf{N}\mathbf{F}_a \subset \mathbf{C}_a$, then we have $\mathbf{F}_a\mathbf{N}\mathbf{F}_a = \mathbf{F}_a\mathbf{C}_a\mathbf{F}_a$, because $\mathbf{N} \supset \mathbf{C}_a$. Since $\mathbf{C}_a$ is adjusted to a by definition, $\mathbf{F}_a\mathbf{C}_a\mathbf{F}_a$ is a basis of $\mathbf{C}_a$, and hence $\mathbf{F}_a\mathbf{N}\mathbf{F}_a$ satisfies the basis conditions. Conversely, if $\mathbf{F}_a\mathbf{N}\mathbf{F}_a$ satisfies the basis conditions, then there exists uniquely a neighbourhood $\mathbf{N}_a$ such that $\mathbf{F}_a\mathbf{N}\mathbf{F}_a$ is a basis of $\mathbf{N}_a$. Then $\mathbf{N}_a$ is obviously adjusted to a and we have $\mathbf{N} \supset \mathbf{N}_a \supset \mathbf{C}_a$. Since $\mathbf{C}_a$ is the strongest among all neighbourhoods which are adjusted to a and included in $\mathbf{N}$, we hence obtain $\mathbf{C}_a = \mathbf{N}_a \supset \mathbf{F}_a\mathbf{N}\mathbf{F}_a$. Referring to Theorem 43.1, we conclude therefore Theorem 43.2.

An adjusted neighbourhood $\mathbf{N}$ is said to be *regularly adjusted,* if for any $\mathbf{n} \in \mathbf{N}$ and $a \in S$ there is $\mathbf{m} \in \mathbf{N}$ such that

$$\mathbf{F}_a\mathbf{n} \supset \mathbf{F}_a\mathbf{m}\mathbf{F}_a.$$

We can show easily that if there is such $\mathbf{m} \in \mathbf{N}$ for a point of S, then there exists such $\mathbf{m} \in \mathbf{N}$ for every point $a \in S$. If $\mathbf{N}$ is regularly adjusted, then $\mathbf{N}$ is strongly adjusted. Because for any $\mathbf{n} \in \mathbf{N}$ there is $\mathbf{n}_1 \in \mathbf{N}$ such that $\mathbf{n}_1\mathbf{n}_1 \subset \mathbf{n}$. If $\mathbf{N}$ is regularly adjusted, then for such $\mathbf{n}_1 \in \mathbf{N}$ there exists $\mathbf{m} \in \mathbf{N}$ such that $\mathbf{F}_a\mathbf{n}_1 \supset \mathbf{F}_a\mathbf{m}\mathbf{F}_a$. Then we have

$$\mathbf{F}_a\mathbf{n} \supset \mathbf{F}_a\mathbf{n}_1\mathbf{n}_1 \supset \mathbf{F}_a\mathbf{m}\mathbf{F}_a\mathbf{n}_1 \supset \mathbf{F}_a\mathbf{m}\mathbf{F}_a\mathbf{m}\mathbf{F}_a \supset \mathbf{m}\mathbf{F}_a\mathbf{m}.$$

If $\mathbf{F}_a\mathbf{n} \supset \mathbf{F}_a\mathbf{m}\mathbf{F}_a$, then we have

$$\mathbf{n}^{-1}\mathbf{F}_a = (\mathbf{F}_a\mathbf{n})^{-1} \supset (\mathbf{F}_a\mathbf{m}\mathbf{F}_a)^{-1} = \mathbf{F}_a\mathbf{m}^{-1}\mathbf{F}_a.$$

Since $\mathbf{n} \in \mathbf{N}$ if and only if $\mathbf{n}^{-1} \in \mathbf{N}$, we also can state that $\mathbf{N}$ is regularly adjusted if and only if for any $\mathbf{n} \in \mathbf{N}$ and $a \in S$ there is $\mathbf{m} \in \mathbf{N}$ such that

$$\mathbf{n}\mathbf{F}_a \supset \mathbf{F}_a\mathbf{m}\mathbf{F}_a.$$

An adjusted neighbourhood $\mathbf{N}$ is said to be *uniformly adjusted,* if for any $\mathbf{n} \in \mathbf{N}$ and $a \in S$ there is $\mathbf{m} \in \mathbf{N}$ such that

$$\mathbf{F}_a \bigcap_{X \in \mathbf{G}} X\mathbf{n}X^{-1} \supset \mathbf{F}_a\mathbf{m}\mathbf{F}_a.$$

We see easily that if there is such $\mathbf{m} \in \mathbf{N}$ for a point $a \in S$, then there exists such $\mathbf{m} \in \mathbf{N}$ for every $a \in S$. It is obvious by definition that if $\mathbf{N}$ is uniformly adjusted, then $\mathbf{N}$ is regularly adjusted. We also can show easily that $\mathbf{N}$ is uniformly adjusted if and only if for any $\mathbf{n} \in \mathbf{N}$ and $a \in S$ there is $\mathbf{m} \in \mathbf{N}$ such that

$$\Big(\bigcap_{X \in \mathbf{G}} X\mathbf{n}X^{-1}\Big)\mathbf{F}_a \supset \mathbf{F}_a\mathbf{m}\mathbf{F}_a.$$

We obviously have by definition

Theorem 43.3. *If* $\mathbf{N}$ *is regularly adjusted and uniformly regular, then* $\mathbf{N}$ *is uniformly adjusted.*

An adjusted neighbourhood $\mathbf{N}$ is said to be *semi-uniformly adjusted,* if for any $\mathbf{n} \in \mathbf{N}$ and $a \in S$ we can find $\mathbf{m} \in \mathbf{N}$ such that

$$\bigcap_{X \in \mathbf{G}} \mathbf{F}_a X\mathbf{n}X^{-1} \supset \mathbf{F}_a\mathbf{m}\mathbf{F}_a.$$

Since $\bigcap_{X \in \mathbf{G}} \mathbf{F}_a X\mathbf{n}X^{-1} \supset \mathbf{F}_a \bigcap_{X \in \mathbf{G}} X\mathbf{n}X^{-1}$, if $\mathbf{N}$ is uniformly adjusted, then $\mathbf{N}$ is semi-uniformly adjusted.

An adjusted neighbourhood $\mathbf{N}$ is said to be *locally uniformly adjusted* if there is $\mathbf{m}_0 \in \mathbf{N}$ such that for any $\mathbf{n} \in \mathbf{N}$ and $a \in S$ there is $\mathbf{m} \in \mathbf{N}$ such that

$$\mathbf{F}_a \bigcap_{X \in \mathbf{m}_0} X\mathbf{n}X^{-1} \supset \mathbf{F}_a\mathbf{m}\mathbf{F}_a.$$

It is obvious by definition that if $\mathbf{N}$ is locally uniformly adjusted, then $\mathbf{N}$ is regularly adjusted, and that if $\mathbf{N}$ is uniformly adjusted, then $\mathbf{N}$ is locally uniformly adjusted. We also see easily that $\mathbf{N}$ is locally uniformly adjusted if and only if there is $\mathbf{m}_0 \in \mathbf{N}$ such that for any $\mathbf{n} \in \mathbf{N}$ and $a \in S$ we can find $\mathbf{m} \in \mathbf{N}$ such that

$$(\bigcap_{X \in \mathbf{m}_0} X\mathbf{n}X^{-1})\mathbf{F}_a \supset \mathbf{F}_a\mathbf{m}\mathbf{F}_a.$$

We obviously have by definition

Theorem 43.4. *If* $\mathbf{N}$ *is regularly adjusted and locally uniformly regular, then* $\mathbf{N}$ *is locally uniformly adjusted.*

An adjusted neighbourhood $\mathbf{N}$ is said to be *locally semi-uniformly adjusted,* if there is $\mathbf{m}_0 \in \mathbf{N}$ such that for any $\mathbf{n} \in \mathbf{N}$ and $a \in S$ there is $\mathbf{m} \in \mathbf{N}$ such that

$$\bigcap_{X \in \mathbf{m}_0} \mathbf{F}_a X\mathbf{n}X^{-1} \supset \mathbf{F}_a\mathbf{m}\mathbf{F}_a.$$

We see easily that if $\mathbf{N}$ is locally uniformly adjusted, then $\mathbf{N}$ is locally semi-uniformly adjusted, and that if $\mathbf{N}$ is semi-uniformly adjusted, then $\mathbf{N}$ is locally semi-uniformly adjusted.

44. **Reflexive Uniformities.** Let $\mathbf{G}$ be a transitive group on a space S. An invariant uniformity $\mathbf{U}$ on S by $\mathbf{G}$ is said to be *semi-regular,* if for any $U \in \mathbf{U}$, $a_\nu \in S$ $(\nu = 1, 2, \ldots, n)$ and $a \in S$ we can find $V \in \mathbf{U}$ such that

$$aU(a_1, \ldots, a_n)\mathbf{F}_a \supset aV.$$

It is obvious by definition that if $\mathbf{U}$ is regular, then $\mathbf{U}$ is semi-regular.

Theorem 44.1. *If* $\mathbf{U}$ *is semi-regular, then* $\mathbf{U}$ *is reflexive and the induced neighbourhood* $\mathbf{N}(\mathbf{U})$ *on* $\mathbf{G}$ *is strongly adjusted.*

Proof. For any $\mathbf{n} \in \mathbf{N}(\mathbf{U})$ we can find $U \in \mathbf{U}$ and $a_\nu \in S$ $(\nu = 1, 2, \ldots, n)$ by Theorem 42.5 such that $\mathbf{n} \supset \bigcap_{\nu=1}^{n} a_\nu U^{\mathbf{G}} M_{a_\nu}^{-1}$. If $\mathbf{U}$ is semi-regular, then for any $a \in S$ we can find $V \in \mathbf{U}$ by definition such that $aU(a_1, \ldots, a_n)\mathbf{F}_a \supset aV$. Since $aU(a_1, \ldots, a_n) = a \bigcap_{\nu=1}^{n} a_\nu U^{\mathbf{G}} M_{a_\nu}^{-1}$ by definition, we hence obtain by (5) in 33

$$\mathbf{F}_a\mathbf{n}\mathbf{F}_a \supset \mathbf{F}_a(\bigcap_{\nu=1}^{n} a_\nu U^{\mathbf{G}} M_{a_\nu}^{-1})\mathbf{F}_a \supset aV^{\mathbf{G}} M_a^{-1} \in \mathbf{N}_a(\mathbf{U}).$$

Thus $\mathbf{F}_a\mathbf{N}(\mathbf{U})\mathbf{F}_a \subset \mathbf{N}_a(\mathbf{U})$. Therefore $\mathbf{N}(\mathbf{U})$ is strongly adjusted by Theorem 43.2. Furthermore $\mathbf{N}_a(\mathbf{U})$ is the component of $\mathbf{N}(\mathbf{U})$ at a, because for the component $\mathbf{C}_a$ of $\mathbf{N}(\mathbf{U})$ at $a \in S$ we have

$$\mathbf{F}_a\mathbf{C}_a\mathbf{F}_a \subset \mathbf{F}_a\mathbf{N}(\mathbf{U})\mathbf{F}_a \subset \mathbf{N}_a(\mathbf{U}) \subset \mathbf{C}_a$$

and $\mathbf{F}_a\mathbf{C}_a\mathbf{F}_a$ is a component of $\mathbf{C}_a$ by definition. Referring to Theorem 42.1, we hence conclude by definition that $\mathbf{U}$ is reflexive.

Theorem 44.2. *If* $\mathbf{U}$ *is reflexive and if* $\mathbf{N}(\mathbf{U})$ *is strongly adjusted, then* $\mathbf{U}$ *is semi-regular.*

Proof. If $\mathbf{N}(\mathbf{U})$ is strongly adjusted, then for any $U \in \mathbf{U}$ and $a_\nu \in S$ $(\nu = 1, 2, \dots, n)$ we have $\mathbf{F}_a(\bigcap_{\nu=1}^{n} a_\nu U^{\mathbf{G}} M_{a_\nu}^{-1})\mathbf{F}_a \in \mathbf{C}_a$ for the component $\mathbf{C}_a$ of $\mathbf{N}(\mathbf{U})$ at $a \in S$ by Theorems 42.5 and 43.2. Since $\mathbf{U}$ is reflexive by assumption, we have $\mathbf{C}_a = \mathbf{N}_a(\mathbf{U})$ by Theorem 42.8. Thus there is $V \in \mathbf{U}$ such that

$$\mathbf{F}_a(\bigcap_{\nu=1}^{n} a_\nu U^{\mathbf{G}} M_{a_\nu}^{-1})\mathbf{F}_a \supset aV^{\mathbf{G}} M_a^{-1},$$

that is, $aU(a_1, \dots, a_n)\mathbf{F}_a \supset aV^{\mathbf{G}}$ and $V^{\mathbf{G}} \in \mathbf{U}$. Therefore $\mathbf{U}$ is semi-regular by definition.

Theorem 44.3. *A reflexive uniformity* $\mathbf{U}$ *is regular if and only if* $\mathbf{N}(\mathbf{U})$ *is regularly adjusted.*

Proof. For any $\mathbf{n} \in \mathbf{N}(\mathbf{U})$ we can find $U \in \mathbf{U}$ and $a_\nu \in S$ $(\nu = 1, 2, \dots, n)$ by Theorem 42.5 such that $\mathbf{n} \supset \bigcap_{\nu=1}^{n} a_\nu U^{\mathbf{G}} M_{a_\nu}^{-1}$. If $\mathbf{U}$ is regular, then for any $a \in S$ we can find an invariant $V \in \mathbf{U}$ by definition such that $aU(a_1, \dots, a_n) \supset aV$. Thus we have

$$\mathbf{F}_a\mathbf{n} \supset \mathbf{F}_a \bigcap_{\nu=1}^{n} a_\nu U^{\mathbf{G}} M_{a_\nu}^{-1} \supset aVM_a^{-1}.$$

Since $aVM_a^{-1} \in \mathbf{N}(\mathbf{U})$ and $\mathbf{F}_a(aVM_a^{-1})\mathbf{F}_a = aVM_a^{-1}$ by (3), (4) in 33, $\mathbf{N}(\mathbf{U})$ is regularly adjusted by definition.

Conversely if $\mathbf{N}(\mathbf{U})$ is regularly adjusted, then for any $U \in \mathbf{U}$ and $a_\nu \in S$ $(\nu = 1, 2, \dots, n)$ there is $\mathbf{m} \in \mathbf{N}(\mathbf{U})$ by definition such that

$$\mathbf{F}_a \bigcap_{\nu=1}^{n} a_\nu U^{\mathbf{G}} M_{a_\nu}{}^{-1} \supset \mathbf{F}_a \mathbf{m} \mathbf{F}_a,$$

because $\bigcap_{\nu=1}^{n} a_\nu U^{\mathbf{G}} M_{a_\nu}{}^{-1} \in \mathbf{N}(\mathbf{U})$ by Theorem 42.5. If **U** is reflexive in addition, then $\mathbf{N}_a(\mathbf{U})$ is the component of **N**(**U**) at a by Theorem 42.8. Since **N**(**U**) is strongly adjusted, we have $\mathbf{F}_a \mathbf{m} \mathbf{F}_a \in \mathbf{N}_a(\mathbf{U})$ by Theorem 43.2. Thus there is $V \in \mathbf{U}$ by definition such that $\mathbf{F}_a \mathbf{m} \mathbf{F}_a \supset a V^{\mathbf{G}} M_a{}^{-1}$, and hence

$$aU(a_1, \ldots, a_n) = a\mathbf{F}_a \bigcap_{\nu=1}^{n} a_\nu U^{\mathbf{G}} M_{a_\nu}{}^{-1} \supset aV^{\mathbf{G}}.$$

Therefore **U** is regular by definition, because $V^{\mathbf{G}} \in \mathbf{U}$.

Theorem 44.4. *If* **U** *is uniformly regular, then* **N**(**U**) *is semi-uniformly adjusted.*

Proof. For any $\mathbf{n} \in \mathbf{N}(\mathbf{U})$ we can find $U \in \mathbf{U}$ and $a_\nu \in S$ $(\nu = 1, 2, \ldots, n)$ by Theorem 42.5 such that $\mathbf{n} \supset \bigcap_{\nu=1}^{n} a_\nu U^{\mathbf{G}} M_{a_\nu}{}^{-1}$. If **U** is uniformly regular, then there is $V \in \mathbf{U}$ by definition such that

$$aXU(a_1, \ldots, a_n) \supset aXV^{\mathbf{G}} \text{ for every } a \in S \text{ and } X \in \mathbf{G}.$$

Since $aXV^{\mathbf{G}} M_a{}^{-1} = aV^{\mathbf{G}} M_a{}^{-1} X$, we hence obtain by (3), (4) in 33

$$\bigcap_{X \in \mathbf{G}} \mathbf{F}_a X \mathbf{n} X^{-1} \supset \bigcap_{X \in \mathbf{G}} \mathbf{F}_a X \Big(\bigcap_{\nu=1}^{n} a_\nu U^{\mathbf{G}} M_{a_\nu}{}^{-1} \Big) X^{-1} \supset aV^{\mathbf{G}} M_a{}^{-1}$$

$$= \mathbf{F}_a (aV^{\mathbf{G}} M_a{}^{-1}) \mathbf{F}_a.$$

Thus **N**(**U**) is semi-uniformly adjusted by definition.

Theorem 44.5. *If* **N**(**U**) *is uniformly adjusted and* **U** *is reflexive, then* **U** *is uniformly regular.*

Proof. If **N**(**U**) is uniformly adjusted, then for any $U \in \mathbf{U}$ and $a_\nu \in S$ $(\nu = 1, 2, \ldots, n)$ there is $\mathbf{m} \in \mathbf{N}(\mathbf{U})$ by definition such that

$$\mathbf{F}_a \bigcap_{X \in \mathbf{G}} X \Big(\bigcap_{\nu=1}^{n} a_\nu U^{\mathbf{G}} M_{a_\nu}{}^{-1} \Big) X^{-1} \supset \mathbf{F}_a \mathbf{m} \mathbf{F}_a.$$

If **U** is reflexive in addition, then $\mathbf{N}_a(\mathbf{U})$ is the component of **N**(**U**) at a by Theorem 42.8. Since **N**(**U**) is strongly adjusted, we have $\mathbf{F}_a \mathbf{m} \mathbf{F}_a \in$

$\mathbf{N}_a(\mathbf{U})$ by Theorem 43.2. Thus there is $V \in \mathbf{U}$ by definition such that $\mathbf{F}_a \mathbf{m} \mathbf{F}_a \supset aV^{\mathbf{G}} M_a^{-1}$. Therefore we obtain $aXU(a_1, \ldots, a_n) \supset aXV^{\mathbf{G}}$ for every $X \in \mathbf{G}$. Thus $\mathbf{U}$ is uniformly regular by definition.

Theorem 44.6. *If* $\mathbf{U}$ *is locally uniformly regular, then* $\mathbf{N}(\mathbf{U})$ *is locally semi-uniformly adjusted.*

Proof. If $\mathbf{U}$ is locally uniformly regular, then there is an invariant $U_0 \in \mathbf{U}$ by definition such that for any $U \in \mathbf{U}$, $a_\nu \in S$ $(\nu = 1, 2, \ldots, n)$ and $a \in S$ we can find $V \in \mathbf{U}$ such that $xU(a_1, \ldots, a_n) \supset xV^{\mathbf{G}}$ for every $x \in aU_0$. Thus, setting $\mathbf{m}_0 = aU_0 M_a^{-1}$, we obtain $\mathbf{m}_0 \in \mathbf{N}(\mathbf{U})$ and

$$aX \bigcap_{\nu=1}^{n} a_\nu U^{\mathbf{G}} M_{a_\nu}^{-1} \supset aV^{\mathbf{G}} X \quad \text{for } X \in \mathbf{m}_0,$$

because $aX \in aU_0$ if and only if $X \in \mathbf{m}_0$. Consequently, if $\mathbf{N}(\mathbf{U}) \ni \mathbf{n} \supset \bigcap_{\nu=1}^{n} a_\nu U^{\mathbf{G}} M_{a_\nu}^{-1}$, then we have

$$\bigcap_{X \in \mathbf{m}_0} \mathbf{F}_a X \mathbf{n} X^{-1} \supset aV^{\mathbf{G}} M_a^{-1}, \quad \mathbf{F}_a (aV^{\mathbf{G}} M_a^{-1}) \mathbf{F}_a = aV^{\mathbf{G}} M_a^{-1} \in \mathbf{N}(\mathbf{U})$$

by (3), (4) in 33. Referring to Theorem 42.5, we hence conclude by definition that $\mathbf{N}(\mathbf{U})$ is locally semi-uniformly adjusted.

Theorem 44.7. *If* $\mathbf{N}(\mathbf{U})$ *is locally uniformly adjusted and* $\mathbf{U}$ *is reflexive, then* $\mathbf{U}$ *is locally uniformly regular.*

Proof. If $\mathbf{N}(\mathbf{U})$ is locally uniformly adjusted, then there is $\mathbf{m}_0 \in \mathbf{N}(\mathbf{U})$ such that for any $U \in \mathbf{U}$, a, $a_\nu \in S$ $(\nu = 1, 2, \ldots, n)$ and $X_0 \in \mathbf{G}$ we can find $\mathbf{m} \in \mathbf{N}(\mathbf{U})$ such that

$$\mathbf{F}_a \bigcap_{X \in \mathbf{m}_0} XX_0 \Big(\bigcap_{\nu=1}^{n} a_\nu U^{\mathbf{G}} M_{a_\nu}^{-1} \Big) X_0^{-1} X^{-1} \supset \mathbf{F}_a \mathbf{m} \mathbf{F}_a,$$

because $X_0 \Big(\bigcap_{\nu=1}^{n} a_\nu U^{\mathbf{G}} M_{a_\nu}^{-1} \Big) X_0^{-1} \in \mathbf{N}(\mathbf{U})$. If $\mathbf{U}$ is reflexive in addition, then $\mathbf{N}_a(\mathbf{U})$ is the component of $\mathbf{N}(\mathbf{U})$ by Theorem 42.8, and hence $\mathbf{F}_a \mathbf{m} \mathbf{F}_a \in \mathbf{N}_a(\mathbf{U})$ by Theorem 43.2, because $\mathbf{N}(\mathbf{U})$ is strongly adjusted. Therefore there is $V \in \mathbf{U}$ by definition such that $\mathbf{F}_a \mathbf{m} \mathbf{F}_a \supset aV^{\mathbf{G}} M_a^{-1}$. Thus we obtain

$$aXX_0 U(a_1, \ldots, a_n) \supset a(aV^{\mathbf{G}} M_a^{-1}) XX_0 = aV^{\mathbf{G}} XX_0 = aXX_0 V^{\mathbf{G}} \quad \text{for } X \in \mathbf{m}_0.$$

Since $\mathbf{N}(\mathbf{U})$ is regularly adjusted, we also can find $U_0 \in \mathbf{U}$ such that $\mathbf{F}_a\mathfrak{m}_0 \supset aU_0{}^{\mathbf{G}}M_a{}^{-1}$. For such $U_0 \in \mathbf{U}$ we have $a\mathfrak{m}_0X_0 \supset aU_0{}^{\mathbf{G}}X_0 = aX_0U_0{}^{\mathbf{G}}$. Thus, if $x \in aX_0U_0{}^{\mathbf{G}}$, then we can find $X \in \mathfrak{m}_0$ such that $x = aXX_0$, and hence

$$xU(a_1, \dots, a_n) \supset xV^{\mathbf{G}} \text{ for every } x \in aX_0U_0{}^{\mathbf{G}}.$$

Since X_0 is arbitrary and $V^{\mathbf{G}} \in \mathbf{U}$, $\mathbf{U}$ is locally uniformly regular by definition.

Theorem 44.8. *An invariant uniformity* $\mathbf{U}$ *on* S *by* $\mathbf{G}$ *is sharp if and only if* $\mathbf{N}(\mathbf{U})$ *is uniformly regular.*

Proof. If $\mathbf{U}$ is sharp, then for any $U \in \mathbf{U}$ we can find $V \in \mathbf{U}$ and $a_\nu \in S$ $(\nu = 1, 2, \dots, n)$ such that $V(a_1, \dots, a_n) \leqq U^{\mathbf{G}}$. Thus we have

$$X \bigcap_{\nu=1}^{n} a_\nu V^{\mathbf{G}} M_{a_\nu}{}^{-1} \subset aXU^{\mathbf{G}}M_a{}^{-1} = aU^{\mathbf{G}}M_a{}^{-1}X \text{ for every } X \in \mathbf{G} \text{ and } a \in S.$$

Consequently we obtain

$$\mathbf{N}(\mathbf{U}) \ni \bigcap_{\nu=1}^{n} a_\nu V^{\mathbf{G}} M_{a_\nu}{}^{-1} \subset \bigcap_{X \in \mathbf{G}} X^{-1}(aU^{\mathbf{G}}M_a{}^{-1})X \text{ for every } a \in S.$$

Therefore we conclude easily that $\mathbf{N}(\mathbf{U})$ is uniformly regular.

Conversely if $\mathbf{N}(\mathbf{U})$ is uniformly regular, then for any $U \in \mathbf{U}$ and $a \in S$ we can find $V \in \mathbf{U}$ and $a_\nu \in S$ $(\nu = 1, 2, \dots, n)$ by Theorem 42.5 such that

$$\bigcap_{\nu=1}^{n} a_\nu V^{\mathbf{G}} M_{a_\nu}{}^{-1} \subset \bigcap_{X \in \mathbf{G}} X^{-1}(aU^{\mathbf{G}}M_a{}^{-1})X,$$

because $aU^{\mathbf{G}}M_a{}^{-1} \in \mathbf{N}(\mathbf{U})$. Thus we have

$$aXV(a_1, \dots, a_n) \subset aXX^{-1}(aU^{\mathbf{G}}M_a{}^{-1})X = aXU^{\mathbf{G}} \text{ for every } X \in \mathbf{G}.$$

Therefore $\mathbf{U}$ is sharp by definition.

Referring to Theorems 34.11, 40.3, 40.4 and 42.6, we obtain

Theorem 44.9. *If* $\mathbf{U}$ *is invariant and normal for* $\mathbf{G}$, *then* $\mathbf{N}(\mathbf{U})$ *is locally uniformly regular and totally bounded.*

Theorem 44.10. *If* $\mathbf{U}$ *is regular and normal for* $\mathbf{G}$, *then* $\mathbf{N}$ *is locally uniformly regular and locally sharp for* $\mathbf{G}$.

Proof. If **U** is normal, then **U** is locally totally bounded by definition and locally sharp by Theorem 35.1, if **U** is invariant by **G** in addition. If **U** is regular, then **U** is invariant by **G** by definition. Thus if **U** is regular and normal, then **U** is locally sharp, and we see by Theorems 44.9 and 44.3 that **N(U)** is locally uniformly regular and regularly adjusted. Consequently **N(U)** is locally uniformly adjusted by Theorem 43.4. Therefore **U** is locally uniformly regular by Theorem 44.7.

45. **Completions.** Let **G** be a transformation group on a space S, but it is not necessary for **G** to be transitive. Let **U** be a uniformity on S invariant by **G**, that is, $\mathbf{U}^{\mathbf{G}} \subset \mathbf{U}$.

Let $\widetilde{\mathbf{U}}$ be a completion of **U** over $\widetilde{S} \supset S$. Since every $X \in \mathbf{G}$ is a unimorphism from S to S for **U**, there exists uniquely a uniformly continuous extension of X over $\widetilde{S}$ as a unimorphism from $\widetilde{S}$ to $\widetilde{S}$ for $\widetilde{\mathbf{U}}$ by Theorem 29.2. Thus we can consider **G** a uniformly continuous transformation group on $\widetilde{S}$ for $\widetilde{\mathbf{U}}$. Since **G** is equi-continuous on S for **U** by Theorem 32.5, **G** also is equi-continuous on $\widetilde{S}$ for $\widetilde{\mathbf{U}}$ by Theorem 15.4. Therefore $\widetilde{\mathbf{U}}$ is invariant by **G** by Theorem 32.5.

For any adding point $\widetilde{x} \in \widetilde{S} - S$ we can find a convergent system $S \ni x_\delta \xrightarrow[\delta \in \Lambda]{} \widetilde{x}$ by definition. Then we have $M_{x_\delta} \xRightarrow[\delta \in \Lambda]{} M_{\widetilde{x}}$ by Theorem 33.6. Therefore the point mapping $M_{\widetilde{x}}$ is uniformly continuous on **G** for **W(U)** for every $\widetilde{x} \in \widetilde{S}$ by Theorem 17.2. Thus we have $\mathbf{W}(\widetilde{\mathbf{U}}) \subset \mathbf{W}(\mathbf{U})$. On the other hand we have by definition

$$\mathbf{W}(\widetilde{\mathbf{U}}) = \mathbf{W}(\widetilde{\mathbf{U}}, \widetilde{S}) \supset \mathbf{W}(\widetilde{\mathbf{U}}, S) = \mathbf{W}(\mathbf{U}).$$

Therefore $\mathbf{W}(\widetilde{\mathbf{U}}) = \mathbf{W}(\mathbf{U})$. We can hence state

Theorem 45.1. *If a transformation group* **G** *on* S *is equi-continuous for* **U**, *then for a completion* $\widetilde{\mathbf{U}}$ *of* **U** *over* $\widetilde{S} \supset S$, **G** *can be extended over* $\widetilde{S}$ *such that* **G** *also is equi-continuous on* $\widetilde{S}$ *for* $\widetilde{\mathbf{U}}$, *and* $\mathbf{W}(\widetilde{\mathbf{U}}) = \mathbf{W}(\mathbf{U})$ *on* **G**.

Let $\overline{\mathbf{G}}$ be the closure of **G** as a system of mappings from S to S for an invariant uniformity **U** on S. Since **G** is equi-continuous by Theorem 32.5, the closure $\overline{\mathbf{G}}$ also is equi-continuous by Theorem 17.1. For any $X, Y \in \overline{\mathbf{G}}$ we can find two convergent systems $\mathbf{G} \ni X_\delta \xrightarrow[\delta \in \Lambda]{} X$ and $\mathbf{G} \ni$

$Y_\gamma \xrightarrow[\gamma\in\Gamma]{} Y$ by definition (1) in 17. For any $U \in \mathbf{U}$ we can find $V \in \mathbf{U}$ such that $xVZ \subset xZU$ for every $Z \in \overline{\mathbf{G}}$ and $x \in S$, because $\overline{\mathbf{G}}$ is equi-continuous for $\mathbf{U}$. For any $x \in S$ we can find $\gamma_0 \in \Gamma$ by definition such that $xXY_\gamma \in xXYU$ for $\gamma \leqq \gamma_0$. We also can find $\delta_0 \in \Delta$ such that $xX_\delta \in xXV$ for $\delta \leqq \delta_0$. Then

$$xX_\delta Y_\gamma \in xXVY_\gamma \subset xXY_\gamma U \subset xXYU^2 \quad \text{for } \delta \leqq \delta_0,\ \gamma \leqq \gamma_0.$$

Therefore we conclude $\mathbf{G} \ni X_\delta Y_\gamma \xrightarrow[(\delta,\gamma)\in\Delta\times\Gamma]{} XY$. Thus, $X, Y \in \overline{\mathbf{G}}$ implies $XY \in \overline{\mathbf{G}}$.

We suppose that $\mathbf{U}$ is complete and $\mathbf{W}(\mathbf{U})$ on $\mathbf{G}$ is locally totally bounded. Referring to Theorem 39.10, we can find a regular neighbourhood $\mathbf{N}$ on $\mathbf{G}$ such that $\mathbf{U}(\mathbf{N}) = \mathbf{W}(\mathbf{U})$. Then $\mathbf{N}$ is right totally bounded by Theorem 40.3. Consequently $\mathbf{N}$ is locally uniformly regular by Theorem 40.4. Thus the inversion on $\mathbf{G}$ is locally uniformly continuous by Theorem 41.11. Therefore, if $\mathbf{G} \ni X_\delta$ $(\delta \in \Delta)$ is a Cauchy system for $\mathbf{W}(\mathbf{U})$, then X_δ^{-1} $(\delta \in \Delta)$ also is a Cauchy system for $\mathbf{W}(\mathbf{U})$ by Theorem 12.12. If $\mathbf{G} \ni X_\delta \xrightarrow[\delta\in\Delta]{} X \in \overline{\mathbf{G}}$ for $\mathbf{U}$, that is, if $xX_\delta \xrightarrow[\delta\in\Delta]{} xX$ for $\mathbf{U}$ for every $x \in S$, then xX_δ $(\delta \in \Delta)$ is a Cauchy system for $\mathbf{U}$ for every $x \in S$. Thus X_δ $(\delta \in \Delta)$ is a Cauchy system for $\mathbf{W}(\mathbf{U})$ by Theorem 23.7. Therefore X_δ^{-1} $(\delta \in \Delta)$ is a Cauchy system for $\mathbf{W}(\mathbf{U})$, and hence xX_δ^{-1} $(\delta \in \Delta)$ is a Cauchy system for $\mathbf{U}$ for every $x \in S$ by Theorem 23.7. Since $\mathbf{U}$ is complete by assumption, xX_δ^{-1} $(\delta \in \Delta)$ is convergent for every $x \in S$, that is, there exists $Y \in \overline{\mathbf{G}}$ such that $X_\delta^{-1} \xrightarrow[\delta\in\Delta]{} Y$ for $\mathbf{U}$. Then we have $X_\delta X_\delta^{-1} \xrightarrow[\delta\in\Delta]{} XY$ and $X_\delta^{-1} X_\delta \xrightarrow[\delta\in\Delta]{} YX$ for $\mathbf{U}$, as proved just above. Since $X_\delta X_\delta^{-1} = X_\delta^{-1} X_\delta = E$, we obtain $xXY \in xI_{\mathbf{U}}$ and $xYX \in xI_{\mathbf{U}}$ for every $x \in S$ by Theorem 7.1.

In the case, where $\mathbf{U}$ is pure, we have $I_{\mathbf{U}} = I$, and hence $XY = YX = E$. Thus both of X and Y are transformations on S and $Y = X^{-1}$. Therefore the closure $\overline{\mathbf{G}}$ forms a transformation group on S. Furthermore, $\mathbf{W}(\mathbf{U})$ on $\overline{\mathbf{G}}$ is complete. Because for any Cauchy system $X_\delta \in \mathbf{G}$ $(\delta \in \Delta)$ for $\mathbf{W}(\mathbf{U})$, xX_δ $(\delta \in \Delta)$ is a Cauchy system for $\mathbf{U}$ for every $x \in S$ by

Theorem 23.7, and hence there exists $X \in \overline{\mathbf{G}}$ such that $X_\delta \xrightarrow[\delta \in \Delta]{} X$ for **U**. Since $\mathbf{G}^{\mathbf{W}(\mathbf{U})-} = \overline{\mathbf{G}}$ by Theorem 7.3, W(U) is complete by Theorem 8.7. Furthermore W(U) is pure by Theorem 33.7. Thus we can state

Theorem 45.2. *If* **U** *is pure, complete and invariant by* **G**, *and if* W(U) *on* **G** *is locally totally bounded, then the closure* $\overline{\mathbf{G}}$ *of* **G** *on S forms a transformation group equi-continuous for* **U**, W(U) *on* $\overline{\mathbf{G}}$ *is pure and complete, and* $\mathbf{G}^{\mathbf{W}(\mathbf{U})-} = \overline{\mathbf{G}}$.

In the case where **U** is not pure, if X is a transformation on S, such that both of X and X^{-1} are uniformly continuous for **U**, then we see easily by Theorem 32.4 that $X\mathbf{U}X^{-1} = \mathbf{U}$, and hence $XI_{\mathbf{U}}X^{-1} = I_{\mathbf{U}}$ for the atom $I_{\mathbf{U}}$ of **U**. Thus $xYX \in xI_{\mathbf{U}}$ implies $xY \in xI_{\mathbf{U}}X^{-1} = xX^{-1}I_{\mathbf{U}}$. Therefore we obtain $X_\delta^{-1} \xrightarrow[\delta \in \Delta]{} X^{-1}$ by Theorem 7.1. Consequently, denoting by $\widetilde{\mathbf{G}}$ the system of all transformations X in $\overline{\mathbf{G}}$ such that both X and X^{-1} are uniformly continuous for **U**, we obtain a transformation group $\widetilde{\mathbf{G}}$ on S, which is equi-continuous for **U** by Theorem 17.1. $\widetilde{\mathbf{G}}$ is called the *transformation closure* of **G**. Thus we can state

Theorem 45.3. *If* **U** *is complete and invariant by* **G** *and if* W(U) *on* **G** *is locally totally bounded, then the transformation closure* $\widetilde{\mathbf{G}}$ *of* **G** *is a transformation group on S, which is equi-continuous for* **U**.

46. **Completion Closures.** According to Theorem 45.1, if a transformation group **G** is equi-continuous on S for a uniformity **U**, then for a completion $\widetilde{\mathbf{U}}$ of **U** over $\widetilde{S} \supset S$, **G** can be extended uniquely over $\widetilde{S}$ such that **G** also is equi-continuous on $\widetilde{S}$ for $\widetilde{\mathbf{U}}$, and

(1) $\mathbf{W}(\widetilde{\mathbf{U}}) = \mathbf{W}(\mathbf{U})$ on **G**.

The closure of **G** on $\widetilde{S}$ is called the *completion closure* of **G** and denoted by $\overline{\mathbf{G}}$. If **U** is pure, then $\widetilde{\mathbf{U}}$ also is pure by definition. If **U** is normal, then W(U) on **G** is locally totally bounded by Theorem 34.11. Since $\mathbf{W}(\widetilde{\mathbf{U}}) = \mathbf{W}(\mathbf{U})$ by (1), $\mathbf{W}(\widetilde{\mathbf{U}})$ also is locally totally bounded. Referring to Theorems 45.2 and 30.1, we hence conclude

Theorem 46.1. *If* **U** *is pure, normal and invariant by* **G**, *then the completion closure* $\overline{\mathbf{G}}$ *of* **G** *is a transformation group equi-continuous*

for the completion $\widetilde{\mathbf{U}}$ *of* $\mathbf{U}$ *over* $\widetilde{S}$, $\mathbf{W}(\widetilde{\mathbf{U}})$ *on* $\overline{\mathbf{G}}$ *is pure and locally compact, and* $\mathbf{G}^{\mathbf{W}(\widetilde{\mathbf{U}})-} = \overline{\mathbf{G}}$.

It is obvious by definition that $\mathbf{W}(\widetilde{\mathbf{U}}) = \mathbf{W}(\widetilde{\mathbf{U}}, \widetilde{S}) \supset \mathbf{W}(\widetilde{\mathbf{U}}, S)$, and we have $\mathbf{W}(\widetilde{\mathbf{U}}) = \mathbf{W}(\mathbf{U}) = \mathbf{W}(\widetilde{\mathbf{U}}, S)$ on $\mathbf{G}$ by (1) and $\mathbf{G}^{\mathbf{W}(\mathbf{U})-} = \overline{\mathbf{G}}$ by Theorem 46.1. Thus we obtain by Theorem 20.6

(2) $\mathbf{W}(\widetilde{\mathbf{U}}) = \mathbf{W}(\widetilde{\mathbf{U}}, S)$ on $\overline{\mathbf{G}}$.

For the completion $\widetilde{\mathbf{U}}$ of $\mathbf{U}$ over $\widetilde{S}$, we have

(3) $(x\widetilde{U}^{\circ S})^- \supset x\widetilde{U}^\circ$ for $x \in S$, $\widetilde{U} \in \widetilde{\mathbf{U}}$.

Because $(x\widetilde{U}^{\circ S})^- = (x\widetilde{U}^\circ \cap S)^- \supset x\widetilde{U}^\circ \cap S^- = x\widetilde{U}^\circ$ by Theorem 3.1

For any $\widetilde{U} \in \widetilde{\mathbf{U}}$ we have

$xX\widetilde{U}^{\overline{\mathbf{G}}S}X^{-1} = xX\widetilde{U}^{\overline{\mathbf{G}}}X^{-1} \cap SX^{-1} = xU^{\overline{\mathbf{G}}} \cap S = xU^{\overline{\mathbf{G}}S}$ for every $x \in S$, $X \in \mathbf{G}$. Thus we obtain $(U^{\overline{\mathbf{G}}S})^{\mathbf{G}} = U^{\overline{\mathbf{G}}S}$. For any $a_\nu \in S$ $(\nu = 1, 2, \ldots, n)$ we have by Theorem 3.1

$$\Big(\bigcap_{\nu=1}^{n} a_\nu U^{\overline{\mathbf{G}}S} M_{a_\nu}^{-1}\Big)^{\mathbf{W}(\widetilde{\mathbf{U}})-} = \Big(\bigcap_{\nu=1}^{n} (a_\nu U^{\overline{\mathbf{G}}} \cap S) M_{a_\nu}^{-1}\Big)^{\mathbf{W}(\widetilde{\mathbf{U}})-}$$

$$= \Big(\bigcap_{\nu=1}^{n} a_\nu \widetilde{U}^{\overline{\mathbf{G}}} \widetilde{M}_{a_\nu}^{-1} \cap \mathbf{G}\Big)^{\mathbf{W}(\widetilde{\mathbf{U}})-} \supset \Big(\bigcap_{\nu=1}^{n} a_\nu \widetilde{U}^{\overline{\mathbf{G}}} \widetilde{M}_{a_\nu}^{-1}\Big)^{\mathbf{W}(\widetilde{\mathbf{U}})\circ} \cap \mathbf{G}^{\mathbf{W}(\widetilde{\mathbf{U}})-}$$

$$\supset \bigcap_{\nu=1}^{n} a_\nu \widetilde{U}^{\overline{\mathbf{G}}\circ} \widetilde{M}_{a_\nu}^{-1}$$

for the point mapping $\widetilde{M}_a$ from $\overline{\mathbf{G}}$ to $\widetilde{S}$ at $a \in S$. Thus we obtain

(4) $\Big(\bigcap_{\nu=1}^{n} a_\nu \widetilde{U}^{\overline{\mathbf{G}}S} M_{a_\nu}^{-1}\Big)^{\mathbf{W}(\mathbf{U})-} \supset \bigcap_{\nu=1}^{n} a_\nu \widetilde{U}^{\overline{\mathbf{G}}\circ} \widetilde{M}_{a_\nu}^{-1}$ for $a_\nu \in S$ $(\nu = 1, 2, \ldots, n)$.

Since $x\widetilde{U}^{\overline{\mathbf{G}}S}(a_1, \ldots, a_n) = \Big(\bigcap_{\nu=1}^{n} a_\nu \widetilde{U}^{\overline{\mathbf{G}}S} M_{a_\nu}^{-1}\Big)\widetilde{M}_x$, we hence obtain by Theorem 12.2

(5) $(x\widetilde{U}^{\overline{\mathbf{G}}S}(a_1, \ldots, a_n))^{\widetilde{\mathbf{U}}-} \supset x\widetilde{U}^{\overline{\mathbf{G}}\circ}(a_1, \ldots, a_n)$ for $x, a_\nu \in S$ $(\nu = 1, 2, \ldots, n)$.

Let U_0 be a normal connector of $\mathbf{U}$ and $U_0 = \widetilde{U}^S$, $\widetilde{U} \in \widetilde{\mathbf{U}}$. For such $\widetilde{U} \in \widetilde{\mathbf{U}}$ there is a symmetric $\widetilde{V} \in \widetilde{\mathbf{U}}$ such that $\widetilde{V}^3 \leqq \widetilde{U}^{\mathbf{G}\circ}$, because $\widetilde{U}^{\mathbf{G}} \in \widetilde{\mathbf{U}}$. Then for any $\widetilde{x} \in \widetilde{S}$ we can find $x \in S$ such that $\widetilde{x} \in x\widetilde{V}$ and we have by (3)

$$\tilde{x}\tilde{V}^2 \subset x\tilde{V}^3 \subset x\tilde{U}^{\circ} \subset (x\tilde{U}^{\circ S})^{-} \subset (xU_0)^{-}.$$

Since xU_0 is totally bounded on S for **U**, $(xU_0)^{-}$ is totally bounded on $\tilde{S}$ for $\tilde{\mathbf{U}}$. Therefore $\tilde{x}\tilde{V}^2$ is totally bounded for $\tilde{\mathbf{U}}$ for every $\tilde{x} \in \tilde{S}$.

For any $\tilde{x}$, $\tilde{a} \in \tilde{S}$ we can find x, $a \in S$ such that $\tilde{x} \in x\tilde{V}^{\overline{\mathbf{G}}}$, $\tilde{a} \in a\tilde{V}^{\overline{\mathbf{G}}}$, and we have by (8) in 32, Theorem 34.3 and (5) in 46

$$\tilde{x}\tilde{V}(\tilde{a}) \subset (x\tilde{V}^{\overline{\mathbf{G}}})\tilde{V}(\tilde{a}) = (x\tilde{V}^{\overline{\mathbf{G}}})(\tilde{a}\tilde{V}^{\overline{\mathbf{G}}}\tilde{M}_{\tilde{a}}^{-1}) = x(\tilde{a}\tilde{V}^{\overline{\mathbf{G}}}\tilde{M}_{\tilde{a}}^{-1})\tilde{V}^{\overline{\mathbf{G}}}$$

$$= \tilde{x}\tilde{V}(\tilde{a})\tilde{V}^{\overline{\mathbf{G}}} \subset x\tilde{V}^3(a)\tilde{V}^{\overline{\mathbf{G}}} \subset x\tilde{U}^{\overline{\mathbf{G}}\circ}(a)\tilde{V}^{\overline{\mathbf{G}}} \subset (x\tilde{U}^{\overline{\mathbf{G}}S}(a))^{-}\tilde{V}^{\overline{\mathbf{G}}} \subset (xU_0(a))^{-}\tilde{V}.$$

Since $xU_0(a)$ is totally bounded for **U**, $(xU_0(a))^{-}$ also is totally bounded for $\tilde{\mathbf{U}}$. Thus we can find $\tilde{x}_\nu \in \tilde{S}$ $(\nu = 1, 2, \ldots, n)$ such that

$$(xU_0(a))^{-} \subset \bigcup_{\nu=1}^{n} \tilde{x}_\nu\tilde{V},$$

and hence $(xU_0(a))^{-}\tilde{V} \subset \bigcup_{\nu=1}^{n} \tilde{x}_\nu\tilde{V}^2$. Since $\tilde{x}\tilde{V}^2$ is totally bounded for $\tilde{\mathbf{U}}$, as proved just above, we conclude that $\tilde{x}\tilde{V}(\tilde{a})$ is totally bounded for $\tilde{\mathbf{U}}$ for every $\tilde{x}$, $\tilde{a} \in \tilde{S}$. Therefore $\tilde{V}$ is a normal connector of $\tilde{\mathbf{U}}$ for $\overline{\mathbf{G}}$. Thus we can state

Theorem 46.2. *If* **U** *is pure, normal and invariant by* **G**, *then the completion* $\tilde{\mathbf{U}}$ *of* **U** *over* $\tilde{S} \supset S$ *also is pure, normal and invariant by the completion closure* $\overline{\mathbf{G}}$ *of* **G**.

For any $\tilde{U} \in \tilde{\mathbf{U}}$, since $\tilde{M}_a\tilde{U}^{\overline{\mathbf{G}}}\tilde{M}_a^{-1} \in \mathbf{W}(\tilde{\mathbf{U}})$ by definition, we have by (4) in 4, (9) in 11 and (7) in 32

$$(a\tilde{U}^{\overline{\mathbf{G}}S}M_a^{-1})^{\mathbf{W}(\tilde{\mathbf{U}})-} \subset (a\tilde{U}^{\overline{\mathbf{G}}S}M_a^{-1})\tilde{M}_a\tilde{U}^{\overline{\mathbf{G}}}\tilde{M}_a^{-1} \subset (a\tilde{U}^{\overline{\mathbf{G}}}\tilde{M}_a^{-1})\tilde{M}_a\tilde{U}^{\overline{\mathbf{G}}}\tilde{M}_a^{-1}$$

$$\subset a\tilde{U}^{\overline{\mathbf{G}}}\tilde{U}^{\overline{\mathbf{G}}}\tilde{M}_a^{-1} \subset a(\tilde{U}^2)^{\overline{\mathbf{G}}}\tilde{M}_a^{-1}.$$

Thus we obtain

$$(6)\quad (\bigcap_{\nu=1}^{n} a_\nu\tilde{U}^{\overline{\mathbf{G}}S}M_{a_\nu}^{-1})^{\mathbf{W}(\tilde{\mathbf{U}})-} \subset \bigcap_{\nu=1}^{n} a_\nu(\tilde{U}^2)^{\overline{\mathbf{G}}}\tilde{M}_{a_\nu}^{-1} \quad \text{for } a_\nu \in S\ (\nu = 1, \ldots, n).$$

We suppose now that **G** is semi-transitive for **U**. Let $\tilde{U}_0$ be a symmetric normal connector of $\tilde{\mathbf{U}}$ such that $x(\tilde{U}_0^{\,3})^S \subset x\mathbf{G}$ for every $x \in S$.

For any $\tilde{x} \in \tilde{S}$ we can find a convergent system $S \ni x_\delta \xrightarrow[\delta\in\Delta]{} \tilde{x}$ by Theorem 7.3. We also can find $\delta_0 \in \Delta$ such that $x_\delta \in \tilde{x}\tilde{U}_0$ for $\delta \leqq \delta_0$. Then $\{x_\delta: \delta \leqq \delta_0\}$ is totally bounded for $\tilde{\mathbf{U}}$, and hence $\{x_\delta: \delta \leqq \delta_0\}\tilde{M}_a^{-1}$ is totally bounded for $\mathbf{W}(\tilde{\mathbf{U}})$ for every $a \in S$ by Theorem 37.11. For any $a \in \tilde{x}\tilde{U}_0 \cap S$ we have $x_\delta \in \tilde{x}\tilde{U}_0 \in a\tilde{U}_0^2$ and hence $x_\delta \in a(\tilde{U}_0^{\,2})^S \subset a\mathbf{G}$ for $\delta \leqq \delta_0$. Thus we can find $X_\delta \in \mathbf{G}$ $(\delta \leqq \delta_0)$ such that $x_\delta = aX_\delta$ for $\delta \leqq \delta_0$ Since

$$\{X_\delta: \delta \leqq \delta_0\} \subset \{x_\delta: \delta \leqq \delta_0\}\tilde{M}_a^{-1},$$

$\{X_\delta: \delta \leqq \delta_0\}$ is totally bounded for $\mathbf{W}(\mathbf{U})$. Thus we can find a partial system $\delta_\gamma \in \Delta$ $(\gamma \in \Gamma)$ by Theorem 29.3 such that $X_{\delta_\gamma} \xrightarrow[\gamma\in\Gamma]{} \tilde{X}$ for $\mathbf{W}(\tilde{\mathbf{U}})$ for some $\tilde{X} \in \overline{\mathbf{G}}$, because $\overline{\mathbf{G}}$ is complete for $\mathbf{W}(\tilde{\mathbf{U}})$ by Theorem 46.1. Then we have by Theorem 12.1

$$x_{\delta_\gamma} = aX_{\delta_\gamma} = X_{\delta_\gamma}\tilde{M}_a \xrightarrow[\gamma\in\Gamma]{} \tilde{X}\tilde{M}_a = a\tilde{X} \text{ for } \tilde{\mathbf{U}}.$$

Consequently $\tilde{x} = a\tilde{X}$, because $\tilde{\mathbf{U}}$ is pure by Theorem 46.2. For any $\tilde{y} \in \tilde{x}\tilde{U}_0$ we also can find similarly $b \in \tilde{y}\tilde{U}_0 \cap S$ and $\tilde{Y} \in \overline{\mathbf{G}}$ such that $\tilde{y} = b\tilde{Y}$. Since $b \in \tilde{y}\tilde{U}_0 \subset \tilde{x}\tilde{U}_0^{\,2} \subset a\tilde{U}_0^{\,3}$, we have $b \in a(\tilde{U}_0^{\,3})^S \subset a\mathbf{G}$. Thus there is $Z \in \mathbf{G}$ such that $b = aZ$, and hence

$$\tilde{y} = b\tilde{Y} = aZ\tilde{Y} = \tilde{x}\tilde{X}^{-1}Z\tilde{Y}, \quad \tilde{X}^{-1}Z\tilde{Y} \in \overline{\mathbf{G}}.$$

Therefore $\tilde{x}\tilde{U}_0 \subset \tilde{x}\overline{\mathbf{G}}$ for every $\tilde{x} \in \tilde{S}$. Thus we can state

Theorem 46.3. *If* $\mathbf{U}$ *is pure, normal and invariant by* $\mathbf{G}$ *and if* $\mathbf{G}$ *is semi-transitive for* $\mathbf{U}$, *then the completion closure* $\overline{\mathbf{G}}$ *also is semi-transitive and for any* $\tilde{x} \in \tilde{S}$ *we can find* $a \in S$ *and* $X \in \overline{\mathbf{G}}$ *such that* $aX = \tilde{x}$.

Theorem 46.4. *If* $\mathbf{U}$ *is pure, normal, invariant and sharp for* $\mathbf{G}$ *and if* $\mathbf{G}$ *is semi-transitive for* $\mathbf{U}$, *then the completion* $\tilde{\mathbf{U}}$ *of* $\mathbf{U}$ *also is sharp for the completion closure* $\overline{\mathbf{G}}$.

Proof. For any $\tilde{U} \in \tilde{\mathbf{U}}$ there is $\tilde{U}_1 \in \tilde{\mathbf{U}}$ such that $\tilde{U}_1^{\,2} \leqq \tilde{U}^{\overline{\mathbf{G}}}$. For such $\tilde{U}_1 \in \tilde{\mathbf{U}}$ we can find $\tilde{V}_1 \in \tilde{\mathbf{U}}$ and $a_\nu \in S$ $(\nu = 1, 2, \ldots, n)$ such that $\tilde{V}_1^{\,\overline{\mathbf{G}}S}(a_1, \ldots, a_n) \leqq \tilde{U}_1^{\,S}$, because $\mathbf{U}$ is sharp for $\mathbf{G}$ by assumption. For such $\tilde{V}_1 \in \tilde{\mathbf{U}}$ there is a symmetric $\tilde{V} \in \tilde{\mathbf{U}}$ such that $\tilde{V}^3 \leqq \tilde{V}_1^{\,\overline{\mathbf{G}}\circ}$. For any $\tilde{x} \in \tilde{S}$ we can find $a \in S$ and $X \in \overline{\mathbf{G}}$ by Theorem 46.3 such that $aX = \tilde{x}$. Since $\mathbf{G}^{\mathbf{W}(\tilde{\mathbf{U}})-} = \overline{\mathbf{G}}$, there is $Y \in \mathbf{G}$ such that

$$Y^{-1} \in (\bigcap_{\nu=1}^{n} a_\nu \tilde{V}^{\bar{\mathbf{G}}} M_{a_\nu}{}^{-1}) X^{-1}.$$

Then we have $aY(Y^{-1}X) = \tilde{x}$ and $a_\nu Y^{-1}X \in a_\nu \tilde{V}^{\bar{\mathbf{G}}}$ $(\nu = 1, 2, \dots, n)$. Thus we obtain by (8) in 34, Theorem 34.3, (5) in 46, and (4) in 4

$$\tilde{x}\tilde{V}(a_1, \dots, a_n) = aY\tilde{V}(a_1X^{-1}Y, \dots, a_nX^{-1}Y)Y^{-1}X$$
$$\subset aY(\tilde{V}^3)(a_1, \dots, a_n)Y^{-1}X \subset aY\tilde{V}_1{}^{\bar{\mathbf{G}}\circ}(a_1, \dots, a_n)Y^{-1}X$$
$$\subset (aY\tilde{V}_1{}^{\bar{\mathbf{G}}S}(a_1, \dots, a_n))^{\tilde{\mathbf{U}}-}Y^{-1}X \subset (aY\tilde{U}_1{}^S)^{\mathbf{U}-}Y^{-1}X$$
$$\subset aY\tilde{U}_1{}^2Y^{-1}X \subset aY\tilde{U}^{\bar{\mathbf{G}}}Y^{-1}X = \tilde{x}\tilde{U}^{\bar{\mathbf{G}}}.$$

Therefore $\tilde{V}(a_1, \dots, a_n) \leqq \tilde{U}^{\bar{\mathbf{G}}}$. Consequently $\mathbf{U}$ is sharp for $\bar{\mathbf{G}}$ by definition.

47. **Transitive Closures.** Let $\mathbf{G}$ be a transformation group on a space S with uniformity $\mathbf{U}$, such that $\mathbf{U}$ is pure, normal and invariant by $\mathbf{G}$. Let $\bar{\mathbf{G}}$ be the completion closure of $\mathbf{G}$ for a completion $\tilde{\mathbf{U}}$ of $\mathbf{U}$ over $\tilde{S} \supset S$. If $\mathbf{G}$ is transitive, then $\mathbf{G}$ is semi-transitive for $\mathbf{U}$. Thus for any $\tilde{x} \in \tilde{S}$ there are $X \in \bar{\mathbf{G}}$ and $x \in S$ by Theorem 46.3 such that $xX = \tilde{x}$. For any $a \in S$, since $S = a\mathbf{G}$ by assumption, we hence obtain $\tilde{x} = xX \in a\mathbf{G}\bar{\mathbf{G}} = a\bar{\mathbf{G}}$. Therefore $\bar{\mathbf{G}}$ also is transitive. Thus we can state

Theorem 47.1. *If* $\mathbf{U}$ *is pure, normal and invariant by* $\mathbf{G}$, *and if* $\mathbf{G}$ *is transitive, then the completion closure* $\bar{\mathbf{G}}$ *also is transitive.*

Now we consider the induced neighbourhoods $\mathbf{N}_a(\mathbf{U}, \mathbf{G})$ and $\mathbf{N}_a(\tilde{\mathbf{U}}, \bar{\mathbf{G}})$ at $a \in S$. Since $\{aU^{\mathbf{G}}M_a{}^{-1}: U \in \mathbf{U}\}$ is a basis of $\mathbf{N}_a(\mathbf{U}, \mathbf{G})$ by definition, for any $\mathbf{n} \in \mathbf{N}_a(\mathbf{U}, \mathbf{G})$ we can find $\tilde{U} \in \tilde{\mathbf{U}}$ such that $a\tilde{U}^{\bar{\mathbf{G}}S}M_a{}^{-1} \subset \mathbf{n}$. Then we have by (4) in 46

$$\mathbf{n}^{\mathrm{W}(\tilde{\mathbf{U}})-} \supset (a\tilde{U}^{\bar{\mathbf{G}}S}M_a{}^{-1})^{\mathrm{W}(\tilde{\mathbf{U}})-} \supset a\tilde{U}^{\bar{\mathbf{G}}\circ}\tilde{M}_a{}^{-1} \in \mathbf{N}_a(\tilde{\mathbf{U}}, \bar{\mathbf{G}}).$$

Therefore $\mathbf{n} \in \mathbf{N}_a(\mathbf{U}, \mathbf{G})$ implies $\mathbf{n}^{\mathrm{W}(\tilde{\mathbf{U}})-} \in \mathbf{N}_a(\tilde{\mathbf{U}}, \bar{\mathbf{G}})$. On the other hand, for any $\tilde{U} \in \tilde{\mathbf{U}}$ we have by (6) in 46

$$(a\tilde{U}^{\bar{\mathbf{G}}S}M_a{}^{-1})^{\mathrm{W}(\tilde{\mathbf{U}})-} \subset a(\tilde{U}^2)^{\bar{\mathbf{G}}}\tilde{M}_a{}^{-1}.$$

Thus $\{\mathbf{n}^{\mathrm{W}(\tilde{\mathbf{U}})-}: \mathbf{n} \in \mathbf{N}_a(\mathbf{U}, \mathbf{G})\}$ is a basis of $\mathbf{N}_a(\tilde{\mathbf{U}}, \bar{\mathbf{G}})$.

Next we consider the relation between $\mathbf{N}(\mathbf{U}, \mathbf{G})$ and $\mathbf{N}(\tilde{\mathbf{U}}, \overline{\mathbf{G}})$. For any $\mathbf{n} \in \mathbf{N}(\mathbf{U}, \mathbf{G})$ we can find $\tilde{U} \in \tilde{\mathbf{U}}$ and $a_\nu \in S$ $(\nu = 1, 2, \ldots, n)$ by Theorem 42.5 such that $\mathbf{n} \supset \bigcap_{\nu=1}^{n} a_\nu \tilde{U}^{\overline{\mathbf{G}}S} M_{a_\nu}{}^{-1}$. Since we have by (4) in 46

$$(\bigcap_{\nu=1}^{n} a_\nu \tilde{U}^{\overline{\mathbf{G}}S} M_{a_\nu}{}^{-1})^{\mathbf{W}(\tilde{\mathbf{U}})-} \supset \bigcap_{\nu=1}^{n} a_\nu \tilde{U}^{\overline{\mathbf{G}}} \circ \tilde{M}_{a_\nu}{}^{-1} \in \mathbf{N}(\tilde{\mathbf{U}}, \overline{\mathbf{G}}),$$

we conclude that $\mathbf{n} \in \mathbf{N}(\mathbf{U}, \mathbf{G})$ implies $\mathbf{n}^{\mathbf{W}(\tilde{\mathbf{U}})-} \in \mathbf{N}(\tilde{\mathbf{U}}, \overline{\mathbf{G}})$. On the other hand, for any $\overline{\mathbf{n}} \in \mathbf{N}(\tilde{\mathbf{U}}, \overline{\mathbf{G}})$ we can find $\tilde{U} \in \tilde{\mathbf{U}}$ and $a_\nu \in S$ $(\nu = 1, 2, \ldots, n)$ by Theorem 42.5 such that $\overline{\mathbf{n}} \supset \bigcap_{\nu=1}^{n} a_\nu \tilde{U}^{\overline{\mathbf{G}}} \tilde{M}_{a_\nu}{}^{-1}$, because $\mathbf{W}(\tilde{\mathbf{U}}) = \mathbf{W}(\tilde{\mathbf{U}}, S)$ by (2) in 46. For such $\tilde{U} \in \tilde{\mathbf{U}}$ there is a symmetric $\tilde{U}_1 \in \tilde{\mathbf{U}}$ such that $\tilde{U}_1{}^2 \leqq \tilde{U}$, and we have by (6) in 46

$$(\bigcap_{\nu=1}^{n} a_\nu \tilde{U}_1{}^{\overline{\mathbf{G}}S} M_{a_\nu}{}^{-1})^{\mathbf{W}(\tilde{\mathbf{U}})-} \subset \bigcap_{\nu=1}^{n} a_\nu (\tilde{U}_1{}^2)^{\overline{\mathbf{G}}} \tilde{M}_{a_\nu}{}^{-1} \subset \overline{\mathbf{n}}.$$

Therefore $\{\mathbf{n}^{\mathbf{W}(\tilde{\mathbf{U}})-} : \mathbf{n} \in \mathbf{N}(\mathbf{U}, \mathbf{G})\}$ is a basis of $\mathbf{N}(\tilde{\mathbf{U}}, \overline{\mathbf{G}})$. Thus we can state

Theorem 47.2. *If* $\mathbf{U}$ *is pure, normal and invariant by a transitive group* $\mathbf{G}$, *then* $(\mathbf{N}_a(\mathbf{U}, \mathbf{G}))^{\mathbf{W}(\tilde{\mathbf{U}})-}$ *is a basis of* $\mathbf{N}_a(\tilde{\mathbf{U}}, \overline{\mathbf{G}})$ *for every* $a \in S$, *and* $(\mathbf{N}(\mathbf{U}, \mathbf{G}))^{\mathbf{W}(\tilde{\mathbf{U}})-}$ *is a basis of* $\mathbf{N}(\tilde{\mathbf{U}}, \overline{\mathbf{G}})$ *for the completion closure* $\overline{\mathbf{G}}$ *of* $\mathbf{G}$.

We suppose in addition that $\mathbf{U}$ is regular for $\mathbf{G}$. For any $\overline{\mathbf{n}} \in \mathbf{N}(\tilde{\mathbf{U}}, \overline{\mathbf{G}})$ there is a symmetric $\overline{\mathbf{n}}_1 \in \mathbf{N}(\tilde{\mathbf{U}}, \overline{\mathbf{G}})$ by definition such that $\overline{\mathbf{n}}_1 \overline{\mathbf{n}}_1 \subset \overline{\mathbf{n}}$. For such $\overline{\mathbf{n}}_1$ we can find $\mathbf{n}_1 \in \mathbf{N}(\mathbf{U}, \mathbf{G})$ by Theorem 47.2 such that $\overline{\mathbf{n}}_1 \supset \mathbf{n}_1$. Since $\mathbf{U}$ is regular for $\mathbf{G}$ by assumption and reflexive by Theorem 44.1, $\mathbf{N}(\mathbf{U}, \mathbf{G})$ is regularly adjusted by Theorem 44.3 and $\mathbf{N}_a(\mathbf{U}, \mathbf{G})$ is the component of $\mathbf{N}(\mathbf{U}, \mathbf{G})$ by Theorem 42.8. Therefore for such $\mathbf{n}_1 \in \mathbf{N}(\mathbf{U}, \mathbf{G})$ we can find $\mathbf{m} \in \mathbf{N}_a(\mathbf{U}, \mathbf{G})$ such that $\mathbf{m} \subset \mathbf{n}_1 \mathbf{F}_a{}^{\mathbf{G}}$, and we have by Theorem 47.2 and (4) in 4

$$\mathbf{N}_a(\tilde{\mathbf{U}}, \overline{\mathbf{G}}) \ni \mathbf{m}^{\mathbf{W}(\tilde{\mathbf{U}})-} \subset (\mathbf{n}_1 \mathbf{F}_a{}^{\mathbf{G}})^{\mathbf{W}(\tilde{\mathbf{U}})-} \subset \mathbf{n}_1 \mathbf{F}_a{}^{\mathbf{G}} W \quad \text{for every } W \in \mathbf{W}(\tilde{\mathbf{U}}).$$

Since $U(\overline{\mathbf{n}}_1) \in \mathbf{W}(\tilde{\mathbf{U}})$ by Theorem 42.6, we hence obtain by (2) in 38

$$\mathbf{m}^{\mathbf{W}(\tilde{\mathbf{U}})-} \subset \mathbf{n}_1 \mathbf{F}_a{}^{\mathbf{G}} U(\overline{\mathbf{n}}_1) = \overline{\mathbf{n}}_1 (\mathbf{n}_1 \mathbf{F}_a{}^{\mathbf{G}}) \subset \overline{\mathbf{n}}_1 \overline{\mathbf{n}}_1 \mathbf{F}_a{}^{\overline{\mathbf{G}}} \subset \overline{\mathbf{n}} \mathbf{F}_a{}^{\overline{\mathbf{G}}},$$

because $\mathbf{F}_a^{\mathbf{G}} \subset \mathbf{F}_a^{\overline{\mathbf{G}}}$. Therefore $\mathbf{N}(\tilde{\mathbf{U}}, \overline{\mathbf{G}})$ is regularly adjusted and $\mathbf{N}_a(\tilde{\mathbf{U}}, \overline{\mathbf{G}})$ is the component of $\mathbf{N}(\tilde{\mathbf{U}}, \overline{\mathbf{G}})$, because $\mathbf{F}_a^{\overline{\mathbf{G}}}\mathbf{N}(\tilde{\mathbf{U}}, \overline{\mathbf{G}})\mathbf{F}_a^{\overline{\mathbf{G}}} \subset \mathbf{N}_a(\tilde{\mathbf{U}}, \overline{\mathbf{G}})$, as proved just above. Thus $\tilde{\mathbf{U}}$ is reflexive by Theorem 42.8. Consequently $\tilde{\mathbf{U}}$ is regular by Theorem 44.3. Since $\tilde{\mathbf{U}}$ is normal for $\overline{\mathbf{G}}$ by Theorem 46.2, $\tilde{\mathbf{U}}$ is locally uniformly regular and locally sharp by Theorem 44.10. Therefore $\tilde{\mathbf{U}} \sim \tilde{\mathbf{U}}^*$ by Theorem 37.6. Since $\tilde{\mathbf{U}}$ is locally compact and $\tilde{\mathbf{U}}^*$ is locally totally bounded by Theorem 37.7, $\tilde{\mathbf{U}}^*$ also is locally compact by Theorem 30.4. Thus we can state

Theorem 47.3. *If* $\mathbf{U}$ *is pure, normal and regular for a transitive group* $\mathbf{G}$, *then the completion* $\tilde{\mathbf{U}}$ *of* $\mathbf{U}$ *is locally uniformly regular, locally sharp,* $\tilde{\mathbf{U}} \sim \tilde{\mathbf{U}}^*$, *and* $\tilde{\mathbf{U}}^*$ *is locally compact for the completion closure* $\overline{\mathbf{G}}$.

The fixer $\mathbf{F}_a^{\overline{\mathbf{G}}}$ is closed for $\mathbf{W}(\tilde{\mathbf{U}})$ by Theorem 33.8, and we obviously have $\mathbf{F}_a^{\overline{\mathbf{G}}} \supset \mathbf{F}_a^{\mathbf{G}}$. Thus $\mathbf{F}_a^{\overline{\mathbf{G}}} \supset (\mathbf{F}_a^{\mathbf{G}})^{\mathbf{W}(\tilde{\mathbf{U}})-}$. For any $\overline{X} \in \mathbf{F}_a^{\overline{\mathbf{G}}}$ we can find a convergent system $\mathbf{G} \ni X_\delta \xrightarrow[\delta \in \Delta]{} \overline{X}$ for $\mathbf{W}(\tilde{\mathbf{U}})$, because $\mathbf{G}^{\mathbf{W}(\tilde{\mathbf{U}})-} = \overline{\mathbf{G}}$ by Theorem 45.2. Then we have by Theorem 12.1

$$aX_\delta = X_\delta \tilde{M}_{a_\delta} \xrightarrow[\delta \in \Delta]{} \overline{X}\tilde{M}_a = a\overline{X} = a.$$

Since $\mathbf{W}(\tilde{\mathbf{U}}) = \mathbf{W}(\tilde{\mathbf{U}}, S)$ by (2) in 46, for any $W \in \mathbf{W}(\tilde{\mathbf{U}})$ we can find $\tilde{U} \in \tilde{\mathbf{U}}$ and $a_\nu \in S\, (\nu = 1, 2, \ldots, n)$ by Theorem 33.2 such that $EW \supset \bigcap_{\nu=1}^{n} a_\nu \tilde{U}^{\overline{\mathbf{G}}} \tilde{M}_{a_\nu}^{-1}$ and we obviously have

$$a(EW \cap \mathbf{G}) \supset a\tilde{U}^{\overline{\mathbf{G}}S}(a_1, \ldots, a_n) \text{ for every } a \in S.$$

Since $\mathbf{U}$ is regular by assumption, we can find $\tilde{V} \in \tilde{\mathbf{U}}$ such that

$$a\tilde{U}^{\overline{\mathbf{G}}S}(a_1, \ldots, a_n) \supset a\tilde{V}^{\overline{\mathbf{G}}S},$$

and hence $a(EW \cap \mathbf{G}) \supset a\tilde{V}^{\overline{\mathbf{G}}S}$. Thus for any $W \in \mathbf{W}(\tilde{\mathbf{U}})$ and $\gamma \in \Delta$ we can find $\delta_{\gamma,W} \in \Delta$ *such* that $\delta_{\gamma,W} \geqq \gamma$ and $aX_{\delta_{\gamma,W}} \in a\tilde{V}^{\overline{\mathbf{G}}S}$, because $S \ni aX_\delta \xrightarrow[\delta \in \Delta]{} a$. Then we also can find $Y_{\gamma,W} \in EW \cap \mathbf{G} \subset \mathbf{G}$ such that $aX_{\delta_{\gamma,W}} = aY_{\gamma,W}$ for $\gamma \in \Delta$ and $W \in \mathbf{W}(\tilde{\mathbf{U}})$, and we obviously have $Y_{\gamma,W} \xrightarrow[(\gamma,W)]{} E$ and $aX_{\delta_{\gamma,W}}Y_{\gamma,W}^{-1} = a$. Therefore we obtain by Theorems 41.3 and 41.11

$$\mathbf{F}_a{}^{\mathbf{G}} \ni X_{\delta_\gamma, W} Y_{\gamma, W}{}^{-1} \xrightarrow[(\gamma, W)]{} \overline{X}E = \overline{X}.$$

Consequently we have $\mathbf{F}_a{}^{\overline{\mathbf{G}}} \subset (\mathbf{F}_a{}^{\mathbf{G}})^{\mathbf{W}(\tilde{\mathbf{U}})-}$. Thus we can state

Theorem 47.4. *If* $\mathbf{U}$ *is pure, normal and regular for a transitive group* $\mathbf{G}$, *then* $(\mathbf{F}_a{}^{\mathbf{G}})^{\mathbf{W}(\tilde{\mathbf{U}})-} = \mathbf{F}_a{}^{\overline{\mathbf{G}}}$ *for the completion closure* $\overline{\mathbf{G}}$ *of* $\mathbf{G}$.

48. **Equivalence.** Let $\mathbf{G}$ be a transitive group on a space S. Let $\mathbf{N}$ be an adjusted neighbourhood on $\mathbf{G}$. For the component $\mathbf{C}_a$ of $\mathbf{N}$ at $a \in S$, the induced uniformity $\mathbf{U}_a(\mathbf{C}_a)$ on S is reflexive by definition. The induced uniformity $\mathbf{U}(\mathbf{N})$ on $\mathbf{G}$ is the weak-uniformity on $\mathbf{G}$ by the system of point mappings M_x $(x \in S)$ for the induced uniformity $\mathbf{U}_a(\mathbf{C}_a)$ on S by Theorem 42.6, that is, $\mathbf{W}(\mathbf{U}_a(\mathbf{C}_a)) = \mathbf{U}(\mathbf{N})$.

If $\mathbf{U}(\mathbf{N})$ on $\mathbf{G}$ is locally totally bounded, then $\mathbf{N}$ is totally bounded by Theorems 40.3, 40.4 and 42.4. Let $\mathbf{n} \in \mathbf{N}$ be totally bounded. If the fixer $\mathbf{F}_a$ is totally bounded, then $\mathbf{F}_a\mathbf{n}\mathbf{F}_a$ is totally bounded for $\mathbf{U}(\mathbf{N})$ by Theorem 40.6. If $\mathbf{N}$ is strongly adjusted, then $\mathbf{F}_a\mathbf{n}\mathbf{F}_a \subset \mathbf{C}_a$ by Theorem 43.2. Thus we have $U_a(\mathbf{F}_a\mathbf{n}\mathbf{F}_a) \in \mathbf{U}_a(\mathbf{C}_a)$ by definition. Since we have by definition (1) in 42

$$aXU_a(\mathbf{F}_a\mathbf{n}\mathbf{F}_a) = (\mathbf{F}_a\mathbf{n}\mathbf{F}_a X)M_a,$$

$aXU_a(\mathbf{F}_a\mathbf{n}\mathbf{F}_a)$ is totally bounded for $\mathbf{U}_a(\mathbf{C}_a)$ for every $X \in \mathbf{G}$. Since we have by (7) in 33 for any $X, Y \in \mathbf{G}$

$$aYU_a(\mathbf{F}_a\mathbf{n}\mathbf{F}_a)(aX) = aY(aXU_a(\mathbf{F}_a\mathbf{n}\mathbf{F}_a)M_{aX}{}^{-1}) = aY(a\mathbf{F}_a\mathbf{n}\mathbf{F}_a XM_{aX}{}^{-1})$$

$$= aYX^{-1}\mathbf{F}_a\mathbf{n}\mathbf{F}_a X = (YX^{-1}\mathbf{F}_a\mathbf{n}\mathbf{F}_a X)M_a,$$

$yU_a(\mathbf{F}_a\mathbf{n}\mathbf{F}_a)(x)$ is totally bounded for $\mathbf{U}_a(\mathbf{C}_a)$ for every $x, y \in S$. Therefore $U_a(\mathbf{F}_a\mathbf{n}\mathbf{F}_a)$ is a normal connector of $\mathbf{U}_a(\mathbf{C}_a)$. Thus we obtain

Theorem 48.1. *If the induced uniformity* $\mathbf{U}(\mathbf{N})$ *on* $\mathbf{G}$ *is locally totally bounded, if the fixer* $\mathbf{F}_a$ *is totally bounded for* $\mathbf{U}(\mathbf{N})$, *and if* $\mathbf{N}$ *is strongly adjusted, then the induced uniformity* $\mathbf{U}_a(\mathbf{C}_a)$ *on* S *is normal for* $\mathbf{G}$ *for the component* $\mathbf{C}_a$ *of* $\mathbf{N}$.

We suppose in addition that $\mathbf{U}(\mathbf{N})$ is complete. Let $U_0 \in \mathbf{U}_a(\mathbf{C}_a)$ be a normal connector. For any Cauchy system $x_\delta \in S$ $(\delta \in \Delta)$ for $\mathbf{U}_a(\mathbf{C}_a)$

we can find $\delta_0 \in \Delta$ by definition such that $x_\delta \in x_{\delta_0} U_0$ for $\delta \leqq \delta_0$. Since $x_{\delta_0} U_0 M_a^{-1}$ is totally bounded for **U**(**N**) by Theorem 37.11, we can find by Theorem 29.3 a partial system $\delta_\gamma \in \Delta$ ($\gamma \in \Gamma$) and $X_{\delta_\gamma} \in \mathbf{G}$ ($\gamma \in \Gamma$) such that $x_{\delta_\gamma} = aX_{\delta_\gamma}$ ($\gamma \in \Gamma$) and $X_{\delta_\gamma} \xrightarrow[\gamma\in\Gamma]{} X \in \mathbf{G}$ for **U**(**N**), because **U**(**N**) is complete by assumption. Then we have $x_{\delta_\gamma} = aX_{\delta_\gamma} = X_{\delta_\gamma} M_a \xrightarrow[\gamma\in\Gamma]{} XM_a = aX$, and hence $x_\delta \xrightarrow[\delta\in\Lambda]{} aX$ for $\mathbf{U}_a(\mathbf{C}_a)$ by Theorem 8.1. Therefore $\mathbf{U}_a(\mathbf{C}_a)$ also is complete. Thus we can state

Theorem 48.2. *If the induced uniformity* **U**(**N**) *on* **G** *is locally compact, if the fixer* $\mathbf{F}_a$ *is compact for* **U**(**N**), *and if* **N** *is strongly adjusted, then the induced uniformity* $\mathbf{U}_a(\mathbf{C}_a)$ *on* S *is locally compact for the component* $\mathbf{C}_a$ *of* **N**.

A transformation group $\mathbf{G}_1$ on a uniform space S_1 with uniformity $\mathbf{U}_1$ is said to be *equivalent* to a transformation group $\mathbf{G}_2$ on a uniform space S_2 with uniformity $\mathbf{U}_2$, if there exists a unimorphism T from S_1 to S_2 such that setting

(1) $(xT)(X\tilde{T}) = (xX)T \quad (x \in S_1,\ X \in \mathbf{G}_1)$,

we obtain a transformation $\tilde{T}$ from $\mathbf{G}_1$ to $\mathbf{G}_2$. Such T is called an *equivalence unimorphism* and $\tilde{T}$ is called its *induced transformation.*

By relation (1), $X\tilde{T}$ is a transformation on S_2 for every $X \in \mathbf{G}_1$. Indeed, $X\tilde{T}$ is obviously a mapping from S_2 to S_2 for every $X \in \mathbf{G}_1$, and

$$(xT)(X\tilde{T})(X^{-1}\tilde{T}) = ((xX)T)(X^{-1}\tilde{T}) = (xXX^{-1})T = xT,$$
$$(xT)(X^{-1}\tilde{T})(X\tilde{T}) = ((xX^{-1})T)(X\tilde{T}) = (xX^{-1}X)T = xT.$$

Thus both $X\tilde{T}$ and $X^{-1}\tilde{T}$ are transformations on S_2 and

(2) $(X^{-1}\tilde{T}) = (X\tilde{T})^{-1}$.

Since $(xT)(X\tilde{T})(Y\tilde{T}) = ((xX)T)(Y\tilde{T}) = (xXY)T = (xT)(XY\tilde{T})$, we obtain

(3) $XY\tilde{T} = (X\tilde{T})(Y\tilde{T})$ for every $X, Y \in \mathbf{G}_1$.

Therefore, if $X\tilde{T} = Y\tilde{T}$, then we have by (2), (3) for any $x \in S_1$

$$xT = (xT)(X\tilde{T})(X^{-1}\tilde{T}) = (xT)(Y\tilde{T})(X^{-1}\tilde{T}) = (xT)(YX^{-1}\tilde{T}) = (xYX^{-1})T,$$

and hence $x = xYX^{-1}$, that is, $xX = xY$ for every $x \in S_1$. Consequently we see that $X\tilde{T} = Y\tilde{T}$ implies $X = Y$. Thus, making use of the notation

$$\mathbf{G}_1\tilde{T} = \{X\tilde{T}: X \in \mathbf{G}_1\},$$

we can say that $\mathbf{G}_1\tilde{T}$ is a transformation group on S_2, and $\tilde{T}$ is a transformation from $\mathbf{G}_1$ to $\mathbf{G}_1\tilde{T}$. Furthermore $\tilde{T}$ satisfies (2) and (3). Such a transformation from a group $\mathbf{G}_1$ to a group $\mathbf{G}_2$, satisfying (2) and (3), is called an *isomorphism* from $\mathbf{G}_1$ to $\mathbf{G}_2$. Thus $\tilde{T}$ is an isomorphism from $\mathbf{G}_1$ to $\mathbf{G}_1\tilde{T}$. $\tilde{T}$ is hence called the *induced isomorphism of* T from $\mathbf{G}_1$ to $\mathbf{G}_1\tilde{T}$. $\mathbf{G}_1$ is equivalent to $\mathbf{G}_1\tilde{T}$ always by definition. If $\mathbf{G}_1$ is equivalent to $\mathbf{G}_2$, then we obviously have $\mathbf{G}_2 = \mathbf{G}_1\tilde{T}$ for the equivalence unimorphism T and its induced isomorphism $\tilde{T}$ by (1).

For a point $a \in S_1$ we have $aX = a$ if and only if $(aX)T = aT$, because T is a transformation from S_1 to S_2. Since $(aT)(X\tilde{T}) = (aX)T$, we hence have $X\tilde{T} \in \mathbf{F}_{aT}^{\mathbf{G}_1\tilde{T}}$ if and only if $X \in \mathbf{F}_a^{\mathbf{G}_1}$, that is, $\mathbf{F}_{aT}^{\mathbf{G}_1\tilde{T}} = \mathbf{F}_a^{\mathbf{G}_1}\tilde{T}$.

Concerning the point mappings we have

(4) $(AM_a^{-1})\tilde{T} = (AT)M_{aT}^{-1}$ for $A \subset S_1$, $a \in S_1$,

Because $AM_a^{-1}\tilde{T} = \{X\tilde{T}: aX \in A\} = \{X\tilde{T}: aXT \in AT\} = \{X\tilde{T}: (aT)(X\tilde{T}) \in AT\} = (AT)M_{aT}^{-1}$.

Now we suppose that $\mathbf{G}_1$ is equivalent to $\mathbf{G}_2$ and $\mathbf{G}_2 = \mathbf{G}_1\tilde{T}$. About the weak-uniformities $\mathbf{W}(\mathbf{U}_1)$ on $\mathbf{G}_1$ and $\mathbf{W}(\mathbf{U}_2)$ on $\mathbf{G}_2$, we have by Theorem 23.6 that $W \in \mathbf{W}(\mathbf{U}_2)$ if and only if we can find $U \in \mathbf{U}_2$ and $a_\nu \in S_1$ ($\nu = 1, 2, \ldots, n$) such that $W \geqq \bigcap_{\nu=1}^{n} M_{a_\nu T} U M_{a_\nu T}^{-1}$, that is,

$$X\tilde{T}W \supset \bigcap_{\nu=1}^{n} X\tilde{T}M_{a_\nu T} U M_{a_\nu T}^{-1} \quad \text{for every } X \in \mathbf{G}_1.$$

On the other hand, we have by (1), (4)

$$X\tilde{T}M_{a_\nu T} U M_{a_\nu T}^{-1} = (a_\nu T)(X\tilde{T}) U M_{a_\nu T}^{-1} = (a_\nu X)TUT^{-1}M_{a_\nu}^{-1}\tilde{T}$$

$$= XM_{a_\nu} TUT^{-1}M_{a_\nu}^{-1}\tilde{T}$$

and $T\mathbf{U}_2T^{-1} = \mathbf{U}_1$, because T is a unimorphism by assumption. Therefore we conclude by Theorem 23.6 that

$$\tilde{T}\mathbf{W}(\mathbf{U}_2)\tilde{T}^{-1} = \mathbf{W}(\mathbf{U}_1),$$

that is, $\tilde{T}$ is a unimorphism between $\mathbf{W}(\mathbf{U}_1)$ and $\mathbf{W}(\mathbf{U}_2)$. Thus we have

Theorem 48.3. *If a transformation group* $\mathbf{G}_1$ *on* S_1 *with uniformity* $\mathbf{U}_1$ *is equivalent to* $\mathbf{G}_2$ *on* S_2 *with* $\mathbf{U}_2$ *by a unimorphism* T *from* S_1 *to* S_2, *then the induced transformation* $\tilde{T}$ *of* T *from* $\mathbf{G}_1$ *to* $\mathbf{G}_2$ *is a unimorphic isomorphism from* $\mathbf{G}_1$ *to* $\mathbf{G}_2$ *for the weak-uniformities* $\mathbf{W}(\mathbf{U}_1)$ and $\mathbf{W}(\mathbf{U}_2)$ *respectively on* $\mathbf{G}_1$ *and* $\mathbf{G}_2$, *and*

$$\mathbf{F}_a{}^{\mathbf{G}_1}\tilde{T} = \mathbf{F}_{aT}{}^{\mathbf{G}_2} \quad \textit{for every } a \in S_1.$$

We suppose now that both $\mathbf{G}_1$ and $\mathbf{G}_2$ are transitive and that there is an isomorphism $\tilde{T}$ from $\mathbf{G}_1$ to $\mathbf{G}_2$ such that $\tilde{T}$ is a unimorphism for $\mathbf{W}(\mathbf{U}_1)$ and $\mathbf{W}(\mathbf{U}_2)$, and $\mathbf{F}_{a_1}{}^{\mathbf{G}_1}\tilde{T} = \mathbf{F}_{a_2}{}^{\mathbf{G}_2}$ for some points $a_1 \in S_1$ and $a_2 \in S_2$. If $a_1 X = a_1 Y$ for some $X, Y \in \mathbf{G}_1$, then $XY^{-1} \in \mathbf{F}_{a_1}{}^{\mathbf{G}_1}$ by definition, and hence

$$(X\tilde{T})(Y\tilde{T})^{-1} = XY^{-1}\tilde{T} \in \mathbf{F}_{a_1}{}^{\mathbf{G}_1}\tilde{T} = \mathbf{F}_{a_2}{}^{\mathbf{G}_2},$$

because $\tilde{T}$ is an isomorphism from $\mathbf{G}_1$ to $\mathbf{G}_2$ by assumption. Thus $a_1 X = a_1 Y$ implies $a_2(X\tilde{T}) = a_2(Y\tilde{T})$. We also can prove similarly that $a_2(X\tilde{T}) = a_2(Y\tilde{T})$ implies $a_1 X = a_1 Y$. Thus setting

$$(a_1 X)T = a_2(X\tilde{T}) \quad \text{for every } X \in \mathbf{G}_1,$$

we obtain a transformation T from S_1 to S_2, and we have

$$(a_1 XY)T = a_2(XY\tilde{T}) = a_2(X\tilde{T})(Y\tilde{T}) = (a_1 XT)(Y\tilde{T}) \quad \text{for every } X, Y \in \mathbf{G}_1.$$

Thus (1) is satisfied for T and $\tilde{T}$. We also can prove easily that for the induced neighbourhoods $\mathbf{N}(\mathbf{W}(\mathbf{U}_1))$ on $\mathbf{G}_1$ and $\mathbf{N}(\mathbf{W}(\mathbf{U}_2))$ on $\mathbf{G}_2$ we have

$$\mathbf{N}(\mathbf{W}(\mathbf{U}_1))\tilde{T} = \mathbf{N}(\mathbf{W}(\mathbf{U}_2)), \quad \mathbf{C}_{a_1}\tilde{T} = \mathbf{C}_{a_2}$$

for the components $\mathbf{C}_{a_1}$ of $\mathbf{N}(\mathbf{W}(\mathbf{U}_1))$ and $\mathbf{C}_{a_2}$ of $\mathbf{N}(\mathbf{W}(\mathbf{U}_2))$. Thus we have

Theorem 48.4. *If both* $\mathbf{G}_1$ *and* $\mathbf{G}_2$ *are transitive, if both* $\mathbf{U}_1$ *and* $\mathbf{U}_2$ *are reflexive, if there is an isomorphism* $\tilde{T}$ *from* $\mathbf{G}_1$ *to* $\mathbf{G}_2$ *such that* $\tilde{T}$ *is a unimorphism for the weak-uniformities* $\mathbf{W}(\mathbf{U}_1)$ *on* $\mathbf{G}_1$ *and* $\mathbf{W}(\mathbf{U}_2)$ *on*

$\mathbf{G}_2$, *and if* $\mathbf{F}_{a_1}{}^{\mathbf{G}_1}\tilde{T} = \mathbf{F}_{a_2}{}^{\mathbf{G}_2}$ *for some* $a_1 \in S_1$ *and* $a_2 \in S_2$, *then* $\mathbf{G}_1$ *is equivalent to* $\mathbf{G}_2$ *and there is an equivalence unimorphism* T *from* S_1 *to* S_2 *for* $\mathbf{U}_1$ *and* $\mathbf{U}_2$ *such that* $\tilde{T}$ *is its induced transformation.*

VI. INTEGRATION THEORY

49. **Measures.** Let $\mathbf{U}$ be a locally totally bounded uniformity on a space S. A function ϕ on S is said to be *totally bounded* for $\mathbf{U}$, if ϕ is bounded on S and the set $\{x: \phi(x) \neq 0\}$ is totally bounded for $\mathbf{U}$. A function ϕ on S is said to be *positive*, and we write $\phi \geqq 0$, if $\phi(x) \geqq 0$ for every $x \in S$.

The system of all functions on S which are positive, totally bounded and uniformly continuous for $\mathbf{U}$, is called the *trunk* of $\mathbf{U}$. With this definition it is obvious that if $\mathbf{U}$ is totally bounded, then the trunk of $\mathbf{U}$ consists of all positive, uniformly continuous functions for $\mathbf{U}$. Let Φ be the trunk of $\mathbf{U}$. We can show easily that $\phi, \psi \in \Phi$ implies $\alpha\phi + \beta\psi \in \Phi$ for $\alpha, \beta \geqq 0$, $\phi\psi \in \Phi$, $\phi \vee \psi \in \Phi$, and $\phi \wedge \psi \in \Phi$. According to Theorem 19.2, we can say that for any totally bounded set $A \subset S$ and for any uniformly continuous, positive function ϕ on A there is $\psi \in \Phi$ such that $\phi(x) = \psi(x)$ for $x \in A$.

A function L on the trunk Φ is called a *measure* on S for $\mathbf{U}$, if

(1) $L(\phi) \geqq 0$ for every $\phi \in \Phi$,

(2) $L(\alpha\phi + \beta\psi) = \alpha L(\phi) + \beta L(\psi)$ for $\phi, \psi \in \Phi$, $\alpha, \beta \geqq 0$.

A measure L is said to be *pure*, if $L(\phi) = 0$ implies $\phi = 0$.

For a measure L it is obvious by definition that $\phi \geqq \psi$ implies $L(\phi) \geqq L(\psi)$. For two measures L, K on S for $\mathbf{U}$, setting

$$(\alpha L + \beta K)(\phi) = \alpha L(\phi) + \beta K(\phi) \quad \text{for } \phi \in \Phi \text{ and } \alpha, \beta \geqq 0,$$

we see easily that $\alpha L + \beta K$ also is a measure on S for $\mathbf{U}$.

For a set $A \subset S$ we denote by χ_A the *characteristic function* of A, that is,

$$\chi_A(x) = \begin{cases} 1 & \text{for } x \in A. \\ 0 & \text{for } x \bar{\in} A. \end{cases}$$

Let L be a measure on S for $\mathbf{U}$. For an open set $G \subset S$

(3) $L(G) = \sup\{L(\phi)\colon \chi_G \geqq \phi \in \Phi\}$

is called the *measure* of G by L. If an open set G is totally bounded, then $L(G) < +\infty$. Because there is $\phi \in \Phi$ such that $\chi_G \leqq \phi$ and then $L(G) \leqq L(\phi) < +\infty$ by (3).

About the measures of open sets, we obviously have by (3)

(4) $G_1 \subset G_2$ implies $L(G_1) \leqq L(G_2)$.

(5) $G_1 \cap G_2 = \emptyset$ implies $L(G_1 \cup G_2) \geqq L(G_1) + L(G_2)$.

Because, if $G_1 \cap G_2 = \emptyset$, then $\chi_{G_1 \cup G_2} = \chi_{G_1} + \chi_{G_2}$, and hence

$$\Phi \ni \phi_1 \leqq \chi_{G_1}, \ \Phi \ni \phi_2 \leqq \chi_{G_2} \ \text{implies}\ \Phi \ni \phi_1 + \phi_2 \leqq \chi_{G_1 \cup G_2}.$$

Theorem 49.1. *For any $\alpha < L(G)$ we can find a totally bounded open set H and $U \in \mathbf{U}$ such that $HU \subset G$ and $\alpha < L(H)$.*

Proof. For any $\alpha < L(G)$ there is $\phi \in \Phi$ by definition such that $\phi \leqq \chi_G$ and $\alpha < L(\phi)$. Setting $G_0 = \{x\colon \phi(x) > 0\}$, we obtain a totally bounded open set G_0 by definition and $L(G_0) < +\infty$. Then there is $\mathcal{E} > 0$ such that $\alpha < L(\phi) - \mathcal{E}L(G_0)$, $\mathcal{E} < 1$. For such $\mathcal{E} > 0$, setting $H = \{x\colon \phi(x) > \mathcal{E}\}$, we obtain an open set H such that $H \subset G_0 \subset G$. Since ϕ is uniformly continuous for $\mathbf{U}$, there is $U \in \mathbf{U}$ such that $HU \subset G_0$. Setting $\psi = \phi \wedge \mathcal{E}$, we obtain $\psi \in \Phi$ such that $\psi \leqq \mathcal{E}$, $\psi(x) = \phi(x)$ for $x \bar{\in} H$, and hence $\Phi \ni \phi - \psi \leqq \chi_H$. Since $\frac{1}{\mathcal{E}}\psi \leqq \chi_{G_0}$, we have $L(\frac{1}{\mathcal{E}}\psi) \leqq L(G_0)$, that is, $L(\psi) \leqq \mathcal{E}L(G_0)$. Thus we have

$$\alpha < L(\phi) - \mathcal{E}L(G_0) = L(\phi - \psi) + L(\psi) - \mathcal{E}L(G_0) \leqq L(H).$$

If $HU \subset G$ for some $U \in \mathbf{U}$, then $H^- \subset G$ by (4) in 4, that is, $H \prec G$. Thus we obtain by Theorem 49.1

Theorem 49.2. *For any $\alpha < L(G)$ we can find a totally bounded open set H such that $H \prec G$ and $\alpha < L(H)$.*

Let $\widetilde{\mathbf{U}}$ be a completion of $\mathbf{U}$ over $\widetilde{S} \supset S$. $\widetilde{\mathbf{U}}$ is locally compact by Theorem 30.2. Let $\widetilde{\Phi}$ be the trunk of $\widetilde{\mathbf{U}}$. For any function $\widetilde{\phi}$ on $\widetilde{S}$ we obtain a function $\tilde{\phi}^S$ on S such that $\tilde{\phi}^S(x) = \tilde{\phi}(x)$ for $x \in S$. This function $\tilde{\phi}^S$ on S is called the *relative function* of $\tilde{\phi}$ on S. We obviously have by definition that $\tilde{\phi} \in \tilde{\Phi}$ implies $\tilde{\phi}^S \in \Phi$. We also see easily by Theorem 19.2 that for any $\phi \in \Phi$ there exists uniquely $\tilde{\phi} \in \tilde{\Phi}$ such that $\tilde{\phi}^S = \phi$, because S is dense in $\tilde{S}$ for $\tilde{\mathbf{U}}$. Furthermore we obviously have

(6) $(\alpha\tilde{\phi} + \beta\tilde{\psi})^S = \alpha\tilde{\phi}^S + \beta\tilde{\psi}^S$,

(7) $\tilde{\phi} = 0$ if and only if $\tilde{\phi}^S = 0$.

Therefore for any measure L on S for $\mathbf{U}$, setting

(8) $\tilde{L}(\tilde{\phi}) = L(\tilde{\phi}^S)$ for $\tilde{\phi} \in \tilde{\Phi}$,

we obtain a measure $\tilde{L}$ on $\tilde{S}$ for $\tilde{\mathbf{U}}$. This measure $\tilde{L}$ is called the *completion* of L over $\tilde{S}$. Conversely for any measure $\tilde{L}$ on $\tilde{S}$ for $\tilde{\mathbf{U}}$, we obtain a measure L on S for $\mathbf{U}$ by (8) such that $\tilde{L}$ is the completion of L. Furthermore we see by (7) that $\tilde{L}$ is pure if and only if L is pure.

For any set $\tilde{A} \subset \tilde{S}$ we have by definition

(9) $\chi_{\tilde{A}}{}^S = \chi_{\tilde{A}^S}$ for the relative set $\tilde{A}^S$ of $\tilde{A}$ on S.

Since $\tilde{\Phi} \ni \tilde{\phi} \leqq \chi_{\tilde{G}}$ implies $\Phi \ni \tilde{\phi}^S \leqq \chi_{\tilde{G}}{}^S = \chi_{\tilde{G}^S}$, we obtain by (3) and (8) $\tilde{L}(\tilde{G}) \leqq L(\tilde{G}^S)$. If $\tilde{\phi}^S \leqq \chi_{\tilde{G}^S}$, then $\tilde{\phi} \leqq 1$ and $\tilde{\phi}(x) = 0$ for $\tilde{x} \in \tilde{G}^{\prime}$, and hence $\tilde{\phi} \leqq \chi_{\tilde{H}}$ for $\tilde{G} \prec \tilde{H}$. Therefore $L(G^S) \leqq \tilde{L}(\tilde{H})$ for $\tilde{G} \prec \tilde{H}$. Thus we obtain

(10) $\tilde{L}(\tilde{G}) \leqq L(\tilde{G}^S) \leqq \inf_{G \prec H} \tilde{L}(\tilde{H})$.

50. Regular Sets. We consider first the case where $\mathbf{U}$ is a locally compact uniformity on a space S. Let L be a measure on S for $\mathbf{U}$ and let Φ be the trunk of $\mathbf{U}$.

Lemma 50.1. *If* $\mathbf{U}$ *is locally compact, then*

$$L(G_1 \cup G_2) \leqq L(G_1) + L(G_2) \quad \textit{for open sets } G_1, G_2 \subset S.$$

Proof. If $\Phi \ni \phi \leqq \chi_{G_0}$, $G_0 \prec G_1 \cup G_2$, then setting $G = \{x\colon \phi(x) > 0\}$, we obtain a totally bounded open set G such that $G^- \subset G_0{}^- \subset G_1 \cup G_2$, and hence

$$G^{-} \cap G_2' \subset (G_1 \cup G_2) \cap G_2' \subset G_1.$$

Since $G^{-} \cap G_2'$ is compact, there is $U \in \mathbf{U}$ by Theorem 9.4 such that $(G^{-} \cap G_2')U \subset G_1$. Therefore setting

$$\phi_0(x) = \begin{cases} \phi(x) & \text{for } x \in G \cap G_2' \\ 0 & \text{for } x \in G_1' \end{cases}$$

we obtain a uniformly continuous, bounded function ϕ_0 on $(G \cap G_2')\cup G_1'$, and we can extend ϕ_0 to be uniformly continuous over S by Theorem 19.2. For an extended ϕ_0 on S, setting $\phi_1 = (\phi_0 \vee 0) \wedge \phi$, we obviously have $0 \leqq \phi_1 \leqq \phi$, $\Phi \ni \phi_1 \leqq \chi_{G_1}$ and $\phi_1(x) = \phi(x)$ for $x \in G \cap G_2'$. Setting $\phi_2 = \phi - \phi_1$, we have $\Phi \ni \phi_2 \leqq \chi_{G_2}$, because $\phi_2(x) = 0$ for $x \in (G \cap G_2') \cup G' \supset G_2'$. Thus we obtain

$$L(\phi) = L(\phi_1) + L(\phi_2) \leqq L(G_1) + L(G_2),$$

and hence

$$L(G_0) \leqq L(G_1) + L(G_2) \quad \text{for } G_0 \prec G_1 \cup G_2.$$

Therefore we conclude Lemma 50.1 by Theorem 49.2.

Referring to (5) in 49, we hence obtain

Lemma 50.2. *If* $\mathbf{U}$ *is locally compact, then*

$$L(G_1 \cup G_2) = L(G_1) + L(G_2) \quad \textit{for } G_1 \cap G_2 = \emptyset.$$

A set $H \subset S$ is said to be *regular* for a measure L, if H is a totally bounded open set and

$$L(H) = \inf_{H \prec G} L(G).$$

Lemma 50.3. *A totally bounded open set* H *is regular for* L *if and only if for any* $\mathcal{E} > 0$ *there is an open set* G *such that*

$$H^{-} \cap H' \subset G \quad \textit{and} \quad L(G) < \mathcal{E}.$$

Proof. If H is regular for L, then for any $\mathcal{E} > 0$ we can find two open sets G_1, G_2 by Theorem 49.2 and by definition such that $G_1 \prec H \prec G_2$ and

$$L(G_2) - \frac{1}{2}\mathcal{E} < L(H) < L(G_1) + \frac{1}{2}\mathcal{E}.$$

Then we have $H^{-} \cap H' \subset G_2 \cap G_1^{-'}$ and, since we have by (4), (5) in 49

$$L(G_1) + L(G_2 \cap G_1^{-'}) \leqq L(G_2),$$

we obtain $L(G_2 \cap G_1^{-'}) < \varepsilon$. Conversely if $H^{-} \cap H' \subset G$ and $L(G) < \varepsilon$, then we have $H \prec H \cup G$ and

$$L(H \cup G) \leqq L(H) + L(G) < L(H) + \varepsilon$$

by Lemma 50.1. Thus we obtain Lemma 50.3.

Theorem 50.4. *If* H_1 *and* H_2 *are regular for* L, *then all of*

$$H_1 \cap H_2, \quad H_1 \cup H_2, \quad H_1 \cap H_2^{-'}$$

are regular for L *too.*

Proof. Since

$(H_1 \cap H_2)^{-} \cap (H_1 \cap H_2)' \subset H_1^{-} \cap H_2^{-} \cap (H_1' \cup H_2') \subset (H_1^{-} \cap H_1') \cup (H_2^{-} \cap H_2')$, $(H_1 \cup H_2)^{-} \cap (H_1 \cup H_2)' = (H_1^{-} \cup H_2^{-}) \cap (H_1' \cap H_2') \subset (H_1^{-} \cap H_1') \cup (H_2^{-} \cap H_2')$, $(H_1 \cap H_2^{-'})^{-} \cap (H_1 \cap H_2^{-'})' \subset H_1^{-} \cap H_2' \cap (H_1' \cup H_2^{-}) \subset (H_1^{-} \cap H_1') \cup (H_2^{-} \cap H_2')$,

we conclude Theorem 50.4 from Lemmas 50.3 and 50.1.

We obviously have by definition

Theorem 50.5. *If* G *is open,* H *is regular for* L *and* $H \subset G \subset H^{-}$, *then* G *also is regular for* L *and* L(H) = L(G).

Theorem 50.6. *If a set* $A \neq \emptyset$ *is totally bounded for* **U**, *then for any* $U \in$ **U** *there is a regular set* H *for* L *such that* $A \subset H \subset AU$.

Proof. We can assume that U is a totally bounded connector of **U**. We can find a uniformly continuous function ϕ on S by Theorem 19.1 such that $0 \leqq \phi \leqq 1$, $\phi(x) = 0$ for $x \in A$ and $\phi(x) = 0$ for $x \in (AU)'$. Then setting

$$G_\alpha = \{x: \phi(x) > \alpha\} \quad (0 < \alpha < 1),$$

we obtain a system of totally bounded open sets G_α $(0 < \alpha < 1)$ such that

$$A \prec G_\alpha \prec G_\beta \prec G_0 \quad \text{for } 1 > \alpha > \beta > 0.$$

Thus setting $\xi_\alpha = \inf_{G_\alpha \prec G} (L(G) - L(G_\alpha))$ $(0 < \alpha < 1)$, we have

$$\xi_\alpha \leqq L(G_\beta) - L(G_\alpha) \quad \text{for } 1 > \alpha > \beta > 0.$$

For any finite system $0 = \alpha_0 < \alpha_1 < \ldots < \alpha_n < 1$ we hence have

$$\sum_{\nu=1}^{n} \xi_{\alpha_\nu} \leqq \sum_{\nu=1}^{n} (L(G_{\alpha_{\nu-1}}) - L(G_{\alpha_\nu})) \leqq L(G_0) < +\infty.$$

Thus we obtain $\sum_{0<\alpha<1} \xi_\alpha < +\infty$. Therefore there is α such that $0 < \alpha < 1$ and $\xi_\alpha = 0$. For such α we see easily by definition that G_α is regular for L.

Theorem 50.7. *If H is regular for L, then for any $U \in \mathbf{U}$ we can find a finite system of regular sets $H_\nu \subset H$ $(\nu = 1, 2, \ldots, n)$ such that*

$$H_\nu \cap H_\mu = \emptyset \ \text{for } \nu \neq \mu, \quad H \subset (\bigcup_{\nu=1}^{n} H_\nu)^-, \quad L(H) = \sum_{\nu=1}^{n} L(H_\nu)$$

and $H_\nu \subset xU$ for every $x \in H_\nu$.

Proof. For a symmetric, totally bounded $V \in \mathbf{U}$ such that $V^4 \leqq U$, we can find a finite system $x_\nu \in H (\nu = 1, 2, \ldots, n)$ such that $H \subset \bigcup_{\nu=1}^{n} x_\nu V$, as H is totally bounded. Then there is a finite system of regular sets K_ν $(\nu = 1, 2, \ldots, n)$ by Theorem 50.6 such that $x_\nu V \subset K_\nu \subset x_\nu V^2$ for every $\nu = 1, 2, \ldots, n$, and we obviously have $H \subset \bigcup_{\nu=1}^{n} K_\nu$, and $x \in K_\nu$ implies $K_\nu \subset x_\nu V^2 \subset xV^4 \subset xU$. Setting $H_1 = H \cap K_1$,

$$H_\mu = H \cap (\bigcup_{\nu=1}^{\mu} K_\nu) \cap (\bigcup_{\nu=1}^{\mu-1} K_\nu^-)' \quad \text{for } \mu = 2, 3, \ldots, n,$$

we obtain regular sets $H_\mu \subset H$ $(\mu = 1, 2, \ldots, n)$ by Theorem 50.4 and

$$(\bigcup_{\mu=1}^{n} H_\mu)^- = \bigcup_{\mu=1}^{n} H_\mu^- \supset \bigcup_{\mu=1}^{n} (H \cap (\bigcup_{\nu=1}^{\mu} K_\nu^-) \cap (\bigcup_{\nu=1}^{\mu-1} K_\nu^-)')$$

$$= H \cap \bigcup_{\nu=1}^{n} K_\nu^- = H.$$

Thus we conclude $L(H) = \sum_{\mu=1}^{n} L(H_\mu)$ by Lemma 50.2 and Theorem 50.5.

Theorem 50.8. *If H is regular for L, then*

$$L(H) = \inf_{\chi_H \leqq \phi \in \Phi} L(\phi).$$

Proof. If $H \prec G$ for an open set G, then there is $U \in \mathbf{U}$ by Theorem 9.4 such that $HU \subset G$. Then we can find $\phi \in \Phi$ by Theorem 19.1 such that $\phi(x) = 1$ for $x \in H$, $\phi(x) = 0$ for $x \bar{\in} G$ and $0 \leqq \phi \leqq 1$. For such ϕ we have $\chi_H \leqq \phi \leqq \chi_G$ by definition, and hence $L(H) \leqq L(\phi) \leqq L(G)$. Thus we obtain Theorem 50.8 by definition.

Now we consider the general case where $\mathbf{U}$ is locally totally bounded. Let $\tilde{\mathbf{U}}$ be a completion of $\mathbf{U}$ over $\tilde{S} \supset S$, and let $\tilde{L}$ be the completion of L over $\tilde{S}$. A set $H \subset S$ is said to be *regular* for L, if there is a regular set $\tilde{H} \subset \tilde{S}$ for $\tilde{L}$ such that $H = \tilde{H}^S$, and then $L(H) = \tilde{L}(\tilde{H})$ by (10) in 49. We see easily by Theorem 29.2 that this definition of regular sets is independent of completions of $\mathbf{U}$. Theorems 50.6 and 50.8 obviously hold in the general case. Referring to Theorem 5.2, we see that Theorems 50.4 and 50.7 hold in the general case too. If $H \subset G \subset H^-$ for a regular set H and an open set G, then there are a regular set $\tilde{H} \subset \tilde{S}$ for $\tilde{L}$ by definition and an open set $\tilde{G} \subset \tilde{S}$ by Theorem 5.1 such that $H = \tilde{H}^S$ and $G = \tilde{G}^S$. Setting $\tilde{G}_1 = (\tilde{G} \cup \tilde{H}) \cap \tilde{H}^{\tilde{\mathbf{U}}-\circ}$, we obtain an open set $\tilde{G}_1$ such that $\tilde{H} \subset \tilde{G}_1 \subset \tilde{H}^{\tilde{\mathbf{U}}-}$. Thus $\tilde{G}_1$ is regular for $\tilde{L}$ by Theorem 50.5, and we have by Theorem 5.2

$$\tilde{G}_1{}^S = (G \cup H) \cap H^{-\circ} = G.$$

Therefore Theorem 50.5 also holds in the general case.

We conclude immediately from Theorems 49.1 and 50.6.

Theorem 50.9. *Let G be an open set. For any $a < L(G)$ we can find a regular set H for L and $U \in \mathbf{U}$ such that $HU \subset G$ and $a < L(H)$.*

Theorem 50.10. *For two regular sets H_1, H_2 for L we have*

$$L(H_1 \cup H_2) + L(H_1 \cap H_2) = L(H_1) + L(H_2).$$

Proof. We need only prove the case where $\mathbf{U}$ is locally compact. Setting $K = H_1 \cap H_2$, we have

$$(H_1 \cap K^{-\prime}) \cap K = \emptyset, \quad (H_1 \cap K^{-\prime}) \cup K \subset H_1 \subset ((H_1 \cap K^{-\prime}) \cup K)^-.$$

Thus we obtain by Lemma 50.2 and Theorem 50.5

$$L(H_1 \cap K^{-\prime}) + L(K) = L(H_1).$$

We can prove similarly

$$L(H_2 \cap K^{-\prime}) + L(K) = L(H_2).$$

Since $(H_1 \cap K^{-\prime}) \cap (H_2 \cap K^{-\prime}) = \emptyset$, $(H_1 \cap K^{-\prime}) \cup (H_2 \cap K^{-\prime}) = (H_1 \cup H_2) \cap K^{-\prime}$, we have by Lemma 50.2

$$L(H_1 \cap K^{-\prime}) + L(H_2 \cap K^{-\prime}) = L((H_1 \cup H_2) \cap K^{-\prime}).$$

Since $((H_1 \cup H_2) \cap K^{-\prime}) \cup K \subset H_1 \cup H_2 \subset (((H_1 \cup H_2) \cap K^{-\prime}) \cup K)^-$ and $((H_1 \cup H_2) \cap K^{-\prime}) \cap K = \emptyset$, we have by Lemma 50.2 and Theorem 50.5

$$L((H_1 \cup H_2) \cap K^{-\prime}) + L(K) = L(H_1 \cup H_2).$$

Thus we obtain Theorem 50.10.

Theorem 50.11. *For a finite system of open sets* G_ν *and regular sets* H_ν *for* L $(\nu = 1, 2, \ldots, n)$, *if* $G_1 \supset G_2 \supset \ldots \supset G_n$, $H_\nu \prec G_\nu$ *and*

$$L(H_\nu) \geqq L(G_\nu) - \varepsilon_\nu \quad (\nu = 1, 2, \ldots, n),$$

then $L(\bigcap_{\nu=1}^{n} H_\nu) \geqq L(G_n) - \sum_{\nu=1}^{n} \varepsilon_\nu$.

Proof. Since $L(H_1) + L(G_1 \cap H_1^{-\prime}) \leqq L(G_1)$ by (5) in 49 and $L(H_1) \geqq L(G_1) - \varepsilon_1$ by assumption, we have $L(G_1 \cap H_1^{-\prime}) \leqq \varepsilon_1$. As $H_2 \subset G_2 \subset G_1$ by assumption, we hence obtain $L(H_2 \cap H_1^{-\prime}) \leqq \varepsilon_1$. Since H_1, H_2 are regular for L, $(H_2 \cap H_1) \cap (H_2 \cap H_1^{-\prime}) = \emptyset$ and

$$((H_2 \cap H_1) \cup (H_2 \cap H_1^{-\prime}))^- = (H_2 \cap (H_1 \cup H_1^{-\prime}))^- \supset H_2 \cap (H_1^- \cup H_1^{-\prime})$$
$$= H_2,$$

we obtain $L(H_2 \cap H_1) + L(H_2 \cap H_1^{-\prime}) = L(H_2)$ by Theorems 50.5 and 50.10, and hence

$$L(H_1 \cap H_2) \geqq L(H_2) - \varepsilon_1 \geqq L(G_2) - (\varepsilon_1 + \varepsilon_2),$$

because $L(H_2) \geqq L(G_2) - \varepsilon_2$ by assumption. Therefore we can conclude Theorem 50.11 by induction.

51. **Integrals.** Let L be a measure on a space S for a locally totally bounded uniformity **U**. Let G_0 be a regular set for L. A finite system of regular sets $\emptyset \neq G_\nu \subset G_0$ $(\nu = 1, 2, \ldots, n)$ is called a *regular partition* of G_0, if $G_\nu \cap G_\mu = \emptyset$ for $\nu \neq \mu$ and $G_0 \subset (\bigcup_{\nu=1}^{n} G_\nu)^-$.

Let ϕ be a uniformly continuous function on G_0 for **U**. Since G_0 is totally bounded, ϕ is bounded on G_0. A regular partition $G_\nu \subset G_0$ $(\nu = 1, 2, \ldots, n)$ of G_0 is called an $\mathcal{E}$ *partition* of G_0 for ϕ and L, if $x, y \in G_\nu$ implies $|\phi(x) - \phi(y)| < \mathcal{E}$ for every $\nu = 1, 2, \ldots, n$. We can prove easily by Theorem 50.7 that for any $\mathcal{E} > 0$ and for any uniformly continuous function ϕ on G_0 there is an $\mathcal{E}$ partition of G_0 for ϕ and L.

For an arbitrary $\mathcal{E}$ partition $G_\nu \subset G_0$ $(\nu = 1, 2, \ldots, n)$ and an arbitrary δ partition $H_\mu \subset G_0$ $(\mu = 1, 2, \ldots, m)$ of G_0 for ϕ and L we have

$$\sum_{\nu=1}^{n} \phi(x_\nu)L(G_\nu) - \sum_{\mu=1}^{m} \phi(y_\mu)L(H_\mu)$$

$$= \sum_{\nu,\mu} \phi(x_\nu)L(G_\nu \cap H_\mu) - \sum_{\nu\ \mu} \phi(y_\mu)L(G_\nu \cap H_\mu)$$

$$= \sum_{\nu,\mu} (\phi(x_\nu) - \phi(y_\mu))L(G_\nu \cap H_\mu).$$

Because $(\bigcup_{\mu=1}^{m} (G_\nu \cap H_\mu))^- \supset G_\nu \cap (\bigcup_{\mu=1}^{m} H_\mu)^- \supset G_\nu \cap G_0 = G_\nu$, and hence we obtain by Theorems 50.5 and 50.10

$$L(G_\nu) = \sum_{\mu=1}^{m} L(G_\nu \cap H_\mu) \quad (\nu = 1, 2, \ldots, n).$$

Similarly we can prove

$$L(H_\mu) = \sum_{\nu=1}^{n} L(G_\nu \cap H_\mu) \quad (\mu = 1, 2, \ldots, m).$$

We assume here that $x_\nu \in G_\nu$ $(\nu = 1, 2, \ldots, n)$ and $y_\mu \in H_\mu$ $(\mu = 1, 2, \ldots, m)$. If $G_\nu \cap H_\mu \neq \emptyset$, then for $z \in G_\nu \cap H_\mu$ we have

$$|\phi(x_\nu) - \phi(z)| < \mathcal{E}, \quad |\phi(y_\mu) - \phi(z)| < \delta,$$

and hence $|\phi(x_\nu) - \phi(y_\mu)| < \mathcal{E} + \delta$. If $G_\nu \cap H_\mu = \emptyset$, then we have $L(G_\nu \cap H_\mu) = 0$. Thus we obtain

$$\left| \sum_{\nu=1}^{n} \phi(x_\nu)L(G_\nu) - \sum_{\mu=1}^{m} \phi(y_\mu)L(H_\mu) \right| \leqq (\mathcal{E} + \delta) \sum_{\nu,\mu} L(G_\nu \cap H_\mu)$$

$$= (\mathcal{E} + \delta)L(G_0).$$

Therefore there exists uniquely a real number a such that

$$\left| \sum_{\nu=1}^{n} \phi(x_\nu)L(G_\nu) - a \right| \leqq \mathcal{E}L(G_0)$$

for any $\mathcal{E}$ partition $G_\nu \subset G_0$ $(\nu = 1, 2, \ldots, n)$ of G_0 for ϕ and L and for any $x_\nu \in G_\nu$ $(\nu = 1, 2, \ldots, n)$. This a is called the *integral* of ϕ on G_0 by L and denoted by

$$L\text{-} \int_{G_0} \phi(x)dx.$$

Thus we have

Theorem 51.1. *For a uniformly continuous function ϕ on a regular set G_0 we have*

$$\left| \sum_{\nu=1}^{n} \phi(x_\nu)L(G_\nu) - L\text{-} \int_{G_0} \phi(x)dx \right| \leqq \mathcal{E}L(G_0)$$

for any $\mathcal{E}$ partition $G_\nu \subset G_0$ $(\nu = 1, 2, \ldots, n)$ of G_0 for ϕ and L and for any $x_\nu \in G_\nu$ $(\nu = 1, 2, \ldots, n)$.

From Theorem 51.1 we conclude easily the following theorems.

Theorem 51.2. *If ϕ and ψ are uniformly continuous functions on a regular set G for L, then*

$$L\text{-} \int_G (a\phi(x) + \beta\psi(x))dx = aL\text{-} \int_G \phi(x)dx + \beta L\text{-} \int_G \psi(x)dx.$$

Theorem 51.3. *If $\phi(x) \leqq \psi(x)$ for every $x \in G$, then*

$$L\text{-} \int_G \phi(x)dx \leqq L\text{-} \int_G \psi(x)dx.$$

If $|\phi(x)| \leqq \psi(x)$ for every $x \in G$, then

$$\left| L\text{-} \int_G \phi(x)dx \right| \leqq L\text{-} \int_G \psi(x)dx.$$

Theorem 51.4. *For two regular sets G, H for L, if $G \cap H = \emptyset$, then*

$$L\text{-} \int_G \phi(x)dx + L\text{-} \int_H \phi(x)dx = L\text{-} \int_{G \cup H} \phi(x)dx.$$

Theorem 51.5. *If $G \subset H \subset G^-$, then*

$$L\text{-}\int_G \phi(x)dx = L\text{-}\int_H \phi(x)dx.$$

Theorem 51.6. *For any regular set G for L we have*

$$L\text{-}\int_G dx = L(G).$$

Theorem 51.7. *For any $\phi \in \Phi$, if $\{x: \phi(x) > 0\} \subset G$ for a regular set G for L, then*

$$L\text{-}\int_G \phi(x)dx = L(\phi).$$

Proof. Let $G_\nu \subset G$ $(\nu = 1, 2, \ldots, n)$ be an $\mathcal{E}$ partition of G for ϕ and L. Then we have by Theorem 51.1

$$\left|\sum_{\nu=1}^{n} \phi(x_\nu)L(G_\nu) - L\text{-}\int_G \phi(x)dx\right| \leqq \mathcal{E}L(G).$$

For any $\delta > 0$ we can find $\phi_\nu, \psi_\nu \in \Phi$ $(\nu = 1, 2, \ldots, n)$ by (3) in 49 and Theorem 50.8 such that $\phi_\nu \leqq \chi_{G_\nu} \leqq \psi_\nu$ and

$$L(G_\nu) - \delta < L(\phi_\nu) \leqq L(\psi_\nu) < L(G_\nu) + \delta.$$

Since $\phi(x_\nu) - \mathcal{E} \leqq \phi(x) \leqq \phi(x_\nu) + \mathcal{E}$ for $x \in G_\nu$, we have

$$(\phi(x_\nu) - \mathcal{E})\phi_\nu \leqq \phi\chi_{G_\nu} \leqq (\phi(x_\nu) + \mathcal{E})\psi_\nu.$$

Since $\{x: \phi(x) > 0\} \subset G \subset (\bigcup_{\nu=1}^{n} G_\nu)^-$ by assumption, we conclude easily

$$\sum_{\nu=1}^{n} (\phi(x_\nu) - \mathcal{E})\phi_\nu \leqq \phi \leqq \sum_{\nu=1}^{n} (\phi(x_\nu) + \mathcal{E})\psi_\nu,$$

that is, $\sum_{\nu=1}^{n} \phi(x_\nu)\phi_\nu \leqq \phi + \mathcal{E} \sum_{\nu=1}^{n} \phi_\nu$, $\phi \leqq \sum_{\nu=1}^{n} (\phi(x_\nu) + \mathcal{E})\psi_\nu$.

Thus we obtain

$$\sum_{\nu=1}^{n} \phi(x_\nu)L(\phi_\nu) \leqq L(\phi) + \mathcal{E} \sum_{\nu=1}^{n} L(\phi_\nu), \quad L(\phi) \leqq \sum_{\nu=1}^{n} (\phi(x_\nu) + \mathcal{E})L(\psi_\nu).$$

Consequently we have

$$\sum_{\nu=1}^{n} \phi(x_\nu)(L(G_\nu) - \delta) \leqq L(\phi) + \mathcal{E} \sum_{\nu=1}^{n} (L(G_\nu) + \delta),$$

$$L(\phi) \leqq \sum_{\nu=1}^{n} (\phi(x_\nu) + \mathcal{E})(L(G_\nu) + \delta)$$

for every $\delta > 0$. Thus we conclude

$$\sum_{\nu=1}^{n} (\phi(x_\nu) - \mathcal{E})L(G_\nu) \leqq L(\phi) \leqq \sum_{\nu=1}^{n} (\phi(x_\nu) + \mathcal{E})L(G_\nu),$$

that is, $|L(\phi) - \sum_{\nu=1}^{n} \phi(x_\nu)L(G_\nu)| \leqq \sum_{\nu=1}^{n} \mathcal{E}L(G_\nu) = \mathcal{E}L(G)$. Therefore

$$|L(\phi) - L\text{-}\int_G \phi(x)dx| \leqq 2\mathcal{E}L(G) \text{ for every } \mathcal{E} > 0.$$

We hence conclude $L(\phi) = L\text{-}\int_G \phi(x)dx$.

For a uniformly continuous function ϕ on S for $\mathbf{U}$, if $\{x: \phi(x) \neq 0\}$ is totally bounded, then there is a regular set G for L by Theorem 50.6 such that $\phi(x) = 0$ for $x \bar{\epsilon} G$. Then for any other regular set H such that $H \supset \{x: \phi(x) \neq 0\}$, we have by Theorems 51.4 and 51.5

$$L\text{-}\int_H \phi(x)dx = L\text{-}\int_{H \cup G} \phi(x)dx = L\text{-}\int_G \phi(x)dx,$$

because $\phi(x) = 0$ for $x \in (H \cup G) \cap (H \cap G)^{-\prime}$. Therefore we denote this integral by $L\text{-}\int \phi(x)dx$, that is,

$$L\text{-}\int \phi(x)dx = L\text{-}\int_G \phi(x)dx \text{ for } G \supset \{x: \phi(x) \neq 0\}.$$

With this definition we have by Theorem 51.7

$$L(\phi) = L\text{-}\int \phi(x)dx \text{ for every } \phi \in \Phi.$$

Theorem 51.8. *If ϕ is a uniformly continuous function on a regular set G for L and H is an open set such that $\phi(x) \leqq \chi_H(x)$ for every $x \in G$, then*

$$L\text{-}\int_G \phi(x)dx \leqq L(H).$$

Proof. We need only show the case where $\phi \geqq 0$. For any $\mathcal{E} > 0$ we can find $U \in \mathbf{U}$ and a regular set $G_1 \subset G$ by Theorems 49.1 and 50.6 such that $G_1 U \subset G$ and $L(G) \leqq L(G_1) + \mathcal{E}$. Then there is $\phi_0 \in \Phi$ by Theorem 19.2 such that $\phi_0(x) = \phi(x)$ for $x \in G_1$, $\phi_0(x) = 0$ for $x \bar{\epsilon} G$ and $\phi_0 \leqq \phi$. For such ϕ_0 we have $\phi_0 \leqq \chi_H$ by assumption, and hence $L(\phi_0) \leqq L(H)$ by definition. On the other hand we have by Theorems 51.4, 51.6, 51.7 and (5) in 49

$$L\text{-}\int_G \phi(x)dx = L\text{-}\int_{G_1} \phi(x)dx + L\text{-}\int_{G\cap G_1^{-\prime}} \phi(x)dx$$
$$\leqq L(\phi_0) + L(G\cap G_1^{-\prime}) \leqq L(\phi_0) + L(G) - L(G_1) \leqq L(\phi_0) + \varepsilon.$$

Thus $L\text{-}\int_G \phi(x)dx \leqq L(H) + \varepsilon$ for every $\varepsilon > 0$.

52. **Binary Integrals.** Let **U** and **V** be locally totally bounded uniformities respectively on spaces S and R. Let L and K be measures respectively for **U** and **V**. For sets $\emptyset \neq A \subset S$ and $\emptyset \neq B \subset R$ a binary mapping $f(x, y)$ $(x \in A, y \in B)$ from the product space $A \times B$ to the space of all real numbers is called a *binary function* on (A, B). A binary function f on (A, B) is said to be *uniformly continuous* for **U** and **V**, if f is uniformly continuous as a binary mapping for the relative uniformities $\mathbf{U}^A$ and $\mathbf{V}^B$.

Let f be a binary function on (A, B). For any point $x \in A$ we obtain a function $f(x, y)$ $(y \in B)$ on B, which will be denoted by $f(x, \ )$. Similarly, for any point $y \in B$ we obtain a function $f(x, y)$ $(x \in A)$ on A, which will be denoted by $f(\ , y)$.

With this definition we have by Theorem 16.1

Theorem 52.1. *A binary function f on (A, B) is uniformly continuous for* **U** *and* **V** *if and only if both of the systems $f(\ , y)$ $(y \in B)$ and $f(x, \ )$ $(x \in A)$ are equi-continuous respectively for* **U** *and* **V**.

Theorem 52.2. *Let G and H be regular sets respectively on S for L and on R for K. For any uniformly continuous, binary function f on (G, H), $L\text{-}\int_G f(x, y)dx$ $(y \in H)$ is a uniformly continuous function on H for* **V**, *$K\text{-}\int_H f(x, y)dy$ $(x \in G)$ is a uniformly continuous function on G for* **U**, *and*

$$L\text{-}\int_G (K\text{-}\int_H f(x, y)dy)dx = K\text{-}\int_H (L\text{-}\int_G f(x, y)dx)dy.$$

Proof. If a binary function f is uniformly continuous on (G, H) for **U** and **V**, then for any $\varepsilon > 0$ we can find $U \in \mathbf{U}$ and $V \in \mathbf{V}$ by definition such that $x_1 \in x_2U$, $x_1, x_2 \in G$, $y_1 \in y_2V$, $y_1, y_2 \in H$ implies

$$|f(x_1, y_1) - f(x_2, y_2)| < \varepsilon.$$

Setting $x = x_1 = x_2$, we hence obtain that $y_1 \in y_2V$, $y_1, y_2 \in H$ implies

$$|f(x, y_1) - f(x, y_2)| < \varepsilon \text{ for every } x \in G.$$

Thus we obtain by Theorems 51.3, 51.4, 51.6 that $y_1 \in y_2V$, $y_1, y_2 \in H$ implies

$$|L\text{-}\int_G f(x, y_1)dx - L\text{-}\int_G f(x, y_2)dx| \leqq \varepsilon L(G).$$

Therefore $L\text{-}\int_G f(x, y)dx$ $(y \in H)$ is a uniformly continuous function on H for **V**. We can prove similarly that $K\text{-}\int_H f(x, y)dy$ $(x \in G)$ is a uniformly continuous function on G for **U**.

According to Theorem 50.7, there is a regular partition $G_\nu \subset G$ $(\nu = 1, 2, \ldots, n)$ of G such that $G_\nu \subset xU$ for $x \in G_\nu$, and there is a regular partition $H_\mu \subset H$ $(\mu = 1, 2, \ldots, m)$ of H such that $H_\mu \subset yV$ for $y \in H_\mu$. Then we have by Theorem 51.1

$$|\sum_{\nu=1}^{n} f(x_\nu, y)L(G_\nu) - L\text{-}\int_G f(x, y)dx| \leqq \varepsilon L(G)$$

for $x_\nu \in G_\nu$ $(\nu = 1, 2, \ldots, n)$, $y \in H$, and

$$|\sum_{\mu=1}^{m} L\text{-}\int_G f(x, y_\mu)dxK(H_\mu) - K\text{-}\int_H (L\text{-}\int_G f(x, y)dx)dy| \leqq \varepsilon L(G)K(H).$$

Therefore we obtain

$$|\sum_{\mu=1}^{m}\sum_{\nu=1}^{n} f(x_\nu, y_\mu)L(G_\nu)K(H_\mu) - K\text{-}\int_H (L\text{-}\int_G f(x, y)dx)dy| \leqq 2\varepsilon L(G)K(H).$$

We can prove similarly

$$|\sum_{\nu=1}^{n}\sum_{\mu=1}^{m} f(x_\nu, y_\mu)L(G_\nu)K(H_\mu - L\text{-}\int_G (K\text{-}\int_H f(x, y)dy)dx| \leqq 2\varepsilon L(G)K(H).$$

Consequently we have

$$|K\text{-}\int_H (L\text{-}\int_G f(x, y)dx)dy - L\text{-}\int_G (K\text{-}\int_H f(x, y)dy)dx| \leqq 4\mathcal{E}L(G)K(H)$$

for every $\mathcal{E} > 0$. Therefore we conclude Theorem 52.2.

In this proof we also obtained

Theorem 52.3. *For a uniformly continuous binary function f on (G, H), if $x_1 \in x_2U$, $x_1, x_2 \in G$, $y_1 \in y_2V$, $y_1, y_2 \in H$ implies*

$$|f(x_1, y_1) - f(x_2, y_2)| < \mathcal{E},$$

then for any regular partition $G_\nu \subset G$ $(\nu = 1, 2, \ldots, n)$ of G such that $G_\nu \subset xU$ for $x \in G_\nu$ and for any regular partition $H_\mu \subset H$ $(\mu = 1, 2, \ldots, m)$ of H such that $H_\mu \subset yV$ for $y \in H_\mu$, we have

$$|\sum_{\mu=1}^{m} \sum_{\nu=1}^{n} f(x_\nu, y_\mu)L(G_\nu)K(H_\mu) - K\text{-}\int_H (L\text{-}\int_G f(x, y)dx)dy| \leqq 2\mathcal{E}L(G)K(H)$$

for $x_\nu \in G_\nu$ and $y_\mu \in H_\mu$ $(\nu = 1, 2, \ldots, n;\ \mu = 1, 2, \ldots, m)$.

53. **Products of Measures.** The product of two spaces S and R will be denoted by (S, R) in the sequel and the points of (S, R) will be denoted by (x, y) $(x \in S, y \in R)$. For sets $A \subset S$ and $B \subset R$ we define a set $(A, B) \subset (S, R)$ by

$$(A, B) = \{(x, y): x \in A, y \in B\}.$$

For functions ϕ and ψ respectively on S and R, we define a function $\phi\psi$ on (S, R) by

$$\phi\psi(x, y) = \phi(x)\psi(y) \quad \text{for } x \in S \text{ and } y \in R.$$

Concerning characteristic functions, we then have

(1) $\chi_{(A,B)} = \chi_A \chi_B$ for $A \subset S$ and $B \subset R$.

For connectors U on S and V on R we define a connector (U, V) on (S, R) by

$$(x, y)(U, V) = (xU, yV) \quad \text{for } x \in S \text{ and } y \in R.$$

The product of two uniformities **U** on S and **V** on R will be denoted by (**U**, **V**). Referring to Theorem 23.6, we can show easily that (U, V) $(U \in \mathbf{U}, V \in \mathbf{V})$ is a basis of $(\mathbf{U}, \mathbf{V})$, because $(xU, yV) = (xU, R) \cap (S, yV)$.

For completions $\tilde{\mathbf{U}}$ of $\mathbf{U}$ over $\tilde{S} \supset S$ and $\tilde{\mathbf{V}}$ of $\mathbf{V}$ over $\tilde{R} \supset R$, the product $(\tilde{\mathbf{U}}, \tilde{\mathbf{V}})$ is a completion of $(\mathbf{U}, \mathbf{V})$ over $(\tilde{S}, \tilde{R})$ by Theorem 24.3. We obviously have by definition

(2) $(A, B)^{(S,R)} = (A^S, B^R)$ for $A \subset \tilde{S}$ and $B \subset \tilde{R}$.

Let Φ, Ψ and Ω be the trunks of $\mathbf{U}$, $\mathbf{V}$ and $(\mathbf{U}, \mathbf{V})$ respectively. We then have by definition

(3) $\phi\psi \in \Omega$ for $\phi \in \Phi$ and $\psi \in \Psi$.

Every function on (S, R) can be considered a binary function on S and R. It is obvious by definition that a function f on (S, R) is uniformly continuous for $(\mathbf{U}, \mathbf{V})$ if and only if f is uniformly continuous as a binary function for $\mathbf{U}$ and $\mathbf{V}$. We consider now a measure L on S for $\mathbf{U}$ and a measure K on R for $\mathbf{V}$. For any totally bounded set $C \subset (S, R)$ for $(\mathbf{U}, \mathbf{V})$, setting

$$A = \{x: (x, y) \in C\}, \quad B = \{y: (x, y) \in C\},$$

we obtain by Theorems 12.5 and 24.2 a totally bounded set A for $\mathbf{U}$ and a totally bounded set B for $\mathbf{V}$. Thus we can find by Theorem 50.6 a regular set G for L and a regular set H for K such that $A \subset G$ and $B \subset H$. Then we have $C \subset (A, B) \subset (G, H)$. Therefore setting

$$(L, K)(\omega) = L\text{-} \int (K\text{-} \int \omega(x, y)dx)dy \quad \text{for } \omega \in \Omega,$$

we see easily by Theorems 51.2 and 51.3 that (L, K) is a measure on (S, R) for $(\mathbf{U}, \mathbf{V})$. This measure (L, K) is called the *product* of L and K. With this definition we obviously have

(4) $(L, K)\phi\psi = L(\phi)K(\psi)$ for $\phi \in \Phi$ and $\psi \in \Psi$.

Theorem 53.1. *For any open sets G for* $\mathbf{U}$ *and H for* $\mathbf{V}$ *we have*

$$(L, K)(G, H) = L(G)K(H)$$

with the convention: $0(+\infty) = (+\infty)0 = 0$. *If G and H are regular respectively for L and K, then (G, H) is regular for (L, K).*

Proof. For any $\alpha < (L, K)(G, H)$ we can find a totally bounded open set $Z \subset (S, R)$ by Theorem 49.1 such that $\alpha < (L, K)(Z)$ and $Z(U, V) \subset (G, H)$ for some $U \in \mathbf{U}$ and $V \in \mathbf{V}$. Setting

$$A = \{x: (x, y) \in Z\}, \quad B = \{y: (x, y) \in Z\},$$

we obtain totally bounded open sets A for **U** and B for **V** by Theorem 24.2 and

$$Z \subset (A, B) \subset (AU, BV) = (A, B)(U, V) \subset (G, H).$$

Since $AU \subset G$ and $BV \subset H$, we can find $\phi \in \Phi$ and $\psi \in \Psi$ by Theorem 19.2 such that $0 \leqq \phi \leqq 1$, $0 \leqq \psi \leqq 1$,

$$\phi(x) = \begin{cases} 1 & \text{for } x \in A \\ 0 & \text{for } x \bar{\in} G \end{cases} \qquad \psi(x) = \begin{cases} 1 & \text{for } x \in B \\ 0 & \text{for } x \bar{\in} H . \end{cases}$$

Then we have

$$\chi_Z \leqq \phi\psi \leqq \chi_{(G,H)}, \quad \phi \leqq \chi_G, \quad \psi \leqq \chi_H$$

because $Z \subset (A, B)$. Therefore we obtain by (4)

$$a < (L, K)(Z) \leqq (L, K)(\phi\psi) = L(\phi)K(\psi) \leqq L(G)K(H).$$

Consequently we have

$$(L, K)(G, H) \leqq L(G)K(H).$$

On the other hand $\Phi \ni \phi \leqq \chi_G$, $\Psi \ni \psi \leqq \chi_H$ implies

$$\Omega \ni \phi\psi \leqq \chi_G\chi_H = \chi_{(G, H)}$$

by (1), and hence by (4)

$$L(\phi)K(\psi) = (L, K)(\phi\psi) \leqq (L, K)(G, H).$$

Thus we conclude $L(G)K(H) \leqq (L, K)(G, H)$ by definition. Therefore

$$(L, K)(G, H) = L(G)K(H)$$

for any open sets G for **U** and H for **V**.

We assume now that both of **U** and **V** are complete. If G is regular for L and H is regular for K, then for any $\mathcal{E} > 0$ we can find open sets G_0 for **U** and H_0 for **V** by definition such that

$$G^- \subset G_0, \quad L(G_0) \leqq L(G) + \mathcal{E}, \quad H^- \subset H_0, \quad K(H_0) \leqq K(H) + \mathcal{E}.$$

Then we have $(G, H)^- \subset (G^-, H^-) \subset (G_0, H_0)$ by Theorem 12.2 and $(L, K)(G_0, H_0) = L(G_0)K(H_0) \leqq (L(G) + \mathcal{E})(K(H) + \mathcal{E}) = (L, K)(G, H) + \mathcal{E}(L(G) + K(H) + \mathcal{E})$ for every $\mathcal{E} > 0$. Thus we conclude by definition that (G, H) is regular for (L, K), because (G, H) is open and totally bounded for (**U**, **V**) by Theorems 24.2 and 24.5. The general case is concluded immediately by (2).

Theorem 53.2. *For regular sets G and H respectively for L and K, if a function f is uniformly continuous on (G, H) for* (**U**, **V**), *then*

$$(L, K)\text{-}\int_{(G,H)} f(x, y)d(x, y) = L\text{-}\int_G (K\text{-}\int_H f(x, y)dy)dx.$$

Proof. If f is uniformly continuous on (G, H) for (**U**, **V**), then for any $\mathcal{E} > 0$ we can find $U \in \mathbf{U}$ and $V \in \mathbf{V}$ by definition such that $x_1 \in x_2 U$, $x_1, x_2 \in G$, $y_1 \in y_2 V$, $y_1, y_2 \in H$ implies

$$|f(x_1, y_1) - f(x_2, y_2)| < \mathcal{E}.$$

Referring to Theorem 50.7, we also can find a regular partition $G_\nu \subset G$ $(\nu = 1, 2, \ldots, n)$ of G for L such that $G_\nu \subset xU$ for $x \in G$, and a regular partition $H_\mu \subset H$ $(\mu = 1, 2, \ldots, m)$ of H for K such that $H_\mu \subset yV$ for $y \in H_\mu$. Then we see easily that (G_ν, H_μ) $(\nu = 1, 2, \ldots, n;\ \mu = 1, 2, \ldots, m)$ is a regular partition of (G, H) for (L, K) and we have by Theorem 51.1

$$\Big|\sum_{\nu=1}^{n}\sum_{\mu=1}^{m} f(x_\nu, y_\mu)(L, K)(G_\nu, H_\mu) - (L, K)\text{-}\int_{(G,H)} f(x, y)d(x, y)\Big| \leqq \mathcal{E}(L, K)(G, H)$$

for $x_\nu \in G_\nu$, $y_\mu \in H_\mu$ $(\nu = 1, 2, \ldots, n;\ \mu = 1, 2, \ldots, m)$. On the other hand we have by Theorem 52.3

$$\Big|\sum_{\nu=1}^{n}\sum_{\mu=1}^{m} f(x_\nu, y_\mu)L(G_\nu)K(H_\mu) - K\text{-}\int_H (L\text{-}\int_G f(x, y)dx)dy\Big| \leqq 2\mathcal{E}L(G)K(H).$$

Since $(L, K)(G_\nu, H_\mu) = L(G_\nu)K(H_\mu)$ by Theorem 53.1, we hence obtain

$$\Big|(L, K)\text{-}\int_{(G,H)} f(x, y)d(x, y) - K\text{-}\int_H (L\text{-}\int_G f(x, y)dx)dy\Big| \leqq 3\mathcal{E}L(G)K(H)$$

for every $\mathcal{E} > 0$. Thus we obtain Theorem 53.2.

We conclude immediately from Theorem 53.2 by definition

Theorem 53.3. *For regular sets G for L and H for K and for a uniformly continuous function f on (S, R) for* (**U**, **V**), *if*

$$\{(x, y): f(x, y) \neq 0\} \subset (G, H),$$

then $(L, K)\text{-}\int f(x, y)d(x, y) = L\text{-}\int(K\text{-}\int f(x, y)dy)dx = K\text{-}\int(L\text{-}\int f(x, y)dx)dy.$

54. **Semi-Invariant Measures.** Let T be a transformation on a space S. For a function ϕ on S we define a function $T\phi$ on S by

$$T\phi(x) = \phi(xT) \quad \text{for every} \quad x \in S.$$

With this definition we obviously have

$$T(\alpha\phi + \beta\psi) = \alpha T\phi + \beta T\psi$$

$$T(\phi \vee \psi) = T\phi \vee T\psi, \quad T(\phi \wedge \psi) = T\phi \wedge T\psi$$

$$T\phi \leqq T\psi \quad \text{if and only if} \quad \phi \leqq \psi.$$

$(T_1 T_2)\phi = T_1(T_2\phi)$ for two transformations T_1, T_2 on S, because $(T_1 T_2)\phi(x) = \phi(xT_1 T_2) = T_2\phi(xT_1) = T_1(T_2\phi)(x)$.

About characteristic functions we have

(1) $\chi_{AT} = T^{-1} \chi_A$ for $A \subset S$,

because $x \in AT$ if and only if $xT^{-1} \in A$, and hence for any $x \in S$ we have

$$\chi_{AT}(x) = \chi_A(xT^{-1}) = T^{-1} \chi_A(x).$$

Let **U** be a locally totally bounded uniformity on S. A transformation T on S is called a *local unimorphism* for **U**, if both of T and T^{-1} are locally uniformly continuous for **U**. We assume that T is a local unimorphism on S for **U**. Then for the trunk Φ of **U** we have

(2) $T\phi \in \Phi$ for $\phi \in \Phi$.

Because for any $\phi \in \Phi$, $T\phi$ is uniformly continuous for **U** by Theorems 12.11 and 14.3, and $\{x: T\phi(x) > 0\}$ is totally bounded for **U** by Theorem 12.5, since

$$\{x: T\phi(x) > 0\} = \{yT^{-1}: T\phi(yT^{-1}) > 0\} = \{y: \phi(y) > 0\}T^{-1}.$$

A measure L on S for **U** is said to *semi-invariant* by T, if there is $\tau > 0$ such that

$$L(T\phi) = \tau L(\phi) \quad \text{for every} \quad \phi \in \Phi.$$

Here τ is called the *coefficient* for L and T. If L is semi-invariant by T with coefficient τ, then it is obvious by definition that L is semi-invariant by T^{-1} with coefficient $\frac{1}{\tau}$. L is said to be *invariant* by T, if L is semi-invariant by T with coefficient 1.

Theorem 54.1. *If a measure* L *for* $\mathbf{U}$ *is semi-invariant by* T *with coefficient* τ, *then*

$$L(GT) = \frac{1}{\tau} L(G) \quad \textit{for any open set } G \subset S.$$

Proof. We see by (1) that $\phi \leqq \chi_{GT}$ if and only if

$$T\phi \leqq T\chi_{GT} = \chi_{GTT^{-1}} = \chi_G.$$

Thus, if L is semi-invariant by T with coefficient τ, then

$$L(GT) = \sup_{\Phi \ni \phi \leqq \chi_{GT}} L(\phi) = \sup_{\Phi \ni T\phi \leqq \chi_G} \frac{1}{\tau} L(T\phi) = \frac{1}{\tau} L(G).$$

Let $\tilde{\mathbf{U}}$ be a completion of $\mathbf{U}$ over $\tilde{S} \supset S$. A local unimorphism T on S for $\mathbf{U}$ can be extended uniquely to a local unimorphism $\tilde{T}$ on $\tilde{S}$ for $\tilde{\mathbf{U}}$ by Theorem 30.5. Then we have

(3) $(\tilde{A}\tilde{T})^S = \tilde{A}^S T$ for $\tilde{A} \subset \tilde{S}$,

because $\tilde{A}\tilde{T} \cap S = \tilde{A}\tilde{T} \cap S\tilde{T} = (\tilde{A} \cap S)\tilde{T} = (\tilde{A} \cap S)T$. For any function $\tilde{\phi}$ on $\tilde{S}$ we have

(4) $(\tilde{T}\tilde{\phi})^S = T\tilde{\phi}^S$,

because $\tilde{T}\tilde{\phi}(x) = \tilde{\phi}(x\tilde{T}) = \tilde{\phi}(xT) = \tilde{\phi}^S(xT) = T\tilde{\phi}^S(x)$ for every $x \in S$. Thus, if L is semi-invariant by T with coefficient τ, then for the completion $\tilde{L}$ of L over $\tilde{S}$ we have by (8) in 49

$$\tilde{L}(\tilde{T}\tilde{\phi}) = L((\tilde{T}\tilde{\phi})^S) = L(T\tilde{\phi}^S) = \tau L(\tilde{\phi}^S) = \tau \tilde{L}(\tilde{\phi})$$

for every $\tilde{\phi} \in \tilde{\Phi}$, that is, $\tilde{L}$ is semi-invariant by $\tilde{T}$ with coefficient τ. Therefore we have by Theorem 54.1

(5) $\tilde{L}(\tilde{G}\tilde{T}) = \frac{1}{\tau} \tilde{L}(\tilde{G})$ for any open set $\tilde{G} \subset \tilde{S}$.

If $\tilde{G}$ is regular for $\tilde{L}$, then for any $\varepsilon > 0$ there is an open set $\tilde{H}$ by definition such that $\tilde{G} \prec \tilde{H}$ and $\tilde{L}(\tilde{H}) \leqq \tilde{L}(\tilde{G}) + \varepsilon$. Since $\tilde{T}$ is a homeomorphism, we have then $\tilde{G}\tilde{T} \prec \tilde{H}\tilde{T}$ and $\tilde{L}(\tilde{H}\tilde{T}) \leqq \tilde{L}(\tilde{G}\tilde{T}) + \frac{\varepsilon}{\tau}$ by (5). Therefore $\tilde{G}\tilde{T}$ also is regular for $\tilde{L}$ by definition. We hence conclude by (3) generally

Theorem 54.2. *If a measure* L *is semi-invariant by* T *and if* G *is regular for* L, *then* GT *also is regular for* L.

Theorem 54.3. *If a measure L is semi-invariant by T with coefficient τ, then for any regular set G for L and for any uniformly continuous function ϕ on GT for* **U** *we have*

$$L\text{-}\int_G \phi(xT)dx = \tau L\text{-}\int_{GT} \phi(x)dx.$$

Proof. Since ϕ is uniformly continuous on GT for **U** by assumption, for any $\mathcal{E} > 0$ we can find $U \in \mathbf{U}$ such that $x \in yU$, $x, y \in GT$ implies

$$|\phi(x) - \phi(y)| < \mathcal{E}.$$

For such $U \in \mathbf{U}$ there is $V \in \mathbf{U}$ such that $xVT \subset xTU$ for every $x \in G$, because T is uniformly continuous on every totally bounded set for **U**. If $x \in yV$, $x, y \in G$, then $xT \in yVT \subset yTU$, $xT, yT \in GT$, which implies

$$|\phi(xT) - \phi(yT)| < \mathcal{E}.$$

Therefore $T\phi$ is uniformly continuous on G for **U**. Furthermore, for a regular partition $G_\nu \subset G$ $(\nu = 1, 2, \ldots, n)$ of G such that $G_\nu \subset xV$ for $x \in G_\nu$, we see easily that $G_\nu T$ $(\nu = 1, 2, \ldots, n)$ is a regular partition of GT such that $G_\nu T \subset yU$ for $y \in G_\nu T$, and we have by Theorem 51.1

$$\left|\sum_{\nu=1}^{n} \phi(x_\nu T)L(G_\nu) - L\text{-}\int_G \phi(xT)dx\right| \leqq \mathcal{E}L(G)$$

$$\left|\sum_{\nu=1}^{n} \phi(x_\nu T)L(G_\nu T) - L\text{-}\int_{GT} \phi(x)dx\right| \leqq \mathcal{E}L(GT)$$

for $x_\nu \in G_\nu$ $(\nu = 1, 2, \ldots, n)$. Since $L(G_\nu) = \tau L(G_\nu T)$ and $L(G) = \tau L(GT)$ by Theorem 54.1, we hence obtain

$$\left|L\text{-}\int_G \phi(xT)dx - \tau L\text{-}\int_{GT} \phi(x)dx\right| \leqq 2\mathcal{E}L(G)$$

for every $\mathcal{E} > 0$. Therefore we obtain Theorem 54.3.

Let **G** be a transformation group on S. If **G** is uniformly continuous for **U**, then every $T \in \mathbf{G}$ is a unimorphism on S for **U** by definition. A measure L on S for **U** is said to be *semi-invariant* by **G**, if L is semi-invariant by every $T \in \mathbf{G}$. L is said to be *invariant* by **G**, if L is invariant by every $T \in \mathbf{G}$. Setting $L(\phi) = 0$ for every $\phi \in \Phi$, we obviously obtain a measure L on S for **U**, which will be denoted by 0.

Theorem 54.4. *Let* **G** *be an equi-continuous, transitive group on S for* **U**. *For any semi-invariant measure $L \neq 0$ on S by* **G** *for* **U** *we have*

$L(\phi) > 0$ for $0 \neq \phi \in \Phi$, and for a uniformly continuous function ϕ on a regular set G for L, if $L\text{-}\int_G \phi(x)dx = 0$ and $\phi(x) \geqq 0$ for every $x \in G$, then $\phi(x) = 0$ for every $x \in G$.

Proof. Since $L \neq 0$ by assumption, there is $\phi_0 \in \Phi$ such that $L(\phi_0) > 0$. If $\phi(a) > \varepsilon > 0$, $\phi \in \Phi$, $a \in S$, then there is $U \in \mathbf{U}$ such that $\phi(x) > \varepsilon$ for every $x \in aU$, because ϕ is uniformly continuous for **U**. For such $U \in \mathbf{U}$ we can find a finite system $x_\nu \in S$ ($\nu = 1, 2, \ldots, n$) such that

$$\{x: \phi_0(x) > 0\} \subset \bigcup_{\nu=1}^{n} x_\nu U^{\mathbf{G}}.$$

Since **G** is transitive by assumption, we can find $T_\nu \in \mathbf{G}$ ($\nu = 1, 2, \ldots, n$) such that $x_\nu = aT_\nu$. For $\gamma = \sup_{x \in S} \phi_0(x)$ we have then

$$\phi_0 \leqq \gamma \chi_{\{x:\ \phi_0(x) > 0\}} \leqq \gamma \sum_{\nu=1}^{n} \chi_{aT_\nu U^{\mathbf{G}}} = \gamma \sum_{\nu=1}^{n} T_\nu^{-1} \chi_{aU^{\mathbf{G}}}$$

$$\leqq \frac{\gamma}{\varepsilon} \sum_{\nu=1}^{n} T_\nu^{-1} \phi,$$

and hence $0 < L(\phi_0) \leqq \frac{\gamma}{\varepsilon} \sum_{\nu=1}^{n} L(T_\nu^{-1}\phi) = \frac{\gamma}{\varepsilon} \left(\sum_{\nu=1}^{n} \frac{1}{\tau_\nu} \right) L(\phi)$ for the coefficients τ_ν for L and T_ν. Consequently $L(\phi) > 0$.

For a uniformly continuous function ϕ on G, if $\phi(x) \geqq 0$ for every $x \in G$ and $\phi(a) > 0$ for some $a \in G$, then we can find $\psi \in \Phi$ by Theorem 19.2 such that $\psi(a) > 0$, $\psi(x) \leqq \phi(x)$ for every $x \in G$ and $\psi(x) = 0$ for $x \,\bar{\in}\, G$. Thus we obtain by Theorem 51.3 and 51.7

$$L\text{-}\int_G \phi(x)dx \geqq L\text{-}\int_G \psi(x)dx = L(\psi) > 0.$$

55. **Theorem of Existence.** Let **U** be a locally totally bounded uniformity on a space S and let **G** be a transformation group on S which is transitive and equi-continuous for **U**. For the trunk Φ of **U**, setting

$$\omega(\phi, U) = \inf \{ \sum_{\nu=1}^{n} \alpha_\nu : \phi \leqq \sum_{\nu=1}^{n} \alpha_\nu \chi_{x_\nu U^{\mathbf{G}}},\ \alpha_\nu \geqq 0,$$
$$x_\nu \in S\ (\nu = 1, 2, \ldots, n),\ n = 1, 2, \ldots \}$$

for $\phi \in \Phi$ and $U \in \mathbf{U}$, we have $0 \leqq \omega(\phi, U) < +\infty$, because we can find $x_\nu \in S$ ($\nu = 1, 2, \ldots, n$) such that

$$\{x: \phi(x) > 0\} \subset \bigcup_{\nu=1}^{n} x_\nu U^{\mathbf{G}}$$

and hence $\phi \leqq \sum_{\nu=1}^{n} \gamma \chi_{x_\nu U^{\mathbf{G}}}$ for $\gamma = \sup_{x \in S} \phi(x)$. Since

$$\phi \leqq \sum_{\nu=1}^{n} a_\nu \chi_{x_\nu U^{\mathbf{G}}} \text{ implies } a\phi \leqq \sum_{\nu=1}^{n} a a_\nu \chi_{x_\nu U^{\mathbf{G}}}$$

for $a \geqq 0$, we have $\omega(a\phi, U) \leqq a\omega(\phi, U)$ for $a \geqq 0$. Thus we also have

$$\omega(\phi, U) = \omega(\frac{1}{a} a\phi, U) \leqq \frac{1}{a} \omega(a\phi, U)$$

for $a > 0$. Consequently we have

(1) $\omega(a\phi, U) = a\omega(\phi, U)$ for $a \geqq 0$.

If $\phi \leqq \sum_{\nu=1}^{n} a_\nu \chi_{x_\nu U^{\mathbf{G}}}$, $\psi \leqq \sum_{\mu=1}^{m} \beta_\mu \chi_{y_\mu U^{\mathbf{G}}}$, then we have

$$\phi + \psi \leqq \sum_{\nu=1}^{n} a_\nu \chi_{x_\nu U^{\mathbf{G}}} + \sum_{\mu=1}^{m} \beta_\mu \chi_{y_\mu U^{\mathbf{G}}}$$

and hence $\omega(\phi + \psi, U) \leqq \sum_{\nu=1}^{n} a_\nu + \sum_{\mu=1}^{m} \beta_\mu$. Consequently

(2) $\omega(\phi + \psi, U) \leqq \omega(\phi, U) + \omega(\psi, U)$.

Since $\phi \leqq \sum_{\nu=1}^{n} a_\nu \chi_{x_\nu U^{\mathbf{G}}}$ implies $T\phi \leqq \sum_{\nu=1}^{n} a_\nu T\chi_{x_\nu U^{\mathbf{G}}} = \sum_{\nu=1}^{n} a_\nu \chi_{x_\nu T^{-1} U^{\mathbf{G}}}$ for $T \in \mathbf{G}$ by (1) in 54, we have $\omega(T\phi, U) \leqq \omega(\phi, U)$. Thus we also have

$$\omega(\phi, U) = \omega(T^{-1}T\phi, U) \leqq \omega(T\phi, U).$$

Consequently we obtain

(3) $\omega(T\phi, U) = \omega(\phi, U)$ for $\phi \in \Phi$, $U \in \mathbf{U}$, $T \in \mathbf{G}$.

Let $U_0 \in \mathbf{U}$ be totally bounded. For a point $a \in S$ we set

$$\omega_a(U) = \inf \{ \sum_{\nu=1}^{n} a_\nu : \chi_{aU_0^{\mathbf{G}}} \leqq \sum_{\nu=1}^{n} a_\nu \chi_{x_\nu U^{\mathbf{G}}},$$
$$a_\nu \geqq 0,\ x_\nu \in S\ (\nu = 1, 2, \ldots, n),\ n = 1, 2, \ldots \}$$

for $U \epsilon \mathbf{U}$. Since $\chi_{aU_0^{\mathbf{G}}} \leqq \sum_{\nu=1}^{n} \alpha_\nu \chi_{x_\nu U^{\mathbf{G}}}$ implies $1 = \chi_{aU_0^{\mathbf{G}}}(a) \leqq \sum_{\nu=1}^{n} \alpha_\nu$, we have $1 \leqq \omega_a(U) < +\infty$. It is obvious that

$$\omega_a(U) \leqq \omega(\phi, U) \quad \text{if} \quad \chi_{aU_0^{\mathbf{G}}} \leqq \phi \epsilon \Phi,$$

and there is really such $\phi \epsilon \Phi$ by Theorem 19.2.

For any $\phi \epsilon \Phi$, since $\{x: \phi(x) > 0\}$ is totally bounded, we can find $a_\mu \epsilon S$ $(\mu = 1, 2, \ldots, m)$ such that

$$\{x: \phi(x) > 0\} \subset \bigcup_{\mu=1}^{m} a_\mu U_0^{\mathbf{G}}.$$

For $\gamma = \sup_{x \epsilon G} \phi(x)$ we then have $\phi \leqq \sum_{\mu=1}^{m} \gamma \chi_{a_\mu U_0^{\mathbf{G}}}$. Since $\mathbf{G}$ is transitive by assumption, we can find $T_\mu \epsilon \mathbf{G}$ $(\mu = 1, 2, \ldots, m)$ such that $a_\mu = aT_\mu$.

For $U \epsilon \mathbf{U}$, if $\chi_{aU_0^{\mathbf{G}}} \leqq \sum_{\nu=1}^{n} \alpha_\nu \chi_{x_\nu U^{\mathbf{G}}}$, then we have by (1) in 54

$$\chi_{a_\mu U_0^{\mathbf{G}}} T_\mu^{-1} \chi_{aU_0^{\mathbf{G}}} \leqq \sum_{\nu=1}^{n} \alpha_\nu \chi_{x_\nu T_\mu U^{\mathbf{G}}}$$

for $\mu = 1, 2, \ldots, m$. Thus we obtain

$$\phi \leqq \sum_{\mu=1}^{m} \sum_{\nu=1}^{n} \gamma \alpha_\nu \chi_{x_\nu T_\mu U^{\mathbf{G}}}$$

Consequently we obtain by definition

$$\omega(\phi, U) \leqq \gamma m \sum_{\nu=1}^{n} \alpha_\nu .$$

We hence conclude $\omega(\phi, U) \leqq \gamma m \omega_a(U)$, that is,

$$\frac{\omega(\phi, U)}{\omega_a(U)} \leqq \gamma m \quad \text{for every } U \epsilon \mathbf{U}.$$

Since $\mathbf{U}$ is a directed space, there is a partial system $U_\delta \epsilon \mathbf{U}$ $(\delta \epsilon \Delta)$ by Theorem 29.7 such that for any bounded function $f(U)$ $(U \epsilon \mathbf{U})$ the partial system $f(U_\delta)$ $(\delta \epsilon \Delta)$ is always convergent. Then setting

$$L(\phi) = \lim_{\delta \epsilon \Delta} \frac{\omega(\phi, U_\delta)}{\omega_a(U_\delta)}$$

we obviously have by (1), (2), (3) and Theorem 18.6

$0 \leqq L(\phi) < +\infty$ for every $\phi \in \Phi$,

$L(a\phi) = aL(\phi)$ for $a \geqq 0$,

$L(T\phi) = L(\phi)$ for every $T \in \mathbf{G}$ and $\phi \in \Phi$,

$L(\phi) \geqq 1$ if $\chi_{aU_0^{\mathbf{G}}} \leqq \phi \in \Phi$,

$L(\phi + \psi) \leqq L(\phi) + L(\psi)$ for $\phi, \psi \in \Phi$.

For $\psi \in \Phi$, if $x \in yU$ implies $|\psi(x) - \psi(y)| < \mathcal{E}$, then

$$\psi \sum_{\nu=1}^{n} a_\nu \chi_{x_\nu U} \leqq \sum_{\nu=1}^{n} a_\nu (\psi(x_\nu) + \mathcal{E}) \chi_{x_\nu U},$$

because for any $x \in S$ we have

$$\psi(x) \sum_{\nu=1}^{n} a_\nu \chi_{x_\nu U}(x) = \sum_{x \in x_\nu U} a_\nu \psi(x)$$

$$\leqq \sum_{x \in x_\nu U} a_\nu (\psi(x_\nu) + \mathcal{E}) = \sum_{\nu=1}^{n} a_\nu (\psi(x_\nu) + \mathcal{E}) \chi_{x_\nu U}(x).$$

If $\phi, \psi_1, \psi_2 \in \Phi$ and $\psi_1 + \psi_2 \leqq 1$, then for any $\mathcal{E} > 0$ we can find $V \in \mathbf{U}$ such that $x \in yV$ implies

$$|\psi_1(x) - \psi_1(y)| < \mathcal{E} \text{ and } |\chi_2(x) - \chi_2(y)| < \mathcal{E}.$$

For any $U \leqq V$ we have naturally that $x \in yU^{\mathbf{G}}$ implies

$$|\psi_1(x) - \psi_1(y)| < \mathcal{E} \text{ and } |\psi_2(x) - \psi_2(y)| < \mathcal{E}.$$

Thus if $\phi \leqq \sum_{\nu=1}^{n} a_\nu \chi_{x_\nu U^{\mathbf{G}}}$, $\mathbf{U} \ni U \leqq V$, then, since $\chi_{x_\nu U^{\mathbf{G}}}(x) \neq 0$ implies $\psi_1(x) \leqq \psi_1(x_\nu) + \mathcal{E}$, we obtain

$$\phi\psi_1 \leqq \psi_1 \sum_{\nu=1}^{n} a_\nu \chi_{x_\nu U^{\mathbf{G}}} \leqq \sum_{\nu=1}^{n} a_\nu (\psi_1(x_\nu) + \mathcal{E}) \chi_{x_\nu U^{\mathbf{G}}}$$

and similarly

$$\phi\psi_2 \leqq \sum_{\nu=1}^{n} a_\nu (\psi_2(x_\nu) + \mathcal{E}) \chi_{x_\nu U^{\mathbf{G}}}.$$

Consequently we have by definition

$$\omega(\phi\psi_1, U) + \omega(\phi\psi_2, U) \leqq \sum_{\nu=1}^{n} a_\nu(\psi_1(x_\nu) + \mathcal{E}) + \sum_{\nu=1}^{n} a_\nu(\psi_2(x_\nu) + \mathcal{E})$$
$$\leqq \sum_{\nu=1}^{n} a_\nu(1 + 2\mathcal{E}).$$

Therefore we have $\omega(\phi\psi_1, U) + \omega(\phi\psi_2, U) \leqq \omega(\phi, U)(1 + 2\mathcal{E})$ for every $\mathcal{E} > 0$ and $\mathbf{U} \ni U \leqq V$. Thus we obtain

$$\omega(\phi\psi_1, U) + \omega(\phi\psi_2, U) \leqq \omega(\phi, U) \text{ for } \mathbf{U} \ni U \leqq V.$$

We hence conclude by definition

$$L(\phi\psi_1) + L(\phi\psi_2) \leqq L(\phi) \text{ if } \psi_1 + \psi_2 \leqq 1,\ \psi_1, \psi_2 \in \Phi.$$

For any $\phi_1, \phi_2 \in \Phi$ there is $\psi \in \Phi$ by Theorem 19.2 such that

$$\psi(x) = \begin{cases} 1 \text{ for } x \in \{y: \phi_1(y) + \phi_2(y) > 0\}U_0^{\,2} \\ 0 \text{ for } x \,\bar{\in}\, \{y: \phi_1(y) + \phi_2(y) > 0\}U_0^{\,3} \end{cases}$$

and we see easily by Theorem 12.10 that $\phi_1 + \phi_2 + \psi \in \Phi$ and

$$\frac{\phi_1}{\phi_1 + \phi_2 + \mathcal{E}\psi}, \frac{\phi_2}{\phi_1 + \phi_2 + \mathcal{E}\psi} \in \Phi \text{ for } \mathcal{E} > 0$$

with the convention: $\frac{0}{0} = 0$. Thus we obtain

$$L(\phi_1) + L(\phi_2) \leqq L(\phi_1 + \phi_2 + \mathcal{E}\psi) \leqq L(\phi_1 + \phi_2) + \mathcal{E}L(\psi)$$

for every $\mathcal{E} > 0$, and hence $L(\phi_1) + L(\phi_2) \leqq L(\phi_1 + \phi_2)$. Consequently

$$L(\phi_1 + \phi_2) = L(\phi_1) + L(\phi_2) \text{ for } \phi_1, \phi_2 \in \Phi.$$

Therefore L is a measure for $\mathbf{U}$ which is invariant by $\mathbf{G}$, and $L \neq 0$. Now we can state

Theorem of Existence. *If a transitive group* $\mathbf{G}$ *on a space* S *is equi-continuous for a locally totally bounded uniformity* $\mathbf{U}$ *on* S, *then there exists an invariant measure* $L \neq 0$ *on* S *by* $\mathbf{G}$ *for* $\mathbf{U}$.

56. **Theorem of Uniqueness.** Let $\mathbf{G}$ be a transitive group on a space S such that $\mathbf{G}$ is equi-continuous for a locally totally bounded uniformity $\mathbf{U}$ on S, that is, $\mathbf{U}^{\mathbf{G}} \subset \mathbf{U}$. We assume in addition that $\mathbf{U}$ is normal for $\mathbf{G}$.

Then the weak-uniformity **W(U)** on **G** by the system of point mappings M_x $(x \in S)$ is locally totally bounded by Theorem 34.11, and for any totally bounded set $A \subset S$ for **U** the inverse image AM_x^{-1} also is totally bounded for **W(U)** for every $x \in S$ by Theorem 37.11. Furthermore the induced neighbourhood **N(U)** on **G** is locally uniformly regular by Theorem 44.9, and hence the inversion Iv on **G** is locally uniformly continuous for **W(U)** by Theorem 41.11, that is, Iv is uniformly continuous on any totally bounded set for **W(U)** by Theorem 12.11.

Since the weak-uniformity **W(U)** on **G** is the induced uniformity of the induced neighbourhood **N(U)** on **G** by Theorem 42.6, **W(U)** is invariant by the right transformation group on the group **G**. Therefore there is an invariant measure $K \neq 0$ on **G** for **W(U)** by the right transformation group by Theorem of Existence in 55, and for a regular set $\mathbf{R} \subset \mathbf{G}$ for K and for a uniformly continuous function ψ on $\mathbf{R}T$ for **W(U)** we have by Theorem 54.3

$$K\text{-}\int_{\mathbf{R}} \psi(XT)dX = K\text{-}\int_{\mathbf{R}T} \psi(X)dX \quad \text{for } T \in \mathbf{G}.$$

Let $L \neq 0$ be an arbitrary invariant measure on S by **G** for **U** and let Φ be the trunk of **U**. For a point $a \in S$ we can find a system $\psi_U \in \Phi$ $(U \in \mathbf{U})$ by Theorem 19.2 such that $\psi_U(a) > 0$ and

$$\{x\colon \psi_U(x) > 0\} \subset aU^{\mathbf{G}} \quad \text{for every } U \in \mathbf{U}.$$

Let $V_0 \in \mathbf{U}$ be symmetric and totally bounded. For any set $A \subset S$ we have

$$\{X\colon \psi_U(xX^{-1}) > 0\} \subset AV_0M_a^{-1} \quad \text{for } x \in A \text{ and } \mathbf{U} \ni U \leqq V_0.$$

Because if $x \in A$ and $xX^{-1} \in aU^{\mathbf{G}}$, then we have $aX \in x(U^{\mathbf{G}})^{-1} \subset xV_0 \subset AV_0$, that is, $X \in AV_0M_a^{-1}$. If A is totally bounded for **U**, then $AV_0M_a^{-1}$ is totally bounded for **W(U)**.

For $\phi \in \Phi$ we can find a regular set $G \subset S$ for L by Theorem 50.6 such that

$$\{x\colon \phi(x) > 0\} \subset G,$$

and there is a regular set $\mathbf{R} \subset \mathbf{G}$ for K *by* Theorem 50.6 such that $GV_0M_a^{-1} \subset \mathbf{R}$, and we have

$$\{(x, X): \phi(x)\psi_U(xX^{-1}) > 0\} \subset (G, \mathbf{R}) \text{ for } \mathbf{U} \ni U \leqq V_0.$$

For a regular set $G_1 \supset GV_0$ for L we have

$$\{(x, X): \phi(aX)\chi_U(xX^{-1}) > 0\} \subset (G_1, \mathbf{R}) \text{ for } \mathbf{U} \ni U \leqq V_0.$$

Because if $aX \in G$ and $xX^{-1} \in aU^{\mathbf{G}}$, then we have $X \in GM_a^{-1} \subset \mathbf{R}$ and

$$x \in aU^{\mathbf{G}}X = aXU^{\mathbf{G}} \subset a(GM_a^{-1})U^{\mathbf{G}} \subset GV_0 \subset G_1.$$

For a regular set $\mathbf{R}_1 \supset G_1V_0M_a^{-1} \cup \mathbf{R}$ for K we have then

$$\{X: \psi_U(xX^{-1}) > 0\} \subset \mathbf{R}_1 \text{ for } x \in G_1 \text{ and } \mathbf{U} \ni U \leqq V_0.$$

Since the inversion Iv is uniformly continuous on $\mathbf{R}_1$, the binary function $\psi_U(xX^{-1})$ $(x \in S,\ X \in \mathbf{G})$ is uniformly continuous on $(G_1, \mathbf{R}_1)$ for $(\mathbf{U}, \mathbf{W}(\mathbf{U}))$ by Theorems 33.3 and 16.1.

For any $\mathcal{E} > 0$ and for any $\phi \in \Phi$ we can find a symmetric $V \in \mathbf{U}$ such that $V \leqq V_0$ and $x \in yV$ implies $|\phi(x) - \phi(y)| < \mathcal{E}$. Then we have

$$|\phi(x)\psi_U(xX^{-1}) - \phi(aX)\psi_U(xX^{-1})| \leqq \mathcal{E}\psi_U(xX^{-1}) \text{ for } \mathbf{U} \ni U \leqq V.$$

Because if $\psi_U(xX^{-1}) > 0$, then $xX^{-1} \in aU^{\mathbf{G}}$, and hence $aX \in x(U^{\mathbf{G}})^{-1} \subset xV$, and consequently $|\phi(x) - \phi(aX)| < \mathcal{E}$. Therefore we obtain by Theorems 51.2, 51.3 and 53.3

$$|L\text{-}\int(K\text{-}\int\phi(x)\psi_U(xX^{-1})dX)dx - K\text{-}\int(L\text{-}\int\phi(aX)\psi_U(xX^{-1})dx)dX|$$

$$\leqq \mathcal{E}L\text{-}\int_{G_1}(K\text{-}\int_{\mathbf{R}_1}\psi_U(xX^{-1})dX)dx = \mathcal{E}L\text{-}\int_{G_1}(K\text{-}\int\psi_U(xX^{-1})dX)dx$$

for $\mathbf{U} \ni U \leqq V$. On the other hand, setting $x = aT$, $T \in \mathbf{G}$, we have by Theorem 54.3

$$K\text{-}\int\psi_U(xX^{-1})dX = K\text{-}\int\psi_U(a(XT^{-1})^{-1})dX = K\text{-}\int\psi_U(aX^{-1})dX,$$

and we have by Theorems 54.3 and 51.7

$$L\text{-}\int\psi_U(xX^{-1})dx = L\text{-}\int\psi_U(x)dx = L(\psi_U) \text{ for every } X \in \mathbf{G}.$$

Thus we obtain by Theorems 51.6 and 51.7

$$|L(\phi)K\text{-}\int\psi_U(aX^{-1})dX - L(\psi_U)K\text{-}\int\phi(aX)dX|$$

$$\leqq \mathcal{E}L(G_1)K\text{-}\int\psi_U(aX^{-1})dX$$

for $\mathbf{U} \ni U \leqq V$. Since $\psi_U(aE^{-1}) = \psi_U(a) > 0$, we have by Theorem 54.4

$$K\text{-} \int \psi_U(aX^{-1})dX > 0,$$

because the right transformation group is transitive and equi-continuous for $\mathbf{W}(\mathbf{U})$. Therefore we obtain

$$\left| L(\phi) - \frac{L(\psi_U)}{K\text{-} \int \psi_U(aX^{-1})dX} K\text{-} \int \phi(aX)dX \right| \leqq \varepsilon L(G_1)$$

for $\mathbf{U} \ni U \leqq V$. We hence conclude that there exists

$$\alpha = \lim_{U \in \mathbf{U}} \frac{L(\psi_U)}{K\text{-} \int \psi_U(aX^{-1})dX}$$

and $L(\phi) = \alpha K\text{-} \int \phi(aX)dX$ for every $\phi \in \Phi$. Therefore for any two invariant measures $L_1, L_2 \neq 0$ on S for $\mathbf{U}$ by $\mathbf{G}$ there exists $\gamma > 0$ such that $L_1(\phi) = \gamma L_2(\phi)$ for every $\phi \in \Phi$. Now we can state

Theorem of Uniqueness. *For a transitive group* $\mathbf{G}$ *on* S, *if a uniformity* $\mathbf{U}$ *on* S *is invariant and normal for* $\mathbf{G}$, *then the invariant measure on* S *for* $\mathbf{U}$ *by* $\mathbf{G}$ *is determined uniquely in the sense that for any two invariant measures* $L_1, L_2 \neq 0$ *on* S *for* $\mathbf{U}$ *by* $\mathbf{G}$ *there is* $\gamma > 0$ *such that* $L_1 = \gamma L_2$, *and for the weak-uniformity* $\mathbf{W}(\mathbf{U})$ *on* $\mathbf{G}$ *there is an invariant measure* $K \neq 0$ *on* $\mathbf{G}$ *by the right transformation group such that setting*

$$L_a(\phi) = K\text{-} \int \phi(aX)dX \quad \text{for } \phi \in \Phi,$$

we obtain an invariant measure $L_a \neq 0$ *on* S *for* $\mathbf{U}$ *by* $\mathbf{G}$ *for every* $a \in S$.

Theorems of Existence and Uniqueness are available for Haar measures on locally compact topological groups.

57. **Measures on Groups.** Let G be a group and let $\mathbf{N}$ be a neighbourhood on G. We suppose that $\mathbf{N}$ is regular and right totally bounded. The induced uniformity $\mathbf{U}(\mathbf{N})$ is invariant by the right transformation group, regular by Theorem 39.1 and locally totally bounded by Theorem 40.3. Thus $\mathbf{U}(\mathbf{N})$ is normal for the right transformation group by Theorem

40.5. Therefore there exists an invariant measure $L \neq 0$ on G for **N** by the right transformation group by Theorem of Existence in 55, and for any two invariant measures L_1, $L_2 \neq 0$ by the right transformation group there is $\gamma > 0$ by Theorem of Uniqueness in 56 such that $L_1 = \gamma L_2$.

A measure L on G for **N** is said to be *right-invariant,* if L is invariant by the right transformation group. L is said to be *left-invariant* if L is invariant by the left transformation group.

Let $L \neq 0$ be a right-invariant measure on G. For the trunk Φ of **U**(**N**) we have by Theorems 54.3 and 51.7

$$L\text{-} \int \phi(xy)dx = L\text{-} \int \phi(x)dx = L(\phi) \quad \text{for } \phi \in \Phi \text{ and } y \in G,$$

that is, making use of the notations:

$$y\phi(x) = \phi(xy), \quad \phi y(x) = \phi(yx) \quad \text{for } x, y \in G,$$

we have $L(y\phi) = L(\phi)$ for every $\phi \in \Phi$ and $y \in G$. Since the left transformations are uniformly continuous for **N** by Theorem 39.3, we have $\phi y \in \Phi$ for $\phi \in \Phi$ and $y \in G$. Thus setting

$$K_y(\phi) = L(\phi y) \quad \text{for } \phi \in \Phi \text{ and } y \in G,$$

we see easily that K_y is a measure on G for **N**. Furthermore K_y is invariant by every right transformation, because

$$z(\phi y)(x) = \phi(yxz) = (z\phi)y(x) \quad \text{for } x, y, z \in G$$

and $K_y(z\phi) = L((z\phi)y) = L(z(\phi y)) = L(\phi y) = K_y(\phi)$ for every $z \in G$. Therefore there is a function τ on G by Theorem of Uniqueness in 56 such that

$$(1) \quad L(\phi y) = \tau(y)L(\phi) \quad \text{for } \phi \in \Phi \text{ and } y \in G,$$

that is, L is semi-invariant by the left transformation L_y with coefficient $\tau(y)$ for every $y \in G$. We see easily by Theorem of Uniqueness that this function τ on G is the same for any other right-invariant measure $L \neq 0$ in (1). Thus τ is called the *coefficient function* of G for **N**.

Concerning the coefficient function τ of G for **N** we obviously have by the definition (1)

$$\tau(e) = 1, \quad 0 < \tau(y) < +\infty \quad \text{for every } y \in G,$$

and $\tau(yz) = \tau(y)\tau(z)$ for $y, z \in G$, because

$$\tau(yz)L(\phi) = L(\phi(yz)) = L((\phi y)z) = \tau(z)L(\phi y) = \tau(z)\tau(y)L(\phi).$$

Setting $z = y^{-1}$, we hence obtain $\tau(y)\tau(y^{-1}) = 1$. Thus we can state

Theorem 57.1. *For the coefficient function τ of G for* **N** *we have*

$$\tau(e) = 1, \quad \tau(yz) = \tau(y)\tau(z), \quad \tau(y)\tau(y^{-1}) = 1 \quad \text{for } y, z \in G.$$

For the characteristic function χ_A of a set $A \subset G$, we have

(2) $\chi_{yA} = \chi_A y^{-1}$ for $y \in G$,

because $x \in yA$ if and only if $y^{-1}x \in A$, and hence

$$\chi_{yA}(x) = \chi_A(y^{-1}x) \quad \text{for every } x \in G.$$

Referring to Theorems 54.1 and 54.2, we obtain

Theorem 57.2. *For any open set $H \subset G$ for* **N** *we have*

$$L(yH) = \frac{1}{\tau(y)} L(H) \quad \text{for every } y \in G.$$

If H is regular for L, then yH also is regular for L for every $y \in G$.

We also obtain by Theorem 54.3

Theorem 57.3. *For a regular set $H \subset G$ for L and for a uniformly continuous function ϕ on yH for* **N**, *we have*

$$L\text{-}\int_H \phi(yx)dx = \tau(y)L\text{-}\int_{yH} \phi(x)dx \quad \text{for every } y \in G.$$

Theorem 57.4. *The coefficient function τ of G for* **N** *is locally uniformly continuous for* **U**(**N**).

Proof. Let $A \subset G$ be an arbitrary totally bounded set for **U**(**N**). Since **N** is locally uniformly regular by Theorem 40.4, the inversion Iv is locally uniformly continuous for **U**(**N**) by Theorem 41.11. Therefore $A^{-1} = A\mathrm{Iv}$ also is totally bounded for **U**(**N**) by Theorem 12.12.

For any $0 \neq \phi \in \Phi$ and for any $\varepsilon > 0$ we can find $\mathbf{n} \in \mathbf{N}$ such that $y \in \mathbf{n}z$ implies $|\phi(y) - \phi(z)| < \varepsilon$. Since $y \in \mathbf{n}z$ implies $yx \in \mathbf{n}zx$, we see that $y \in \mathbf{n}z$ implies $|\phi(yx) - \phi(zx)| < \varepsilon$ for every $x \in G$.

Setting $B = \{x: \phi(x) > 0\}$, we obtain a totally bounded set B for **U**(**N**) by definition. Thus $A^{-1}B$ also is totally bounded for **U**(**N**) by Theorems 40.1 and 40.6, and there is a regular set $H \supset A^{-1}B$ for L by Theorem 50.6. Referring to Theorems 51.2, 51.3 and 51.6, we hence conclude

$$|L\text{-}\int_H \phi(yx)dx - L\text{-}\int_H \phi(zx)dx| \leqq \varepsilon L\text{-}\int_H dx = \varepsilon L(H)$$

for $y \in \mathbf{n}z$. Thus we have by Theorem 57.3

$$|\tau(y)L\text{-}\int_{yH} \phi(x)dx - \tau(x)L\text{-}\int_{zH} \phi(x)dx| \leqq \varepsilon L(H)$$

for $y \in \mathbf{n}z$. Since $y \in A$ implies $yH \supset yA^{-1}B \supset yy^{-1}B = B$, we have by Theorem 51.7

$$L\text{-}\int_{yH} \phi(x)dx = L\text{-}\int_{zH} \phi(x)dx = L(\phi) \quad \text{for } y,\ z \in A.$$

We conclude therefore that $y \in \mathbf{n}z$, $y, z \in A$ implies

$$|\tau(y) - \tau(z)| \leqq \varepsilon \frac{L(H)}{L(\phi)}.$$

Thus τ is locally uniformly continuous for $\mathbf{U}(\mathbf{N})$ by definition.

Theorem 57.5. *For a regular set H for L, H^{-1} also is regular for L and*

$$L(H^{-1}) = L\text{-}\int_H \tau(x)dx.$$

For a uniformly continuous function ϕ on H for $\mathbf{U}(\mathbf{N})$ *we have*

$$L\text{-}\int_{H^{-1}} \phi(x^{-1})dx = L\text{-}\int_H \tau(x)\phi(x)dx.$$

Proof. Since the inversion Iv is locally uniformly continuous for $\mathbf{U}(\mathbf{N})$ by Theorem 41.11, setting

$$K(\phi) = L\text{-}\int \tau(x)\phi(x^{-1})dx \quad \text{for } \phi \in \Phi,$$

we obtain a measure K on G for $\mathbf{N}$. Since we have by Theorems 57.1 and 57.3

$$\begin{aligned} K(y\phi) &= L\text{-}\int \tau(x)\phi(x^{-1}y)dx = \tau(y)L\text{-}\int \tau(y^{-1}x)\phi((y^{-1}x)^{-1})dx \\ &= \tau(y)\tau(y^{-1})L\text{-}\int \tau(x)\phi(x^{-1})dx = K(\phi) \end{aligned}$$

for every $y \in G$, K also is right-invariant. Thus there exists $\gamma > 0$ by Theorem of Uniqueness in 56 such that $K(\phi) = \gamma L(\phi)$ for every $\phi \in \Phi$, that is,

$$L\text{-}\int \tau(x)\phi(x^{-1})dx = \gamma L\text{-}\int \phi(x)dx \quad \text{for every } \phi \in \Phi.$$

Since $\phi \in \Phi$ implies $\tau(\mathrm{Iv}\phi) \in \Phi$, we have then by Theorem 57.1

$$L(\phi) = L\text{-}\int \tau(x)\tau(x^{-1})\phi(x)dx = \gamma L\text{-}\int \tau(x)\phi(x^{-1})dx = \gamma^2 L(\phi)$$

for every $\phi \in \Phi$. Thus we obtain $\gamma = 1$. Therefore we have

$$L\text{-}\int \tau(x)\phi(x^{-1})dx = L\text{-}\int \phi(x)dx \quad \text{for every } \phi \in \Phi.$$

Since $\mathrm{Iv}\phi \in \Phi$ for every $\phi \in \Phi$, we hence obtain

$$L\text{-}\int \tau(x)\phi(x)dx = L\text{-}\int \phi(x^{-1})dx \quad \text{for every } \phi \in \Phi.$$

Since Iv is a homeomorphism for $\mathbf{U}(\mathbf{N})$ by Theorem 22.6 and $H^{-1} = H\mathrm{Iv}$, if H is regular for L, then H^{-1} is open by definition and we have that $\Phi \ni \phi \leqq \chi_H$ if and only if $\phi(x^{-1}) \leqq \chi_{H^{-1}}(x)$ for every $x \in G$. For any $\mathcal{E} > 0$ we can find a regular set K and $U \in \mathbf{U}(\mathbf{N})$ by Theorem 50.9 such that $KU \subset H$ and $L(K) > L(H) - \mathcal{E}$. Then there is $\phi \in \Phi$ by Theorem 19.2 such that $\phi(x) = 1$ for $x \in K$ and $\phi \leqq \chi_H$, and hence $\phi(x^{-1}) \leqq \chi_{H^{-1}}(x)$ for every $x \in G$. Thus we have

$$L(H^{-1}) \geqq L\text{-}\int \phi(x^{-1})dx = L\text{-}\int \tau(x)\phi(x)dx \geqq L\text{-}\int_K \tau(x)dx.$$

Since $L(H \cap K^{-\prime}) \leqq L(H) - L(K) < \mathcal{E}$ by Theorem 50.10, we have by Theorems 51.3, 51.4, 51.5 and 51.6

$$L\text{-}\int_K \tau(x)dx = L\text{-}\int_H \tau(x)dx - L\text{-}\int_{H\cap K^{-\prime}} \tau(x)dx$$

$$\geqq L\text{-}\int_H \tau(x)dx - \mathcal{E}\sup_{x\in H} \tau(x) \quad \text{for every } \mathcal{E} > 0.$$

Thus we obtain

$$L(H^{-1}) \geqq L\text{-}\int_H \tau(x)dx.$$

On the other hand, for any $a < L(H^{-1})$ we can find a regular set K_1 for L and $U_1 \in \mathbf{U}(\mathbf{N})$ by Theorem 50.9 such that $a < L(K_1)$ and $K_1U_1 \subset H^{-1}$. Since Iv is locally uniformly continuous for $\mathbf{U}(\mathbf{N})$, we see by Theorem 12.11 that there is $V \in \mathbf{U}(\mathbf{N})$ such that $x\mathrm{Iv}V \subset xU_1\mathrm{Iv}$ for every $x \in K_1$, and we have

$$K_1^{-1}V = K_1\mathrm{Iv}V \subset K_1U_1\mathrm{Iv} \subset H^{-1}\mathrm{Iv} = H.$$

Thus there is $\phi \in \Phi$ by Theorem 19.2 such that $\phi(x) = 1$ for every $x \in K_1^{-1}$ and $\phi \leqq \chi_H$, and we have by Theorems 51.6 and 51.3

$$L(K_1) = L\text{-}\int_{K_1} dx \leqq L\text{-}\int \phi(x^{-1})dx = L\text{-}\int \tau(x)\phi(x)dx \leqq L\text{-}\int_H \tau(x)dx.$$

Consequently $\alpha < L\text{-}\int_H \tau(x)dx$. Therefore we obtain

$$L\text{-}\int_H \tau(x)dx = L(H^{-1}).$$

Let $\tilde{\mathbf{U}}$ be a completion of $\mathbf{U}(\mathbf{N})$ over $\tilde{G} \supset G$ and let $\tilde{L}$ be the completion of L over $\tilde{G}$. Since Iv is a local unimorphism on G for $\mathbf{U}(\mathbf{N})$, Iv can be extended uniquely to a local unimorphism $\tilde{\mathrm{I}}\mathrm{v}$ over $\tilde{G}$ by Theorem 30.5. Since τ is locally uniformly continuous for $\mathbf{U}(\mathbf{N})$, τ can be extended to a locally uniformly continuous function $\tilde{\tau}$ on $\tilde{G}$ by Theorem 12.13. For a regular set $\tilde{H}$ for $\tilde{L}$, if $\tilde{H}_\nu \subset \tilde{H}$ $(\nu = 1, 2, \ldots, n)$ is an $\mathcal{E}$ partition of $\tilde{H}$ for $\tilde{\tau}$, then $\tilde{H}_\nu{}^G$ $(\nu = 1, 2, \ldots, n)$ is an $\mathcal{E}$ partition of $\tilde{H}^G$ for τ. Therefore we have by Theorem 51.1 and (10) in 49

$$\tilde{L}\text{-}\int_{\tilde{H}} \tilde{\tau}(x)dx = L\text{-}\int_{\tilde{H}^G} \tau(x)dx = L((\tilde{H}^G)^{-1}) \geqq \tilde{L}(\tilde{H}\tilde{\mathrm{I}}\mathrm{v}),$$

because $(\tilde{H}\tilde{\mathrm{I}}\mathrm{v})^G = \tilde{H}^G\mathrm{Iv} = (\tilde{H}^G)^{-1}$. If $\tilde{H}^- \cap \tilde{H}' \subset \tilde{K}$ for a regular set $\tilde{K}$ for $\tilde{L}$, then $(\tilde{H}\tilde{\mathrm{I}}\mathrm{v})^- \cap (\tilde{H}\tilde{\mathrm{I}}\mathrm{v})' \subset \tilde{K}\tilde{\mathrm{I}}\mathrm{v}$ and

$$\tilde{L}(\tilde{K}\tilde{\mathrm{I}}\mathrm{v}) \leqq \tilde{L}\text{-}\int_{\tilde{K}} \tilde{\tau}(x)dx \leqq \tilde{L}(\tilde{K}) \sup_{x \in K} \tilde{\tau}(x),$$

as proved just above. Thus we see easily by Lemma 50.3 that if $\tilde{H}$ is regular for $\tilde{L}$, then $\tilde{H}\tilde{\mathrm{I}}\mathrm{v}$ also is regular for $\tilde{L}$, and hence $(\tilde{H}^G)^{-1} = (\tilde{H}\tilde{\mathrm{I}}\mathrm{v})^G$ is regular for L by definition. Therefore if H is regular for L, then H^{-1} also is regular for L.

Let ϕ be a uniformly continuous function on a regular set H for L. For any $\mathcal{E}$ partition $H_\nu \subset H$ $(\nu = 1, 2, \ldots, n)$ of H for ϕ, $H_\nu{}^{-1}$ $(\nu = 1, 2, \ldots, n)$ is a regular partition of H^{-1}, and we have

$$\sum_{\nu=1}^{n} \phi(x_\nu)L(H_\nu{}^{-1}) = \sum_{\nu=1}^{n} L\text{-}\int_{H_\nu} \tau(x)\phi(x_\nu)dx$$

for any $x_\nu \in S$ $(\nu = 1, 2, \ldots, n)$. Thus we have by Theorems 51.2, 51.3 and 51.4

$$\left| \sum_{\nu=1}^{n} L\text{-}\int_{H_\nu} \tau(x)\phi(x_\nu)dx - L\text{-}\int_H \tau(x)\phi(x)dx \right|$$

$$\leqq \sum_{\nu=1}^{n} L\text{-}\int_{H_\nu} \tau(x)|\phi(x_\nu) - \phi(x)|dx \leqq \mathcal{E}L\text{-}\int_H \tau(x)dx = \mathcal{E}L(H^{-1})$$

for $x_\nu \in H_\nu$ $(\nu = 1, 2, \ldots, n)$. On the other hand we obtain by Theorem 51.1

$$\left|L\text{-}\int_{H^{-1}} \phi(x^{-1})dx - \sum_{\nu=1}^{n} \phi(x_\nu)L(H_\nu^{-1})\right| \leq \varepsilon L(H^{-1})$$

for $x_\nu \in H_\nu$ $(\nu = 1, 2, ..., n)$. Therefore we conclude

$$L\text{-}\int_{H^{-1}} \phi(x^{-1})dx = L\text{-}\int_{H} \tau(x)\phi(x)dx.$$

58. **Steady Groups.** Let a neighbourhood **N** on a group G be regular and right totally bounded, as assumed in 57. Let τ be the coefficient function of G for **N**.

Theorem 58.1. *For $x \in G$, if $\{x^\nu: \nu = 1, 2, ...\}$ is totally bounded for* **U(N)**, *then $\tau(x) = 1$.*

Proof. Since the inversion Iv is locally uniformly continuous for **U(N)** by Theorem 41.11, if $\{x^\nu: \nu = 1, 2, ...\}$ is totally bounded for **U(N)**, then $\{x^\nu, x^{-\nu}: \nu = 1, 2, ...\}$ also is totally bounded by Theorem 12.12. Since τ is locally uniformly continuous for **U(N)** by Theorem 57.4, τ is bounded on $\{x^\nu, x^{-\nu}. \nu = 1, 2, ...\}$ by Theorems 18.5 and 12.11. On the other hand we have by Theorem 57.1

$$\tau(x^\nu) = \tau(x)^\nu, \quad \tau(x^{-\nu}) = \tau(x)^{-\nu} \quad (\nu = 1, 2, ...).$$

Thus we conclude $\tau(x) = 1$.

A set $A \subset G$ is called a *subgroup* of G, if $A \neq \emptyset$ and $x, y \in A$ implies $x^{-1}y \in A$. Every subgroup A of G contains $e \in G$, because $x \in A$ implies $e = x^{-1}x \in A$. For any subgroup A of G, we see easily that $x \in A$ implies $x^{-1} \in A$, and $x, y \in A$ implies $xy \in A$.

As an immediate consequence of Theorem 58.1, we have

Theorem 58.2. *If a subgroup A of G is totally bounded for* **U(N)**, *then $\tau(x) = 1$ for every $x \in A$.*

A group G is said to be *steady* for a neighbourhood **N** on G, if $\tau(x) = 1$ for every $x \in G$. With this definition we have by (1) in 57

Theorem 58.3. *G is steady for* **N** *if and only if the right-invariant measure $L \neq 0$ on G for* **N** *is invariant by every left transformation.*

Thus we can state

Theorem 58.4. *If G is commutative, that is, if $xy = yx$ for every $x, y \in G$, then G is steady for any neighbourhood* **N** *on G.*

If $\tau(x)^{\nu} = \tau(x^{\nu})$ and $\tau(x)^{-\nu} = \tau(x^{-\nu})$ are bounded for $\nu = 1, 2, \ldots$, then $\tau(x) = 1$. Thus we have

Theorem 58.5. *The coefficient function τ of G for* **N** *is bounded if and only if G is steady for* **N**.

As an immediate consequence of Theorem 58.2 we have

Theorem 58.6. *If* **U(N)** *is totally bounded, then G is steady for* **N**.

Theorem 58.7. *If* **N** *is uniformly regular and right totally bounded, then G is steady for* **N**.

Proof. If **N** is uniformly regular, then for any open set $A \ni e$ for **U(N)** we can find an open set $B \ni e$ such that $B \subset xAx^{-1}$ for every $x \in G$. Since **N** is right totally bounded by assumption, we can assume by Theorem 40.3 that A is totally bounded for **U(N)**. Then for a right-invariant measure $L \neq 0$ on G for **N**, we have by Theorems 54.4 and 57.2

$$0 < L(B) \leqq L(xAx^{-1}) = L(xA) = \frac{1}{\tau(x)} L(A) < +\infty,$$

that is, $\tau(x) \leqq \dfrac{L(A)}{L(B)}$ for every $x \in G$. Therefore $\tau = 1$ by Theorem 58.5.

Theorem 58.8. *G is steady for* **N** *if and only if for a right-invariant measure $L \neq 0$ on G for* **N** *we have*

$$L\text{-}\int \phi(x^{-1})dx = L\text{-}\int \phi(x)dx \quad \textit{for every } \phi \in \Phi,$$

or $L(H^{-1}) = L(H)$ for any open set $H \subset G$ for **U(N)**.

Proof. If G is steady for **N**, then we have by Theorem 57.5

$$L\text{-}\int \phi(x^{-1})dx = L\text{-}\int \phi(x)dx \quad \text{for every } \phi \in \Phi,$$

that is, L is invariant by the inversion Iv. Therefore we obtain by Theorem 54.1 that $L(H^{-1}) = L(H)$ for any open set H for **U(N)**.

Conversely if $L\text{-}\int \phi(x^{-1})dx = L\text{-}\int \phi(x)dx$ for every $\phi \in \Phi$, then by by Theorem 57.5

$$L\text{-}\int (\tau(x) - 1)\phi(x)dx = 0 \quad \text{for every } \phi \in \Phi.$$

If $\tau(x_0) > 1$, then there is $\phi \in \Phi$ by Theorem 19.1 such that $\phi(x_0) = 1$ and

$$\{x: \phi(x) > 0\} \subset \{x: \tau(x) > 1\}.$$

Then we have $(\tau - 1)\phi \in \Phi$ and $L((\tau - 1)\phi) = 0$ by Theorem 51.7, contradicting Theorem 54.4. If $\tau(x_0) < 1$, then $\tau(x_0^{-1}) > 1$ by Theorem 57.1 and we obtain the same contradiction. Thus we conclude $\tau = 1$.

If $L(H^{-1}) = L(H)$ for any regular set H for L, then we have by Theorem 57.5

$$L\text{-}\int_H (\tau(x) - 1)dx = 0 \quad \text{for any regular set } H.$$

If $\tau(x_0) > 1$, then we can find a regular set H for L by Theorem 50.9 such that $x_0 \in H \subset \{x: \tau(x) > 1\}$, and we have

$$L\text{-}\int_H (\tau(x) - 1)dx = 0 \text{ and } \tau(x) - 1 \geqq 0 \text{ for every } x \in H.$$

Thus we obtain $\tau(x) = 1$ for every $x \in H$ by Theorem 54.4, contradicting $x_0 \in H$. If $\tau(x_0) < 1$, then $\tau(x_0^{-1}) > 1$. Thus we conclude $\tau = 1$.

59. **Invariant Subgroups.** Let S be a subgroup of a group G. Concerning relative sets $A^S = A \cap S$ of $A \subset S$, we obviously have

(1) $A \subset B$ implies $A^S \subset B^S$,

(2) $(\bigcup_{\lambda \in \Lambda} A_\lambda)^S = \bigcup_{\lambda \in \Lambda} A_\lambda{}^S$,

(3) $(\bigcap_{\lambda \in \Lambda} A_\lambda)^S = \bigcap_{\lambda \in \Lambda} A_\lambda{}^S$,

(4) $(AB)^S \supset A^S B^S$,

(5) $(AB)^S = A^S B$ and $(BA)^S = BA^S$ for $B \subset S$,

(6) $(A^{-1})^S = (A^S)^{-1}$.

If $A^S \subset B \subset S$, then there is $B_1 \subset G$ such that $B_1 \supset A$ and $B_1{}^S = B$. Because setting $B_1 = B \cup S'$, we have $B_1{}^S = (B \cup S') \cap S = B$ and $B \cup S' \supset (A \cap S) \cup S' \supset A$. Therefore for a neighbourhood $\mathbf{N}$ on G, making use of the notation

$$\mathbf{N}^S = \{\mathbf{n}^S: \mathbf{n} \in \mathbf{N}\},$$

we see easily that $\mathbf{N}^S$ satisfies the neighbourhood conditions in 38. Thus $\mathbf{N}^S$ is a neighbourhood on S. $\mathbf{N}^S$ is called the *relative neighbourhood* of $\mathbf{N}$ on $S \subset G$. It is obvious by definition that if $\mathbf{B}$ is a basis of $\mathbf{N}$, then $\mathbf{B}^S$ is a basis of $\mathbf{N}^S$.

Since $(\mathbf{n}x)^S = \mathbf{n}^S x$ for $x \in S$ and $\mathbf{n} \in \mathbf{N}$ by (5), we have

Theorem 59.1. *For the induced uniformity* $\mathbf{U}(\mathbf{N})$ *on* G *and* $\mathbf{U}(\mathbf{N}^S)$ *on* S *we have*

$$\mathbf{U}(\mathbf{N}^S) = \mathbf{U}(\mathbf{N})^S,$$

that is, $\mathbf{U}(\mathbf{N}^S)$ *is the relative uniformity of* $\mathbf{U}(\mathbf{N})$ *on* S.

Since $\mathbf{n} \subset x^{-1}\mathbf{m}x$ implies $\mathbf{n}^S \subset x^{-1}\mathbf{m}^S x$ for every $x \in S$ by (5), we conclude easily

Theorem 59.2. *If* $\mathbf{N}$ *is regular, locally uniformly regular or uniformly regular, then* $\mathbf{N}^S$ *also is so respectively.*

Theorem 59.3. *If a set* $A \subset G$ *is right or left totally bounded for* $\mathbf{N}$, *then* A^S *also is so for* $\mathbf{N}^S$ *respectively.*

Proof. If A is right totally bounded for $\mathbf{N}$, then $A \cap S$ also is right totally bounded for $\mathbf{N}$. Thus for any $\mathbf{n} \in \mathbf{N}$ we can find $a_\nu \in A \cap S$ $(\nu = 1, 2, \ldots, n)$ such that $A \cap S \subset \bigcup_{\nu=1}^{n} \mathbf{n}a_\nu$ and we have by (1), (2), (5)

$$A^S \subset \bigcup_{\nu=1}^{n} \mathbf{n}^S a_\nu, \quad a_\nu \in A^S \ (\nu = 1, 2, \ldots, n).$$

The proof is quite similar for left totally bounded sets.

A subgroup N of G is said to be *invariant,* if $uNu^{-1} = N$ for every $u \in G$. Let N be an arbitrary invariant subgroup of G. For any $u \in G$, setting

$$xI_u = uxu^{-1} \quad \text{for every } x \in N,$$

we obtain a transformation I_u on N. This transformation I_u is called the *inner transformation* on N by $u \in G$. About inner transformations, we obviously have by definition

$$I_u I_v = I_{vu}, \quad I_u I_{u^{-1}} = E, \quad I_u^{-1} = I_{u^{-1}}.$$

Thus all inner transformations on N form a transformation group on N, which will be called the *inner transformation group* on N by G.

Theorem 59.4. *If* $\mathbf{N}$ *is uniformly regular and right totally bounded, then for any invariant subgroup* $N \subset G$, N *is steady for the relative neighbourhood* $\mathbf{N}^N$, *and the right-invariant measure* $L \neq 0$ *on* N *for* $\mathbf{N}^N$ *is invariant by the inner transformation group on* N *by* G *and*

$$L\text{-}\int_H \phi(uxu^{-1})dx = L\text{-}\int_{uHu^{-1}} \phi(x)dx \quad \textit{for every } u \in G$$

for any regular set H for L and for any uniformly continuous function ϕ on H for $\mathbf{N}^N$.

Proof. Since $\mathbf{N}$ is uniformly regular by assumption, setting

$$\mathbf{B} = \{ \bigcap_{u \in G} u\mathbf{n}u^{-1} : \mathbf{n} \in \mathbf{N}\},$$

we obtain a basis $\mathbf{B}$ of $\mathbf{N}$ and we have $u\mathbf{n}u^{-1} = \mathbf{n}$ for every $\mathbf{n} \in \mathbf{B}$ and $u \in G$. Then $\mathbf{B}^N$ is a basis of the relative neighbourhood $\mathbf{N}^N$. Therefore

$$\{U(\mathbf{n}) : \mathbf{n} \in \mathbf{B}^N\}$$

is a basis of the induced uniformity $\mathbf{U}(\mathbf{N}^N)$. Here $xU(\mathbf{n}) = \mathbf{n}x$ for every $x \in N$ by (1) in 38. We have then

$$xI_u U(\mathbf{n}) I_u^{-1} = u^{-1}(\mathbf{n}uxu^{-1})u = \mathbf{n}x = xU(\mathbf{n})$$

for every $x \in N$ and $\mathbf{n} \in \mathbf{B}^N$, because $u^{-1}(\mathbf{n} \cap N)u = u^{-1}\mathbf{n}u \cap N = \mathbf{n} \cap N$ for every $\mathbf{n} \in \mathbf{B}$ and $u \in G$ by (3). Let $\mathbf{G}$ be the system of all transformations X on N such that $XU(\mathbf{n})X^{-1} = U(\mathbf{n})$ for every $\mathbf{n} \in \mathbf{B}^N$. Then $\mathbf{G}$ is obviously a transformation group on N and $\mathbf{G} \ni R_x, I_u$ for every $x \in N$ and $u \in G$. In addition $\mathbf{U}(\mathbf{N}^N)$ is invariant by $\mathbf{G}$. Since $\mathbf{U}(\mathbf{N}^N) = \mathbf{U}(\mathbf{N})^N$ by Theorem 59.1, $\mathbf{U}(\mathbf{N}^N)$ is locally totally bounded. Therefore there is an invariant measure $L \neq 0$ on N for $\mathbf{U}(\mathbf{N}^N)$ by $\mathbf{G}$ by Theorem of Existence in 55. Then L is invariant by R_x and I_u for every $x \in N$ and $u \in G$. On the other hand the invariant measure on N for $\mathbf{U}(\mathbf{N}^N)$ by the right transformation group R_x $(x \in N)$ is determined uniquely in the sense of Theorem of Uniqueness in 56. Therefore the right invariant measure L is invariant by I_u for every $u \in G$, and we have by Theorems 54.2 and 54.3 that if $H \subset N$ is regular for L, then $uHu^{-1} = HI_u$ also is regular for L for every $u \in G$ and

$$L\text{-}\int_H \phi(uxu^{-1})dx = L\text{-}\int_H \phi(xI_u)dx = L\text{-}\int_{HI_u} \phi(x)dx = L\text{-}\int_{uHu^{-1}} \phi(x)dx.$$

Since $\mathbf{N}^N$ is uniformly regular by Theorem 59.2, N is steady for $\mathbf{N}^N$ by Theorem 58.7.

60. **Measure Characters.** We suppose again that **G** is a transitive group on a space S and a uniformity **U** on S is invariant and normal for **G**. According to Theorems 42.6, 42.4 and 40.3, the induced neighbourhood **N**(**U**) on **G** is regular and right totally bounded. Thus **G** has the coefficient function τ for **N**(**U**), as defined by (1) in 57. A function χ on S is called a *measure character* of **G** for **U**, if $0 < \chi(x) < +\infty$ for every $x \in S$ and

$$\chi(xX) = \chi(x)\tau(X) \text{ for every } x \in S \text{ and } X \in \mathbf{G}.$$

For two measure characters χ_1, χ_2 of **G** for **U** we have then

$$\frac{\chi_1(xX)}{\chi_2(xX)} = \frac{\chi_1(x)}{\chi_2(x)} \text{ for every } X \in \mathbf{G}.$$

Since **G** is transitive by assumption, there is $\alpha > 0$ such that $\chi_1(x) = \alpha\chi_2(x)$ for every $x \in S$.

For a right-invariant measure $K \neq 0$ on **G** for **N**(**U**), setting

$$\chi_\phi(x) = K\text{-}\int \phi(xX)dX \text{ for } 0 \neq \phi \in \Phi,$$

we have by Theorem 57.3 that $\chi_\phi(xY) = \chi_\phi(x)\tau(Y)$ for every $Y \in \mathbf{G}$, and $0 < \chi_\phi(x) < +\infty$ for every $x \in S$ by Theorem 54.4. Thus we can state

Theorem 60.1. *There exists a measure character of* **G** *for* **U** *and it is unique in the sense that for two measure characters* χ_1, χ_2 *we can find* $\alpha > 0$ *such that* $\chi_1(x) = \alpha\chi_2(x)$ *for every* $x \in S$.

Theorem 60.2. *The measure character of* **G** *for* **U** *is locally uniformly continuous on* S *for* **U**.

Proof. χ_ϕ is a measure character of **G** for **U** for any $0 \neq \phi \in \Phi$. Let $A \subset S$ be an arbitrary totally bounded set for **U** such that

$$A \supset \{x: \phi(x) > 0\}.$$

According to Theorem 37.12, $\bigcup_{x \in A} AM_x^{-1}$ is totally bounded for the weak-uniformity **W**(**U**) on **G**. Thus there is a regular set $\mathbf{H} \subset \mathbf{G}$ for K by Theorem 50.6 such that

$$\mathbf{H} \supset \bigcup_{x \in A} AM_x^{-1}.$$

Then we have $\{x: \phi(x) > 0\}M_y^{-1} \subset \mathbf{H}$ for every $y \in A$. Thus

$$\chi_\phi(x) = K\text{-}\int_{\mathbf{H}} \phi(xX)dX \quad \text{for every } x \in A.$$

Since ϕ is uniformly continuous on S for $\mathbf{U}$, for any $\mathcal{E} > 0$ we can find $U \in \mathbf{U}$ such that $x \in yU$ implies $|\phi(x) - \phi(y)| < \mathcal{E}$. Then $x \in yU$, $x, y \in A$, implies

$$|\chi_\phi(x) - \chi_\phi(y)| \leqq K\text{-}\int_{\mathbf{H}} |\phi(xX) - \phi(yX)|dX \leqq \mathcal{E}K(\mathbf{H}).$$

Therefore χ_ϕ is uniformly continuous on A.

Theorem 60.3. *For the invariant measure $L \neq 0$ on S for* **U** *by* **G** *and for the measure character χ of* **G** *for* **U** *we have*

$$L\text{-}\int_{HX} \chi(x)dx = \tau(X)L\text{-}\int_{H} \chi(x)dx \quad \textit{for every } X \in \mathbf{G}.$$

for any regular set $H \subset S$ for L.

Proof. Since L is invariant by **G**, we have by Theorem 54.3

$$L\text{-}\int_{HX} \chi(x)dx = L\text{-}\int_{H} \chi(xX)dx \quad \text{for every } X \in \mathbf{G}.$$

On the other hand we have $\chi(xX) = \chi(x)\tau(X)$ by definition.

It is obvious by definition

Theorem 60.4. **G** *is steady for* $\mathbf{N}(\mathbf{U})$ *if and only if the measure character of* **G** *for* **U** *is constant on S.*

Since $\chi(xX) = \chi(x)\tau(X)$ for every $X \in \mathbf{G}$ and **G** is transitive by assumption, we see easily that χ is bounded on S if and only if τ is bounded on **G**. Thus we obtain by Theorem 58.5

Theorem 60.5. **G** *is steady for* $\mathbf{N}(\mathbf{U})$ *if and only if the measure character of* **G** *for* **U** *is bounded on S.*

As an immediate consequence of Theorem 60.5 we have

Theorem 60.6. *If* **U** *is totally bounded, then* **G** *is steady for* $\mathbf{N}(\mathbf{U})$.

61. **Double Integrals.** In addition to the assumptions in 60 about S, **U**, **G**, we assume now that the induced neighbourhood $\mathbf{N}(\mathbf{U})$ on **G** is uniformly regular. Let $\mathbf{H} \subset \mathbf{G}$ be an invariant subgroup of **G**, that is, $X\mathbf{H}X^{-1} = \mathbf{H}$ for every $X \in \mathbf{G}$.

According to Theorem 36.1, the system $x\mathbf{H}$ $(x \in S)$ gives a partition of S. Thus we obtain a *partition space* of S by $x\mathbf{H}$ $(x \in S)$. This partition space of S is denoted by $S/\mathbf{H}$, that is,

(1) $S/\mathbf{H} = \{x\mathbf{H}: x \in S\}$.

Let P be the *partition mapping* from S to $S/\mathbf{H}$, that is,

(2) $xP = x\mathbf{H}$ for every $x \in S$.

Then we obviously have

(3) $AP = \{x\mathbf{H}: x \in A\}$ for $A \subset S$,

(4) $APP^{-1} = A\mathbf{H}$ for $A \subset S$.

For any connector U on S, setting

(5) $aP(U/\mathbf{H}) = aU^{\mathbf{G}}P$,

we obtain a connector $U/\mathbf{H}$ on $S/\mathbf{H}$. Then we obviously have

(6) $U \geqq V$ implies $U/\mathbf{H} \geqq V/\mathbf{H}$.

Consequently we obtain

(7) $\bigcap_{\lambda \in \Lambda} (U_\lambda/\mathbf{H}) \geqq \bigcap_{\lambda \in \Lambda} U_\lambda/\mathbf{H}$.

Since $aP(U/\mathbf{H})P^{-1} = aU^{\mathbf{G}}PP^{-1} = aU^{\mathbf{G}}\mathbf{H}$ by (4) and (5), we have

(8) $P(U/\mathbf{H})P^{-1} = U^{\mathbf{G}}\mathbf{H}$.

Since the partition mapping P is full, we have by (7) in 32

$$\begin{aligned} P(U/\mathbf{H})(V/\mathbf{H})P^{-1} &= P(U/\mathbf{H})P^{-1}P(V/\mathbf{H})P^{-1} = U^{\mathbf{G}}\mathbf{H}V^{\mathbf{G}}\mathbf{H} \\ &= U^{\mathbf{G}}V^{\mathbf{G}}\mathbf{H} \leqq (UV)^{\mathbf{G}}\mathbf{H} = P(UV/\mathbf{H})P^{-1}. \end{aligned}$$

Thus we obtain

$xP(U/\mathbf{H})(V/\mathbf{H}) \subset xP(UV/\mathbf{H})$ for every $x \in S$.

Therefore we have

(9) $(U/\mathbf{H})(V/\mathbf{H}) \leqq (UV/\mathbf{H})$.

We have $aP \in xP(U/\mathbf{H})$ if and only if $a \in xP(U/\mathbf{H})P^{-1} = xU^{\mathbf{G}}\mathbf{H}$, that is, if and only if $aX \in xU^{\mathbf{G}}$ for some $X \in \mathbf{H}$. On the other hand we see easily by (5) in 32 that $aX \in xU^{\mathbf{G}}$ if and only if $xX^{-1} \in a(U^{-1})^{\mathbf{G}}$. Therefore we obtain

(10) $(U/\mathbf{H})^{-1} = U^{-1}/\mathbf{H}$.

For the uniformity **U** on S we see easily by (7), (9), (10) that $\{U/\mathbf{H}: U \in \mathbf{U}\}$ satisfied the basis conditions in 2. Therefore there exists uniquely a uniformity on $S/\mathbf{H}$ such that $\{U/\mathbf{H}: U \in \mathbf{U}\}$ is a basis. This uniformity on $S/\mathbf{H}$ is called the *partition uniformity* of **U** by **H** and denoted by **U**/**H**.

Theorem 61.1. *The partition mapping P is uniformly continuous for the partition uniformity* **U**/**H**.

Proof. For any $U \in \mathbf{U}$ we have by (8)

$$P(U/\mathbf{H})P^{-1} = U^{\mathbf{G}}\mathbf{H} \geqq U^{\mathbf{G}} \in \mathbf{U}$$

because **U** is invariant by **G** by assumption. Since $\{U/\mathbf{H}: U \in \mathbf{U}\}$ is a basis of **U**/**H**, P is uniformly continuous by definition.

For any $Z \in \mathbf{G}$, setting

(11) $xP(Z/\mathbf{H}) = xZP$ for every $x \in S$,

we obtain a transformation $Z/\mathbf{H}$ on $S/\mathbf{H}$. Because we see by (2) that $xP = yP$ if and only if $x = yX$ for some $X \in \mathbf{H}$. If $x = yX$ for some $X \in \mathbf{H}$, then $xZ = yXZ = yZ(Z^{-1}XZ)$ and $Z^{-1}XZ \in \mathbf{H}$. Thus $xP = yP$ implies $xZP = yZP$. Therefore $Z/\mathbf{H}$ is a mapping from $S/\mathbf{H}$ to $S/\mathbf{H}$ for any $Z \in \mathbf{G}$. Furthermore we obviously have by (11)

(12) $(Y/\mathbf{H})(Z/\mathbf{H}) = YZ/\mathbf{H}$ for $Y, Z \in \mathbf{G}$.

Thus we have

$$(Z/\mathbf{H})(Z^{-1}/\mathbf{H}) = (Z^{-1}/\mathbf{H})(Z/\mathbf{H}) = E/\mathbf{H}$$

and $E/\mathbf{H}$ is obviously the identity transformation on $S/\mathbf{H}$. Therefore $Z/\mathbf{H}$ is a transformation on $S/\mathbf{H}$, and we have

(13) $Z^{-1}/\mathbf{H} = (Z/\mathbf{H})^{-1}$ for every $Z \in \mathbf{G}$.

We see by (12) and (13) that $Z/\mathbf{H}$ $(Z \in \mathbf{G})$ form a transformation group on $S/\mathbf{H}$, which is called the *partition* of **G** by **H** and denoted by **G**/**H**.

We obviously have by (2) that $xYP = xZP$ for every $x \in S$ if and only if $Y \in Z\mathbf{H} = \mathbf{H}Z$. Thus we have

(14) $Y/\mathbf{H} = Z/\mathbf{H}$ if and only if $Y \in \mathbf{H}Z$.

Theorem 61.2. **U**/**H** *is invariant and normal for* **G**/**H** *and* $U/\mathbf{H}$ *is invariant by* **G**/**H** *for every* $U \in \mathbf{U}$.

Proof. For any $x \in S$ and $Z \in \mathbf{G}$ we have by (11), (13) and (5)

$$xP(Z/\mathbf{H})(U/\mathbf{H})(Z/\mathbf{H})^{-1} = xZP(U/\mathbf{H})(Z^{-1}/\mathbf{H}) = xZU^{\mathbf{G}}P(Z^{-1}/\mathbf{H})$$
$$= xZU^{\mathbf{G}}Z^{-1}P = xU^{\mathbf{G}}P = xP(U/\mathbf{H}).$$

Thus $U/\mathbf{H}$ is invariant by $\mathbf{G}/\mathbf{H}$ for every $U \in \mathbf{U}$. Since $U/\mathbf{H}$ $(U \in \mathbf{U})$ is a basis of $\mathbf{U}/\mathbf{H}$, $\mathbf{U}/\mathbf{H}$ is invariant by $\mathbf{G}/\mathbf{H}$ by definition.

For a normal connector $U \in \mathbf{U}$, we see by (1) in 34 that for any x, $a \in S$ we have

$$xP(U/\mathbf{H})(aP) = \{xP(Z/\mathbf{H}) \colon aP(Z/\mathbf{H}) \in aP(U/\mathbf{H})\}$$
$$= \{xZP \colon aZP \in aU^{\mathbf{G}}P\} = \{xZ \colon aZ \in aU^{\mathbf{G}}\}P = xU(a)P.$$

Since $xU(a)$ is totally bounded for $\mathbf{U}$ and P is uniformly continuous by Theorem 61.1, $xU(a)P$ is totally bounded for $\mathbf{U}/\mathbf{H}$. Since $xU^{\mathbf{G}}$ is totally bounded for $\mathbf{U}$, $xP(U/\mathbf{H})$ is totally bounded for $\mathbf{U}/\mathbf{H}$ by (5). Therefore $U/\mathbf{H}$ is a normal connector of $\mathbf{U}/\mathbf{H}$.

According to Theorem of Existence in 55, there exists an invariant measure $L \neq 0$ on $S/\mathbf{H}$ for $\mathbf{U}/\mathbf{H}$ by $\mathbf{G}/\mathbf{H}$, and it is unique in the sense of Theorem of Uniqueness in 56.

Since the induced neighbourhood $\mathbf{N}(\mathbf{U})$ on $\mathbf{G}$ is right totally bounded by Theorem 40.3 and uniformly regular by assumption, we conclude from Theorem 59.4 that $\mathbf{H}$ is steady for the relative neighbourhood $\mathbf{N}(\mathbf{U})^{\mathbf{H}}$ and for the right-invariant measure $K \neq 0$ on $\mathbf{H}$ for $\mathbf{N}(\mathbf{U})^{\mathbf{H}}$

$$K\text{-} \int \psi(ZXZ^{-1})dX = K\text{-} \int \psi(X)dX \quad \text{for every } Z \in \mathbf{G} \text{ and } \psi \in \Psi$$

for the trunk Ψ of $\mathbf{W}(\mathbf{U})^{\mathbf{H}}$, because the relative uniformity $\mathbf{W}(\mathbf{U})^{\mathbf{H}}$ is the induced uniformity of the relative neighbourhood $\mathbf{N}(\mathbf{U})^{\mathbf{H}}$ by Theorems 42.6 and 59.1

For the trunk Φ of $\mathbf{U}$, setting

$$\psi_x(X) = \phi(xX) \quad \text{for } \phi \in \Phi,\ x \in S,\ X \in \mathbf{H},$$

we have $\psi_x \in \Psi$ for every $x \in S$, because the point mapping M_x is uniformly continuous and

$$\{X \colon \phi(xX) > 0\} = \{y \colon \phi(y) > 0\}M_x^{-1}$$

is totally bounded for $\mathbf{W}(\mathbf{U})$ by Theorem 37.11. Thus setting

$$\omega(x) = K\text{-} \int \phi(xX)dX \quad \text{for every } x \in S,$$

we obtain a function ω on S. If $xP = yP$, then there is $T \in \mathbf{H}$ by (2) such that $x = yT$ and we have by Theorem 59.4

$$\omega(x) = K\text{-} \int \phi(yTX)dX = K\text{-} \int T\phi(yTXT^{-1})dX = K\text{-} \int T\phi(yX)dX$$
$$= K\text{-} \int \phi(yXT)dX = K\text{-} \int \phi(yX)dX = \omega(y).$$

Thus we can consider ω a function on $S/\mathbf{H}$, that is, $\omega(xP) = \omega(x)$ for every $x \in S$.

We set $A = \{y: \phi(y) > 0\}$ for $\phi \in \Phi$. If $x \bar{\in} A\mathbf{H}$, then $x\mathbf{H} \cap A = \emptyset$, and hence $\phi(xX) = 0$ for every $X \in \mathbf{H}$. Thus $\omega(x) = 0$ for $x \bar{\in} A\mathbf{H} = APP^{-1}$. Therefore

$$\{xP: \omega(xP) > 0\} \subset AP$$

and AP is totally bounded for $\mathbf{U}/\mathbf{H}$ by Theorem 61.1.

Let $U_0 \in \mathbf{U}$ be a normal connector. Then we have by Theorem 37.12 that $\bigcup_{x \in A U_0} AM_x^{-1}$ is totally bounded for $\mathbf{W}(\mathbf{U})$. Thus there is a regular set $\mathbf{K} \subset \mathbf{H}$ by Theorem 50.6 for K such that

$$(\bigcup_{x \in A U_0} AM_x^{-1}) \cap \mathbf{H} \subset \mathbf{K}.$$

Then we have $\{X: \phi(xX) > 0,\ X \in \mathbf{H}\} = AM_x^{-1} \cap \mathbf{H} \subset \mathbf{K}$ for every $x \in AU_0$, and hence

$$K\text{-} \int \phi(xX)dX = K\text{-} \int_{\mathbf{K}} \phi(xX)dX \text{ for every } x \in AU_0.$$

Since ϕ is uniformly continuous for $\mathbf{U}$ and $\mathbf{G}$ is equi-continuous for $\mathbf{U}$, for any $\mathcal{E} > 0$ we can find a symmetric $U \in \mathbf{U}$ such that $U \leqq U_0$ and $x \in yU$ implies

$$|\phi(xX) - \phi(yX)| < \mathcal{E} \text{ for every } X \in \mathbf{G}.$$

Then we have by Theorems 51.2, 51.3 and 51.6 that if $x \in yU$, $x, y \in AU_0$, then

$$|K\text{-} \int_{\mathbf{K}} \phi(xX)dX - K\text{-} \int_{\mathbf{K}} \phi(yX)dX| \leqq K\text{-} \int_{\mathbf{K}} \mathcal{E}dX = \mathcal{E}K(\mathbf{K}),$$

that is, $|\omega(x) - \omega(y)| \leqq \mathcal{E}K(\mathbf{K})$ for $x \in yU$, $x, y \in AU_0$.

If $xP \in yP(U/\mathbf{H})$, then $x\mathbf{H} \subset y\mathbf{H}U^{\mathbf{G}}$ by (5). If $x\mathbf{H} \cap A = \emptyset$ and $y\mathbf{H} \cap A = \emptyset$, then $\omega(xP) = \omega(yP) = 0$, as proved just above. If $y\mathbf{H} \cap A \neq \emptyset$, then there is $Y \in \mathbf{H}$ such that $yY \in A$, and we have $x \in yYU^{\mathbf{G}}\mathbf{H}$. Thus there is $X \in \mathbf{H}$ such that $xX \in yYU^{\mathbf{G}}$. Then we have $xX \in AU_0$, and hence

$$|\omega(xP) - \omega(yP)| = |\omega(xX) - \omega(yY)| \leqq \mathcal{E}K(\mathbf{K}).$$

In the case where $x\mathbf{H} \cap A \neq \emptyset$, we obtain the same result in a similar manner, because U is symmetric. Thus we conclude that ω is uniformly continuous on $S/\mathbf{H}$ for $\mathbf{U}/\mathbf{H}$ and $\{xP: \omega(xP) > 0\}$ is totally bounded for $\mathbf{U}/\mathbf{H}$. Therefore setting

$$(L, K)(\phi) = L\text{-} \int (K\text{-} \int \phi(xX)dX)d(xP) \quad \text{for } \phi \in \Phi,$$

we obtain a measure $(L, K) \neq 0$ on S for $\mathbf{U}$. For any $Z \in \mathbf{G}$ we have by Theorem 59.4

$$K\text{-} \int \phi(xXZ)dX = K\text{-} \int \phi(xZX)dX \quad \text{for } \phi \in \Phi,$$

as proved just above, and hence we obtain by (11)

$$(L, K)(Z\phi) = L\text{-} \int \omega(xZP)d(xP) = L\text{-} \int \omega(xP(Z/\mathbf{H}))d(xP)$$
$$= L\text{-} \int \omega(xP)d(xP) = (L, K)(\phi)$$

for every $\phi \in \Phi$ and $Z \in \mathbf{G}$. Therefore we can state

Theorem 61.3. *Let Φ be the trunk of* $\mathbf{U}$ *and let $\Phi_{\mathbf{H}}$ be the trunk of* $\mathbf{U}/\mathbf{H}$. *For the right-invariant measure $K \neq 0$ on* $\mathbf{H}$ *for* $\mathbf{N}(\mathbf{U})^{\mathbf{H}}$, *setting*

$$\omega_\phi(xP) = K\text{-} \int \phi(xX)dX \quad \text{for } \phi \in \Phi,$$

we have $\omega_\phi \in \Phi_{\mathbf{H}}$ for every $\phi \in \Phi$. For the invariant measure $L \neq 0$ on $S/\mathbf{H}$ *for* $\mathbf{U}/\mathbf{H}$ *by* $\mathbf{G}/\mathbf{H}$, *setting*

$$(L, K)(\phi) = L\text{-} \int \omega_\phi(xP)d(xP) \quad \text{for } \phi \in \Phi,$$

we obtain an invariant measure $(L, K) \neq 0$ on S for $\mathbf{U}$ *by* $\mathbf{G}$.

62. **Almost Uniformly Continuous Functions.**

We suppose in the sequel that a uniformity $\mathbf{U}$ on a space S is locally compact, that is, $\mathbf{U}$ is locally totally bounded and complete. Let L be a measure on S for $\mathbf{U}$.

Theorem 62.1. *For any sequence of open sets $G_\nu \subset S$ ($\nu = 1, 2, \ldots$) we have*

$$L(\bigcup_{\nu=1}^{\infty} G_\nu) = \sup_{n \geq 1} L(\bigcup_{\nu=1}^{n} G_\nu) \leq \sum_{\nu=1}^{\infty} L(G_\nu).$$

Proof. For any $\alpha < L(\bigcup_{\nu=1}^{\infty} G_\nu)$ there is a totally bounded open set $G \subset S$ by Theorem 49.2 such that $G^- \subset \bigcup_{\nu=1}^{\infty} G_\nu$ and $\alpha < L(G)$. Since $\mathbf{U}$

is complete, G^- is compact by Theorem 9.1. Thus we can find n such that $G^- \subset \bigcup_{\nu=1}^{n} G_\nu$ and we have by Lemma 50.1

$$L(G) \leqq L(\bigcup_{\nu=1}^{n} G_\nu) \leqq \sum_{\nu=1}^{n} L(G_\nu).$$

Consequently $\alpha < \sup_{n\geqq 1} L(\bigcup_{\nu=1}^{n} G_\nu) \leqq \sum_{\nu=1}^{\infty} L(G_\nu)$. On the other hand we have by (4) in 49

$$L(\bigcup_{\nu=1}^{\infty} G_\nu) \geqq \sup_{n\geqq 1} L(\bigcup_{\nu=1}^{n} G_\nu).$$

Theorem 62.2. *For a sequence of open sets* $G_1 \supset G_2 \supset \ldots$, *if* $L(G_1) < +\infty$ *and* $\bigcap_{\nu=1}^{\infty} G_\nu \neq \emptyset$, *then* $\inf_{n\geqq 1} L(G_n) = 0$.

Proof. For any $\varepsilon > 0$ we can find a sequence of regular sets H_ν ($\nu = 1, 2, \ldots$) for L by Theorem 50.9 such that

$$H_\nu^- \subset G_\nu \text{ and } L(H_\nu) > L(G_\nu) - \frac{1}{2^\nu}\varepsilon \text{ for } \nu = 1, 2, \ldots .$$

Then we have $\bigcap_{\nu=1}^{\infty} H_\nu^- = \emptyset$ by assumption, and hence

$$\bigcup_{\nu=1}^{\infty} (G_1 \cap H_\nu^{-\prime}) = G_1 \cap (\bigcap_{\nu=1}^{\infty} H_\nu^-)' = G_1 .$$

Since $(\bigcap_{\nu=1}^{n} H_\nu) \cap (\bigcup_{\nu=1}^{n} (G_1 \cap H_\nu^{-\prime})) = \emptyset$ for every $n = 1, 2, \ldots$, we have by Lemma 50.2

$$L(\bigcap_{\nu=1}^{n} H_\nu) + L(\bigcup_{\nu=1}^{n} (G_1 \cap H_\nu^{-\prime})) \leqq L(G_1) \text{ for } n = 1, 2, \ldots,$$

and $\sup_{n\geqq 1} L(\bigcup_{\nu=1}^{n} (G_1 \cap H_\nu^{-\prime})) = L(G_1)$ by Theorem 62.1. Consequently we obtain $\inf_{n\geqq 1} L(\bigcap_{\nu=1}^{n} H_\nu) = 0$. Since we have by Theorem 50.11

$$L(\bigcap_{\nu=1}^{n} H_\nu) \geqq L(G_n) - \sum_{\nu=1}^{n} \frac{1}{2^\nu} \mathcal{E} \geqq L(G_n) - \mathcal{E} \quad \text{for } n = 1, 2, \ldots,$$

we hence obtain $\inf_{n \geqq 1} L(G_n) \leqq \mathcal{E}$ for any $\mathcal{E} > 0$. Therefore $\inf_{n \geqq 1} L(G_n) = 0$.

Let H be a regular set for L. A bounded function f on H is said to be *almost uniformly continuous* on H for **U** by L, if for any $\mathcal{E} > 0$ we can find an open set $G \subset H$ such that $L(G) \leqq \mathcal{E}$ and f is uniformly continuous on $H \cap G'$ for **U**. With this definition we can prove easily by Lemma 50.1

Theorem 62.3. *For two almost uniformly continuous functions f and g on H for* **U** *by L, all of the functions: $\alpha f + \beta g$, fg, $f \vee g$, $f \wedge g$, $|f|$ and $\frac{1}{f}$, if $f(x) \neq 0$ for $x \in H$, are almost uniformly continuous on H for* **U** *by L.*

For a function f on H, a uniformly continuous function g on S for **U** is called an *$\mathcal{E}$ approximation* of f on H for **U** by L, if there is an open set $G \subset H$ such that $L(G) \leqq \mathcal{E}$ and $f(x) = g(x)$ for every $x \in H \cap G'$.

Theorem 62.4. *A bounded function f on H is almost uniformly continuous on H for* **U** *by L if and only if f has an $\mathcal{E}$ approximation on H for any $\mathcal{E} > 0$.*

Proof. If f is almost uniformly continuous on H for **U** by L, then for any $\mathcal{E} > 0$ we can find an open set $G \subset H$ such that $L(G) \leqq \mathcal{E}$ and f is uniformly continuous on $H \cap G'$. Then there is a uniformly continuous function $f_{\mathcal{E}}$ on S for **U** by Theorem 19.2 such that $f_{\mathcal{E}}(x) = f(x)$ for $x \in H \cap G'$, that is, $f_{\mathcal{E}}$ is an $\mathcal{E}$ approximation of f on H for **U** by L. If f has an $\mathcal{E}$ approximation on H for every $\mathcal{E} > 0$, then f is obviously almost uniformly continuous on H by definition.

We obviously have by definition

Theorem 62.5. *If $f_{\mathcal{E}}$ is an $\mathcal{E}$ approximation of f on H, then $\alpha f_{\mathcal{E}}$, $|f_{\mathcal{E}}|$, $f_{\mathcal{E}} \vee a$, $f_{\mathcal{E}} \wedge a$ are $\mathcal{E}$ approximations of αf, $|f|$, $f \vee a$, $f \wedge a$ respectively for any real number a. If $f_{\mathcal{E}}$ and $g_{\mathcal{E}}$ are $\mathcal{E}$ approximations of f and g respectively, then $\alpha f_{\mathcal{E}} + \beta g_{\mathcal{E}}$, $f_{\mathcal{E}} g_{\mathcal{E}}$, $f_{\mathcal{E}} \vee g_{\mathcal{E}}$, $f_{\mathcal{E}} \wedge g_{\mathcal{E}}$ are $2\mathcal{E}$ approximations of $\alpha f + \beta g$, fg, $f \vee g$, $f \wedge g$ respectively.*

Theorem 62.6. *If a sequence of almost uniformly continuous functions f_ν ($\nu = 1, 2, \ldots$) on H is convergent to a function f on H and*

$|f_\nu(x)| \leqq \gamma$ for every $\nu = 1, 2, \ldots$ and $x \in H$, then f also is almost uniformly continuous on H and for any $\varepsilon > 0$ there is an open set $G \subset H$ such that $L(G) \leqq \varepsilon$ and f_ν $(\nu = 1, 2, \ldots)$ is uniformly convergent on $H \cap G'$.

Proof. We consider first the case where all of the f_ν $(\nu = 1, 2, \ldots)$ are uniformly continuous and $f_1 \leqq f_2 \leqq \ldots$ on H. Setting

$$G_{m,n} = \bigcup_{\nu=1}^{\infty} \{x\colon f_{n+\nu}(x) - f_n(x) > \frac{1}{m}\} \cap H \ (m,\ n = 1, 2, \ldots),$$

we obtain open sets $G_{m,n} \subset H$, and $G_{m,n} \supset G_{m,n+1}$, $\bigcap_{\nu=1}^{\infty} G_{m,\nu} = \emptyset$ for every $m = 1, 2, \ldots$, because f_ν $(\nu = 1, 2, \ldots)$ is convergent on H. Thus we have by Theorem 62.2

$$\inf_{n \geqq 1} L(G_{m,n}) = 0 \ \text{ for every } m = 1, 2, \ldots .$$

Therefore we can find n_m $(m = 1, 2, \ldots)$ such that $L(G_{m,n_m}) < \frac{1}{2^m}$ for every $m = 1, 2, \ldots$. Then setting

$$G_m = \bigcup_{\mu=1}^{\infty} G_{m+\mu, n_{m+\mu}} \ (m = 1, 2, \ldots),$$

we have by Theorem 62.1

$$L(\bigcup_{\mu=m}^{\infty} G_\mu) \leqq \sum_{\mu=m}^{\infty} \frac{1}{2^\mu} = \frac{1}{2^{m-1}} \ (m = 1, 2, \ldots)$$

and f_ν $(\nu = 1, 2, \ldots)$ is uniformly convergent to f on $H \cap (\bigcup_{\mu=m}^{\infty} G_\mu)'$, because for any $x \in H \cap (\bigcup_{\mu=m}^{\infty} G_\mu)'$ we have

$$0 \leqq f_{n+\nu}(x) - f_n(x) \leqq \frac{1}{\mu} \ \text{ for } n \geqq n_\mu,\ \mu \geqq m,\ \nu = 1, 2, \ldots,$$

and hence $0 \leqq f(x) - f_n(x) \leqq \frac{1}{\mu}$ for $n \geqq n_\mu$, $\mu \geqq m$. Thus f is uniformly continuous on $H \cap (\bigcup_{\mu=m}^{\infty} G_\mu)'$ for every $m = 1, 2, \ldots$ by Theorem 17.2. Since $\lim_{m\to\infty} \frac{1}{2^{m-1}} = 0$, f is almost uniformly continuous on H by definition.

We suppose now that f_ν $(\nu = 1, 2, \ldots)$ are almost uniformly continuous and $f_1 \leqq f_2 \leqq \ldots$ on H. For any $\varepsilon > 0$ there is a $\frac{1}{2^{\nu+1}}\varepsilon$ approximation g_ν of f_ν $(\nu = 1, 2, \ldots)$ by Theorem 62.4. Then we can find open sets $G_\nu \subset H$ $(\nu = 1, 2, \ldots)$ such that $L(G_\nu) \leqq \frac{1}{2^{\nu+1}}\varepsilon$ and $g_\nu(x) = f_\nu(x)$ for every $x \in H \cap G_\nu'$. Setting $G_\varepsilon = \bigcup_{\nu=1}^{\infty} G_\nu$, we have by Theorem 62.1

$$L(G_\varepsilon) \leqq \sum_{\nu=1}^{\infty} \frac{1}{2^{\nu+1}}\varepsilon = \frac{1}{2}\varepsilon,$$

and $f_\nu(x) = g_\nu(x)$ for every $\nu = 1, 2, \ldots$ and $x \in H \cap G_\varepsilon'$. Setting

$$f_{\varepsilon,n} = \bigvee_{\nu=1}^{n} (g_\nu \wedge \gamma) \quad (n = 1, 2, \ldots),$$

we hence have $f_{\varepsilon,1} \leqq f_{\varepsilon,2} \leqq \ldots$ and $f_{\varepsilon,n}(x) = f_n(x)$ for every $n = 1, 2, \ldots$ and $x \in H \cap G_\varepsilon'$. Thus setting

$$f_\varepsilon(x) = \lim_{n\to\infty} f_{\varepsilon,n}(x) \quad (x \in H)$$

we have $f_\varepsilon(x) = f(x)$ for every $x \in H \cap G_\varepsilon'$. Since there is an open set $H_\varepsilon \subset H$ such that $L(H_\varepsilon) \leqq \frac{1}{2}\varepsilon$ and $f_{\varepsilon,n}$ $(n = 1, 2, \ldots)$ is uniformly convergent to f_ε on $H \cap H_\varepsilon'$, as proved just above, $f_{\varepsilon,n}$ $(n = 1, 2, \ldots)$ is uniformly convergent to f on $H \cap (H_\varepsilon \cup G_\varepsilon)'$ and $L(H_\varepsilon \cup G_\varepsilon) \leqq \varepsilon$ by Theorem 62.1. Therefore f is almost uniformly continuous on H by definition, and for any $\varepsilon > 0$ there is an open set $G \subset H$ such that $L(G) < \varepsilon$ and f_ν $(\nu = 1, 2, \ldots)$ is uniformly convergent to f on $H \cap G'$.

If $f_1 \geqq f_2 \geqq \ldots$, then $-f_1 \leqq -f_2 \leqq \ldots$. Thus we can say the same thing for the case: $f_1 \geqq f_2 \geqq \ldots$. Generally we have

$$\lim_{\nu\to\infty} f_\nu(x) = \lim_{m\to\infty} \lim_{n\to\infty} \operatorname*{Max}_{m \leqq \nu \leqq m+n} f_\nu(x),$$

if f_ν $(\nu = 1, 2, \ldots)$ is convergent. Therefore, if f_ν $(\nu = 1, 2, \ldots)$ are almost uniformly continuous on H, then f also is almost uniformly continuous on H. Furthermore, setting

$$g_n(x) = \sup_{\nu \geqq n} |f_\nu(x) - f(x)| \quad (n = 1, 2, \ldots),$$

we obtain a sequence of almost uniformly continuous functions $g_1 \geqq g_2 \geqq \ldots$ on H and $\lim_{n\to\infty} g_n(x) = 0$ for every $x \epsilon H$. Therefore for any $\mathcal{E} > 0$ there is an open set $G \subset H$ such that $L(G) \leqq \mathcal{E}$ and g_n $(n = 1, 2, \ldots)$ is uniformly convergent to 0 on $H \cap G'$. Consequently f_ν $(\nu = 1, 2, \ldots)$ also is uniformly convergent to f on $H \cap G'$.

63. **Integration.** Let f be an almost uniformly continuous function on a regular set $H \subset S$ for L and $|f(x)| \leqq \gamma$ for $x \epsilon H$. For any $\mathcal{E}$ approximation $f_\mathcal{E}$ and δ approximation f_δ of f on H such that $|f_\mathcal{E}(x)| \leqq \gamma$, $|f_\delta(x)| \leqq \gamma$ for $x \epsilon H$, we can find an open set $G \subset H$ by definition such that $L(G) \leqq \mathcal{E} + \delta$ and

$$\{x: f_\mathcal{E}(x) \neq f(x),\ x \epsilon H\} \cup \{x: f_\delta(x) \neq f(x),\ x \epsilon H\} \subset G.$$

Thus we have $|f_\mathcal{E}(x) - f_\delta(x)| \leqq 2\gamma\chi_G(x)$ for $x \epsilon H$. We hence obtain by Theorem 51.8

$$L\text{-} \int_H |f_\mathcal{E}(x) - f_\delta(x)| dx \leqq 2\gamma L(G).$$

Therefore we have by Theorems 51.2 and 51.3

$$|L\text{-} \int_H f_\mathcal{E}(x)dx - L\text{-} \int_H f_\delta(x)dx| \leqq 2\gamma(\mathcal{E} + \delta)$$

for any $\mathcal{E}$ approximation $f_\mathcal{E}$ and δ approximation f_δ of f such that $|f_\mathcal{E}(x)| \leqq \gamma$ and $|f_\delta(x)| \leqq \gamma$ for $x \epsilon H$. Thus we conclude easily that there exists a unique real number α such that $\alpha = \lim_{\delta\to 0} L\text{-} \int_H f_\delta(x)dx$ for any δ approximations f_δ such that $|f_\delta(x)| \leqq \gamma$ for $x \epsilon H$. This α is called the *integral* of f on H and denoted by $L\text{-} \int_H f(x)dx$. With this definition we obviously have

Theorem 63.1. *For an almost uniformly continuous function f on H, if $|f(x)| \leqq \gamma$ for $x \epsilon H$, then we have*

$$|L\text{-} \int_H f_\mathcal{E}(x)dx - L\text{-} \int_H f(x)dx| \leqq 2\gamma\mathcal{E}$$

for any $\mathcal{E}$ approximation $f_\mathcal{E}$ of f such that $|f_\mathcal{E}(x)| \leqq \gamma$ for $x \epsilon H$.

A function f on a regular set H is said to be *measurable* on H by L, if there is a sequence of almost uniformly continuous functions f_ν ($\nu = 1, 2, \ldots$) on H such that $f(x) = \lim_{\nu\to 0} f_\nu(x)$ for every $x \in H$. If f is measurable on H by L, then setting

$$f|_\beta^\alpha = (f \wedge \alpha) \vee \beta \quad \text{for } \alpha \geqq \beta$$

we obtain an almost uniformly continuous function $f|_\beta^\alpha$ on H by Theorems 62.3 and 62.6, because $f(x) = \lim_{\nu\to\infty} f_\nu(x)$ implies $f|_\beta^\alpha(x) = \lim_{\nu\to\infty} f_\nu|_\beta^\alpha(x)$. Conversely if $f|_\beta^\alpha$ is almost uniformly continuous on H for any $\alpha \geqq \beta$, then f is measurable on H by L, because $f(x) = \lim f|_{-\nu}^{\nu}(x)$ for every $x \in H$.

Concerning measurable functions we conclude from Theorem 62.3

Theorem 63.2. *For two measurable functions f and g on H by L, all of the functions $\alpha f + \beta g$, fg, $f \vee g$, $f \wedge g$, $|f|$ and $\frac{1}{f}$, if $f(x) \neq 0$ for every $x \in H$, are measurable on H by L.*

For a sequence of almost uniformly continuous functions $f_1 \leqq f_2 \leqq \ldots$ on H, if $f_\nu(x) \leqq \gamma$ for every $\nu = 1, 2, \ldots$ and $x \in H$, then the limit f_0 of f_ν ($\nu = 1, 2, \ldots$) also is almost uniformly continuous on H by Theorem 62.6. In addition, for any $\mathcal{E} > 0$ there is an open set $G \subset H$ such that $L(G) \leqq \mathcal{E}$ and f_ν ($\nu = 1, 2, \ldots$) is uniformly convergent to f_0 on $H \cap G'$, that is, we can find n_m ($m = 1, 2, \ldots$) such that $f_0(x) - f_\nu(x) \leqq \frac{1}{m}$ for every $\nu \geqq n_m$ and $x \in H \cap G'$. Thus for any $\mathcal{E} > 0$ and m we can find $\mathcal{E}$ approximations g_ν of f_ν ($\nu = 0, n_m, n_m + 1, \ldots$) on H by Theorem 19.2 such that

$$g_\nu(x) \leqq g_{\nu+1}(x) \leqq g_0(x) \leqq \gamma \text{ and } 0 \leqq g_0(x) - g_\nu(x) \leqq \frac{1}{m}$$
$$\text{for } x \in H,\ \nu \geqq n_m.$$

Then we have by Theorems 51.2 and 51.3

$$0 \leqq L\text{-} \int_H g_0(x)dx - L\text{-} \int_H g_\nu(x)dx \leqq \frac{1}{m} L(H) \quad \text{for } \nu \geqq n_m.$$

We hence obtain by Theorem 63.1

$$-4\gamma\mathcal{E} \leqq L\text{-}\int_H f_0(x)dx - L\text{-}\int_H f_\nu(x)dx \leqq \frac{1}{m} L(H) + 4\gamma\mathcal{E} \quad \text{for } \nu \geqq n_m.$$

for any $\mathcal{E} > 0$ and $m = 1, 2, \ldots$. Thus we conclude

$$L\text{-}\int_H f_0(x)dx = \lim_{\nu\to\infty} L\text{-}\int_H f_\nu(x)dx.$$

Therefore we define the integral of a positive measurable function f on H by

$$(1)\ L\text{-}\int_H f(x)dx = \sup_{\alpha>0} L\text{-}\int_H f|_0^\alpha(x)dx.$$

A function f on S is said to be *measurable* by L, if f is measurable on H for any regular set H for L. We define the integral of positive measurable functions f by

$$(2)\ L\text{-}\int f(x)dx = \sup_H L\text{-}\int_H f(x)dx.$$

Theorem 63.3. *For a sequence of positive measurable functions* $0 \leqq f_1 \leqq f_2 \leqq \ldots$ *by* L, *if* $f(x) = \lim_{\nu\to\infty} f_\nu(x)$ *for every* $x \in S$, *then* f *also is measurable by* L *and*

$$L\text{-}\int f(x)dx = \lim_{\nu\to\infty} L\text{-}\int f_\nu(x)dx.$$

Proof. Since $f|_0^\alpha(x) = \lim_{\nu\to\infty} f_\nu|_0^\alpha(x)$ for every $x \in S$, we see easily by Theorem 62.6 that f also is measurable by L and

$$L\text{-}\int_H f|_0^\alpha(x)dx = \lim_{\nu\to\infty} L\text{-}\int_H f_\nu|_0^\alpha(x)dx$$

on every regular set H, as proved just above. Since we have by definition

$$L\text{-}\int_H f_\nu|_0^\alpha(x)dx \leqq L\text{-}\int f_\nu(x)dx,$$

we hence conclude

$$L\text{-}\int f(x)dx \leqq \lim_{\nu\to\infty} L\text{-}\int f_\nu(x)dx.$$

On the other hand $f \geqq f_\nu$ $(\nu = 1, 2, \ldots)$ implies by definition

$$L\text{-}\int f(x)dx \geqq \lim_{\nu\to\infty} L\text{-}\int f_\nu(x)dx.$$

Theorem 63.4. *For a sequence of positive measurable functions* $f_\nu \geqq 0$ $(\nu = 1, 2, \ldots)$ *we have*

$$L\text{-}\int \varliminf_{\nu\to\infty} f_\nu(x)dx \leqq \varliminf_{\nu\to\infty} L\text{-}\int f_\nu(x)dx.$$

Proof. Setting $g_n(x) = \inf_{\nu \geqq 1} f_{n+\nu}(x)$ $(n = 1, 2, \ldots)$, we have

$$0 \leqq g_1 \leqq g_2 \leqq \ldots \text{ and } \varliminf_{\nu\to\infty} f_\nu(x) = \lim_{\nu\to\infty} g_\nu(x).$$

Since $\varliminf_{\nu\to\infty} f_\nu|_0^\alpha(x) = \lim_{\nu\to\infty} g_\nu|_0^\alpha(x)$ and $g_n|_0^\alpha(x) = \inf_{\nu\geqq 1} f_{n+\nu}|_0^\alpha(x)$ for $\alpha \geqq 0$, we see easily that g_n $(n = 1, 2, \ldots)$ and $\varliminf_{\nu\to\infty} f_\nu$ are measurable by L. Furthermore we have by Theorem 63.3

$$L\text{-}\int \varliminf_{\nu\to\infty} f_\nu(x)dx = \lim_{\nu\to\infty} L\text{-}\int g_\nu(x)dx \leqq \varliminf_{\nu\to\infty} L\text{-}\int f_\nu(x)dx.$$

Applying Theorem 63.1, we can show easily that Theorem 51.4 also holds for almost uniformly continuous functions. We also can prove easily by Theorem 49.1 and Lemma 50.2 that the characteristic function χ_G of an open set G is almost uniformly continuous on every regular set for L. Thus for any two regular sets $G \supset H$ for L we have

$$L\text{-}\int_G f|_0^\alpha(x)\chi_H(x)dx = L\text{-}\int_H f|_0^\alpha(x)dx \quad \text{for every } \alpha \geqq 0,$$

if f is positive and measurable by L. Therefore we obtain

(3) $L\text{-}\int_H f(x)dx = L\text{-}\int f(x)\chi_H(x)dx.$

If f and g are positive and measurable by L, then $\alpha f + \beta g$ also is positive and measurable by L for $\alpha, \beta \geqq 0$, because

$$(\alpha f + \beta g)(x) = \lim_{n\to\infty} (\alpha f|_0^n + \beta g|_0^n)(x) \quad \text{for } x \in S.$$

Applying Theorem 63.1, we can hence conclude from Theorem 51.2

(4) $L\text{-}\int (\alpha f(x) + \beta g(x))dx = \alpha L\text{-}\int f(x)dx + \beta L\text{-}\int g(x)dx$ for $\alpha, \beta \geqq 0$.

If f is measurable by L, then $f^+ = f \vee 0$ and $f^- = (-f) \vee 0$ also are measurable by L, because $f^+|_0^\alpha = (f|_0^\alpha)^+$ and $f^-|_0^\alpha = (f|_{-\alpha}^0)^-$. For a measurable function f by L, if

$$L\text{-} \int f^+(x)dx < +\infty \quad \text{and} \quad L\text{-} \int f^-(x)dx < +\infty$$

then f is said to be *integrable* by L and the integral of f is defined by

(5) $L\text{-} \int f(x)dx = L\text{-} \int f^+(x)dx - L\text{-} \int f^-(x)dx.$

Theorem 63.5. *A measurable function f by L is integrable by L if and only if $L\text{-} \int |f(x)|dx < +\infty$, and then*

$$|L\text{-} \int f(x)dx| \leqq L\text{-} \int |f(x)|dx.$$

Proof. Since $|f| = f^+ + f^-$, we have by (4)

$$L\text{-} \int |f(x)|dx = L\text{-} \int f^+(x)dx + L\text{-} \int f^-(x)dx.$$

Thus $L\text{-} \int |f(x)|dx < +\infty$ if and only if $L\text{-} \int f^+(x)dx < +\infty$ and $L\text{-} \int f^-(x)dx < +\infty$, and then

$$L\text{-} \int |f(x)|dx \geqq |L\text{-} \int f^+(x)dx - L\text{-} \int f^-(x)dx| = |L\text{-} \int f(x)dx|.$$

Theorem 63.6. *For two integrable functions f and g by L, $\alpha f + \beta g$ also is integrable by L and*

$$L\text{-} \int (\alpha f(x) + \beta g(x))dx = \alpha L\text{-} \int f(x)dx + \beta L\text{-} \int g(x)dx.$$

Proof. Since $|\alpha f(x) + \beta g(x)| \leqq |\alpha||f(x)| + |\beta||g(x)|$, if both f and g are integrable by L, then $\alpha f + \beta g$ also is integrable by L by Theorem 63.5. We conclude easily from (4) that

$$L\text{-} \int \alpha f(x)dx = \alpha L\text{-} \int f(x)dx.$$

Since $(f + g)^+ + f^- + g^- = (f + g)^- + f^+ + g^+$, we also obtain by (4)

$$L\text{-} \int (f + g)^+(x)dx - L\text{-} \int (f + g)^-(x)dx = L\text{-} \int f(x)dx + L\text{-} \int g(x)dx.$$

A set $A \subset S$ is said to be *measurable* by L, if χ_A is measurable by L. Every open set is measurable and

(6) $L(G) = L\text{-} \int \chi_G(x)dx$ for any open set G.

Because we see easily by Theorem 49.1 and Lemma 50.2 that χ_G is measurable by L. If $\Phi \ni \phi \leqq \chi_G$, then we have by Theorem 51.7

$$L(\phi) = L\text{-} \int \phi(x)dx \leqq L\text{-} \int \chi_G(x)dx.$$

Thus we obtain by definition

$$L(G) \leqq L\text{-} \int \chi_G(x)dx.$$

If $L(G) < +\infty$, then for any $\mathcal{E} > 0$ there is a regular set G_1 by Theorem 50.9 such that $L(G_1) > L(G) - \mathcal{E}$ and $G_1 U \subset G$ for some $U \in \mathbf{U}$. We can find then a uniformly continuous function f on S by Theorem 19.1 such that $f(x) = 1$ for $x \in G_1$, $f(x) = 0$ for $x \bar{\in} G$ and $0 \leqq f(x) \leqq 1$ for $x \in G$. Such a function f is obviously an $\mathcal{E}$ approximation of both χ_{G_1} and χ_G. Thus we have by Theorem 63.1

$$|L\text{-}\int_H f(x)dx - L\text{-}\int_H \chi_{G_1}(x)dx| \leqq 2\mathcal{E},$$

$$|L\text{-}\int_H f(x)dx - L\text{-}\int_H \chi_G(x)dx| \leqq 2\mathcal{E}$$

for every regular set H for L. Therefore we conclude by Theorem 51.6

$$L\text{-}\int \chi_G(x)dx \leqq L\text{-}\int \chi_{G_1}(x)dx + 4\mathcal{E} = L(G_1) + 4\mathcal{E} \leqq L(G) + 4\mathcal{E},$$

that is, $L\text{-}\int \chi_G(x)dx \leqq L(G) + 4\mathcal{E}$ for any $\mathcal{E} > 0$. Thus we obtain (6).

For any measurable set A by L we define $L(A)$ by

(7) $L(A) = L\text{-}\int \chi_A(x)dx.$

$L(A)$ is called the *measure* of A by L. With this definition we have by (2)

(8) $L(A) = \sup_H L(A \cap H)$ for every regular set H.

Because $\chi_{A \cap H} = \chi_A \chi_H$ and $A \cap H$ also is measurable by Theorem 63.2

64. Transformation Theorems. Let $\mathbf{G}$ be a transitive group on a space S. We assume first that a locally compact uniformity $\mathbf{U}$ on S is invariant by $\mathbf{G}$. Then there is an invariant measure $L \neq 0$ on S by $\mathbf{G}$ by Theorem of Existence in 55. Since $L(G) = L(GT)$ for every open set $G \subset S$ and $T \in \mathbf{G}$ by Theorem 54.1, if a function ϕ is almost uniformly continuous on a regular set H for L, then $T\phi$ also is almost uniformly continuous on HT^{-1} and for an $\mathcal{E}$ approximation $\phi_{\mathcal{E}}$ of ϕ, $T\phi_{\mathcal{E}}$ also is an $\mathcal{E}$ approximation of $T\phi$ for every $T \in \mathbf{G}$. Thus we can show easily by Theorem 63.1

$$L\text{-}\int_H \phi(x)dx = L\text{-}\int_{HT^{-1}} T\phi(x)dx \quad (T \in \mathbf{G})$$

for any almost uniformly continuous function ϕ on H. Therefore we see easily by definition that if f is a positive measurable function on S by L, then Tf also is positive and measurable by L, and

$$L\text{-}\int f(x)dx = L\text{-}\int f(xT)dx \quad \text{for every } T \in \mathbf{G}.$$

Furthermore, if f is integrable by L, then Tf also is integrable by L and has the same integral as f for every $T \in \mathbf{G}$.

As a generalization of the Lebesgue's translation theorem we have

Theorem 64.1. *If f is integrable by L, then*

$$\lim_{X\to E} L\text{-}\int |f(x) - f(xX)|dx = 0$$

for the weak-uniformity $\mathbf{W}(\mathbf{U})$ *on* $\mathbf{G}$.

Proof. We can assume by definition that f is a positive measurable function on S by L. Since $\lim_{\alpha\to\infty} f|_0^\alpha(x) = f(x)$ for every $x \in S$, for any $\mathcal{E} > 0$ we can find $\alpha > 0$ by Theorem 63.3 such that

$$L\text{-}\int f(x)dx \leqq L\text{-}\int f|_0^\alpha(x)dx + \mathcal{E}.$$

Then we have

$$L\text{-}\int f(xT)dx = L\text{-}\int f(x)dx \leqq L\text{-}\int f|_0^\alpha(x)dx + \mathcal{E} = L\text{-}\int f|_0^\alpha(xT)dx + \mathcal{E}$$

for every $T \in \mathbf{G}$. Thus we obtain by Theorem 63.6

$$L\text{-}\int |f(x) - f(xT)|dx \leqq L\text{-}\int |f|_0^\alpha(x) - f|_0^\alpha(xT)|dx + L\text{-}\int (f(x) - f|_0^\alpha(x))dx$$

$$+ L\text{-}\int (f(xT) - f|_0^\alpha(xT))dx \leqq L\text{-}\int |f|_0^\alpha(x) - f|_0^\alpha(xT)|dx + 2\mathcal{E}.$$

Therefore we can also assume that $0 \leqq f(x) \leqq \alpha$ for every $x \in S$.

For any $\mathcal{E} > 0$ we can find a regular set H for L by definition such that

$$L\text{-}\int f(x)dx \leqq L\text{-}\int_H f(x)dx + \mathcal{E} = L\text{-}\int f(x)\chi_H(x)dx + \mathcal{E}.$$

Let $V \in \mathbf{U}$ be a totally bounded connector. Since the system of point mappings M_x $(x \in H)$ is equi-continuous on $\mathbf{G}$ for $\mathbf{W}(\mathbf{U})$ by Theorem 33.3, we can find $W \in \mathbf{W}(\mathbf{U})$ such that $X \in YW$ implies $xX \in xYV$ for every $x \in H$. Here we can assume by Theorem 42.6 that W is invariant by the right transformation group on **G** and symmetric. We then have $HX \subset HV$ for every $X \in EW$. Since HV also is totally bounded, we can find a regular set $H_1 \supset HV$ by Theorem 50.6 and we have $H_1 T \supset H$ for every $T \in EW$, because $T \in EW$ implies $T^{-1} \in EW$. Thus we obtain by (4) in 63

$$L\text{-} \int |f(x) - f(xT)|(1 - \chi_{H_1}(x))dx$$

$$\leqq L\text{-} \int f(x)(1 - \chi_{H_1}(x))dx + L\text{-} \int f(xT)(1 - \chi_{H_1}(x))dx$$

$$\leqq L\text{-} \int f(x)(1 - \chi_H(x))dx + L\text{-} \int f(x)(1 - \chi_{H_1}(xT^{-1}))dx \leqq 2\varepsilon$$

because $\chi_{H_1}(xT^{-1}) = \chi_{H_1 T}(x) \geqq \chi_H(x)$ by (1) in 54.

We consider a regular set H_2 for L such that $H_2 \supset H_1 V$. Let f_δ be a δ approximation of f on H_2. Since f_δ is uniformly continuous on H_2, we can find $U \in \mathbf{U}$ such that $U \leqq V$ and $x \in yU$, $x, y \in H_2$, implies

$$|f_\delta(x) - f_\delta(y)| \leqq \frac{\varepsilon}{L(H_1)}.$$

We also can find $W_1 \in \mathbf{W}(\mathbf{U})$ such that $W_1 \leqq W$ and $X \in YW_1$ implies $xX \in xYU$ for every $x \in H_1$. Then we have

$$|f_\delta(x) - f_\delta(xT)| \leqq \frac{\varepsilon}{L(H_1)} \quad \text{for every } x \in H_1 \text{ and } T \in EW_1,$$

because $x \in H_1$, $T \in EW_1$ implies $xT \in xU \subset H_1 U \subset H_2$. Thus we obtain

$$L\text{-} \int_{H_1} |f_\delta(x) - f_\delta(xT)|dx \leqq \varepsilon \quad \text{for } T \in EW_1.$$

Since $|f_\delta(x) - f_\delta(xT)|$ is a 2δ approximation of $|f(x) - f(xT)|$ on H_1, we have by Theorem 63.1

$$L\text{-} \int_{H_1} |f(x) - f(xT)|dx \leqq 4a\delta + \varepsilon.$$

We hence conclude

$$L\text{-} \int |f(x) - f(xT)|dx \leqq L\text{-} \int |f(x) - f(xT)|\chi_{H_1}(x)dx + 2\varepsilon \leqq 3\varepsilon + 4a\delta$$

for every $T \in EW_1$. Since $\delta > 0$ is arbitrary, setting $\delta = \frac{\varepsilon}{a}$, we obtain

$$L\text{-} \int |f(x) - f(xT)|dx \leqq 7\varepsilon \text{ for every } T \in EW_1.$$

Therefore $\lim_{T \to E} L\text{-} \int |f(x) - f(xT)|dx = 0.$

We suppose in the sequel that a locally compact uniformity **U** on S is invariant and normal for a transitive group **G** on S and the weak-uniformity **W(U)** on **G** is complete. Then **W(U)** also is locally compact by Theorem 34.11 and invariant by the right transformation group on **G** by Theorem 42.6. Thus there is a right-invariant measure $K \neq 0$ on **G**. Setting

(1) $L_a(\phi) = K\text{-} \int \phi(aX)dX$ for $\phi \in \Phi$ and $a \in S$

for the trunk Φ of **U**, we obtain an invariant measure $L_a \neq 0$ on S for **U** by **G**, because for any $T \in \mathbf{G}$ we have

$$L_a(T\phi) = K\text{-} \int \phi(aXT)dX = K\text{-} \int \phi(aX)dX \text{ for every } \phi \in \Phi.$$

For any open set $G \subset S$, GM_a^{-1} is an open set *of* **G** for **W(U)**, because the point mapping M_a is uniformly continuous for **W(U)**. We have

(2) $L_a(G) = K(GM_a^{-1})$ $(a \in S)$

for any open set $G \subset S$. Because $\Phi \ni \phi \leqq \chi_G$ implies

$$\phi(aX) \leqq \chi_G(aX) = \chi_{GM_a^{-1}}(X)$$

since $aX \in G$ if and only if $X \in GM_a^{-1}$. Thus we obtain by definition

$$L_a(G) = \sup_{\Phi \ni \phi \leqq \chi_G} L_a(\phi) \leqq K(GM_a^{-1}).$$

Let Ψ be the trunk of **W(U)** on **G**. For any $\alpha < K(GM_a^{-1})$ we can find $\psi \in \Psi$ by Theorem 49.2 such that $\alpha < K(\psi)$, $\psi \leqq 1$ and

$$\{X: \psi(X) > 0\}^- \subset GM_a^{-1}.$$

Then we also can find an open set $G_1 \subset S$ by Theorem 9.4 such that

$$\{X: \psi(X) > 0\}^- M_a \subset G_1 \prec G,$$

because $\{X: \psi(X) > 0\}^- M_a$ is compact by Theorem 12.3. For such G_1 we can find $\phi \in \Phi$ by Theorem 19.2 such that $\phi(x) = 1$ for $x \in G_1$, $\phi(x) = 0$ for $x \bar{\in} G$ and $\phi \leqq 1$. Then we have $\Phi \ni \phi \leqq \chi_G$ and $\psi(X) \leqq \phi(aX)$ for every $X \in \mathbf{G}$. Thus

$$a < K(\psi) \leqq K\text{-} \int \phi(aX)dX = L_a(\phi) \leqq L_a(G).$$

Therefore we conclude $K(GM_a^{-1}) \leqq L_a(G)$.

Since $H \prec G$ implies $HM_a^{-1} \prec GM_a^{-1}$, we conclude from (2)

Theorem 64.2. *If G is a regular set for L_a, then GM_a^{-1} is a regular set for K.*

Let ϕ be a positive uniformly continuous function on a regular set G for L_a. For any $\mathcal{E}$ partition $G_\nu \subset G$ $(\nu = 1, 2, \ldots, n)$ of G for ϕ, we see easily that $G_\nu M_a^{-1} (\nu = 1, 2, \ldots, n)$ is an $\mathcal{E}$ partition of $\bigcup_{\nu=1}^{n} G_\nu M_a^{-1}$ for $\phi(aX)$ and $\bigcup_{\nu=1}^{n} G_\nu M_a^{-1} \subset GM_a^{-1}$. Thus we obtain by Theorem 51.1

$$L_a\text{-} \int_G \phi(x)dx \leqq K\text{-} \int_{GM_a^{-1}} \phi(aX)dX.$$

For any positive uniformly continuous function ϕ on G we can find $\phi_0 \in \Phi$ by Theorem 19.2 such that $\phi(x) = \phi_0(x)$ for $x \in G$. For a regular set G_1 for L_a such that

$$G_1 \supset \{x: \phi_0(x) > 0\} \cup G$$

we hence have by Theorems 51.7 and 51.4

$$\begin{aligned} L_a(\phi_0) &= L_a\text{-} \int_G \phi(x)dx + L_a\text{-} \int_{G_1 \cap G'} \phi_0(x)dx \\ &\leqq K\text{-} \int_{GM_a^{-1}} \phi(aX)dX + K\text{-} \int_{(G_1 \cap G')M_a^{-1}} \phi_0(aX)dX \\ &= K\text{-} \int_{G_1 M_a^{-1}} \phi_0(aX)dX = K\text{-} \int \phi_0(aX)dX = L_a(\phi_0). \end{aligned}$$

Thus we obtain

$$(3) \quad L_a\text{-} \int_G \phi(x)dx = K\text{-} \int_{GM_a^{-1}} \phi(aX)dX$$

for any positive uniformly continuous function ϕ on G. For an arbitrary uniformly continuous function ϕ on G we can find $\gamma > 0$ such that $\phi(x) + \gamma \geqq 0$ for $x \in G$, and we have by (2) and Theorem 51.6

$$L_a\text{-} \int_G \gamma dx = \gamma L_a(G) = \gamma K(GM_a^{-1}) = K\text{-} \int_{GM_a^{-1}} \gamma dX.$$

Therefore (3) holds for any uniformly continuous function ϕ on G.

From (2) and (3) we conclude immediately

Theorem 64.3. *If f is almost uniformly continuous on a regular set G for L_a, then $f(aX)$ is almost uniformly continuous on GM_a^{-1} for K. For any $\mathcal{E}$ approximation $f_{\mathcal{E}}$ of f on G, $f_{\mathcal{E}}(aX)$ is an $\mathcal{E}$ approximation of $f(aX)$ on GM_a^{-1}, and (3) holds for any almost uniformly continuous function f on G.*

Therefore we have by definition

Theorem 64.4. *If f is measurable by L_a, then $f(aX)$ is measurable by K. For any positive measurable function f on S by L_a we have*

$$L_a\text{-} \int f(x)dx = K\text{-} \int f(aX)dX.$$

For the coefficient function τ of G for K, we have by (1)

$$L_{aT}(\phi) = K\text{-} \int \phi(aTX)dX = \tau(T)K\text{-} \int \phi(aX)dX = \tau(T)L_a(\phi),$$

for every $\phi \in \Phi$, that is,

(4) $L_{aT}(\phi) = \tau(T)L_a(\phi)$ for every $T \in \mathbf{G}$ and $\phi \in \Phi$.

Thus we obtain by definition

(5) $L_{aT}(H) = \tau(T)L_a(H)$ for any open set H and $T \in \mathbf{G}$.

Theorem 64.5. *Let L be an invariant measure on S for $\mathbf{U}$ by $\mathbf{G}$ and let K be a right-invariant measure for $\mathbf{W}(\mathbf{U})$ on $\mathbf{G}$. For a measurable set A by L and for a measurable set $\mathbf{A}$ by K, if $L(A) > 0$ and $K(\mathbf{A}) > 0$, then $(A\mathbf{A})^\circ \neq \emptyset$.*

Proof. If $L(A) > 0$, then $L_a(A) > 0$ by Theorem of Uniqueness in 56. Referring to (8) in 63, we can assume that A is totally bounded for $\mathbf{U}$ and $\mathbf{A}$ is totally bounded for $\mathbf{W}(\mathbf{U})$. Then we can find a regular set $H_0 \supset A$ for L_a and a regular set $\mathbf{H}_0 \subset \mathbf{G}$ for K by Theorem 50.6 such that

$$\mathbf{H}_0 \supset \mathbf{A} \cup H_0 M_a^{-1},$$

because $H_0 M_a^{-1}$ is totally bounded for $\mathbf{W}(\mathbf{U})$ by Theorem 37.11. Here we can assume $\mathbf{H}_0^{-1} = \mathbf{H}_0$ by Theorem 57.5, because otherwise we could replace $\mathbf{H}_0$ by $\mathbf{H}_0 \cup \mathbf{H}_0^{-1}$. There is a regular set H_1 for L_a such that $H_1 \supset H_0\mathbf{H}_0 \cup H_0$, because $H_0\mathbf{H}_0$ is totally bounded for $\mathbf{U}$ by Theorems 33.3 and 16.2. We also can find a regular set H_2 for L_a by the same reason such that $H_2 \supset H_1 \mathbf{H}_0 \cup H_1$. Since τ is uniformly continuous on $H_1 M_a^{-1}$ by Theorem 57.4, we can find $\gamma > 0$ such that $\tau(X) \leqq \gamma$ for every $X \in H_1 M_a^{-1}$. Let $\mathcal{E} > 0$ be arbitrary but $2\mathcal{E} < L_a(A)$, $2\mathcal{E} < K(\mathbf{A})$. Let f be an $\mathcal{E}$ approximation of χ_A on H_2 for L_a such that $0 \leqq f \leqq 1$. Then we have by Theorem 63.1

$$|L_a\text{-}\int_{H_0} f(x)dx - L_a\text{-}\int_{H_0} \chi_A(x)dx| \leqq 2\mathcal{E}$$

and hence $L_a\text{-}\int_{H_0} f(x)dx \geqq L_a(A) - 2\mathcal{E}$.

For any $x \in H_1$ we can find $T \in H_1 M_a^{-1}$ such that $x = aT$, and then $L_x(H) = L_{aT}(H) \leqq \gamma L_a(H)$ for any open set H by (5). Therefore f is a $\gamma\mathcal{E}$ approximation of χ_A on H_2 for L_x for every $x \in H_1$, and $f(xX)$ is a $\gamma\mathcal{E}$ approximation of $\chi_A(xX)$ on $\mathbf{H}_0$ for K by Theorem 64.3, because $H_2 M_x^{-1} \supset H_2 \mathbf{H}_0 M_x^{-1} \supset \mathbf{H}_0$. Since we have by Theorem 57.5

$$K(\mathbf{H}^{-1}) = K\text{-}\int_{\mathbf{H}} \tau(X)dX \leqq \gamma K(\mathbf{H})$$

for any regular set $\mathbf{H}$ for K such that $\mathbf{H} \subset \mathbf{H}_0$, we obtain by Theorem 50.9

$$K(\mathbf{H}^{-1}) \leqq \gamma K(\mathbf{H}) \text{ for any open set } \mathbf{H} \subset \mathbf{H}_0.$$

Therefore $f(xX^{-1})$ is a $\gamma^2\mathcal{E}$ approximation of $\chi_A(xX^{-1})$ on $\mathbf{H}_0$, because $\mathbf{H}_0^{-1} = \mathbf{H}_0$.

Let g be an $\mathcal{E}$ approximation of $\chi_{\mathbf{A}}$ on $\mathbf{H}_0$ such that $0 \leqq g \leqq 1$. Then we have by Theorem 63.1

$$|K\text{-}\int_{\mathbf{H}_0} g(X)dX - K\text{-}\int_{\mathbf{H}_0} \chi_{\mathbf{A}}(X)dX| \leqq 2\mathcal{E}$$

and hence $K(\mathbf{A}) + 2\mathcal{E} \geqq K\text{-}\int_{\mathbf{H}_0} g(X)dX \geqq K(\mathbf{A}) - 2\mathcal{E}$. Since $f(xX^{-1})g(X)$ is a $(\gamma^2 + 1)\mathcal{E}$ approximation of $\chi_A(xX^{-1})\chi_{\mathbf{A}}(X)$ on $\mathbf{H}_0$ for every $x \in H_1$, setting

$$k(x) = K\text{-}\int_{\mathbf{H}_0} \chi_A(xX^{-1})\chi_{\mathbf{A}}(X)dX \quad \text{for } x \in H_1,$$

we have by Theorem 63.1

$$|K\text{-}\int_{\mathbf{H}_0} f(xX^{-1})g(X)dX - k(x)| \leqq 2(\gamma^2 + 1)\mathcal{E}$$

for every $x \in H_1$. Since $\mathbf{G}$ is equi-continuous for $\mathbf{U}$ and f is uniformly continuous on H_2, we can find $U \in \mathbf{U}$ such that $x \in yU^{\mathbf{G}}$, $x, y \in H_2$, implies $|f(x) - f(y)| < \mathcal{E}$. Then $x \in yU^{\mathbf{G}}$, $x, y \in H_1$ implies

$$|f(xX^{-1}) - f(yX^{-1})| < \mathcal{E} \quad \text{for every } X \in \mathbf{H}_0,$$

because $x \in yU^{\mathbf{G}}$ implies $xX^{-1} \in yX^{-1}U^{\mathbf{G}}$, and $x, y \in H_1$ implies xX^{-1}, $yX^{-1} \in H_2$ for every $X \in \mathbf{H}_0$. Thus we have

$$\begin{aligned} &|K\text{-}\int_{\mathbf{H}_0} f(xX^{-1})g(X)dX - K\text{-}\int_{\mathbf{H}_0} f(yX^{-1})g(X)dX| \\ &\leqq \mathcal{E}K\text{-}\int_{\mathbf{H}_0} g(X)dX \leqq \mathcal{E}(K(\mathbf{A}) + 2\mathcal{E}) \end{aligned}$$

and hence $|k(x) - k(y)| \leqq 4(\gamma^2 + 1)\mathcal{E} + \mathcal{E}(K(\mathbf{A}) + 2\mathcal{E})$ for $x \in yU^{\mathbf{G}}$, x, $y \in H_1$. Since $\mathcal{E} > 0$ is arbitrary, we conclude therefore that k is a uniformly continuous function on H_1 for $\mathbf{U}$, and

$$\begin{aligned} &|L_a\text{-}\int_{H_1} (K\text{-}\int_{\mathbf{H}_0} f(xX^{-1})g(X)dX)dx - L_a\text{-}\int_{H_1} k(x)dx| \\ &\leqq 2(\gamma^2 + 1)\mathcal{E}L_a(H_1). \end{aligned}$$

On the other hand we have by Theorem 52.2

$$\begin{aligned} L_a\text{-}\int_{H_1} (K\text{-}\int_{\mathbf{H}_0} f(xX^{-1})g(X)dX)dx &= K\text{-}\int_{\mathbf{H}_0} (L_a\text{-}\int_{H_1} f(xX^{-1})g(X)dx)dX \\ &= K\text{-}\int_{\mathbf{H}_0} (L_a\text{-}\int_{H_1X^{-1}} f(x)g(X)dx)dX \end{aligned}$$

$$\geqq K\text{-}\int_{\mathbf{H}_0} (L_a\text{-}\int_{H_0} f(x)g(X)dx)dX = (L_a\text{-}\int_{H_0} f(x)dx)(K\text{-}\int_{\mathbf{H}_0} g(X)dX)$$

because $H_1X^{-1} \supset H_0$ for every $X \in \mathbf{H}_0$. Thus we have

$$L_a\text{-}\int_{H_1} k(x)dx \geqq (L_a(A) - 2\mathcal{E})(K(\mathbf{A}) - 2\mathcal{E}) - 2(\gamma^2 + 1)\mathcal{E}L_a(H_1).$$

Since $\mathcal{E} > 0$ is arbitrary, we hence conclude

$$L_a\text{-}\int_{H_1} k(x)dx \geqq L_a(A)K(\mathbf{A}) > 0.$$

Thus $\{x: k(x) > 0,\ x \in H_1\} \neq \emptyset$. If $k(x) > 0$, then there is $X \in \mathbf{H}_0$ such that $\chi_A(xX^{-1})\,\chi_{\mathbf{A}}(X) > 0$, that is, $X \in \mathbf{A}$ and $xX^{-1} \in A$, and hence $x \in A\mathbf{A}$. Therefore $A\mathbf{A} \supset \{x: k(x) > 0,\ x \in H_1\}$. Since k is uniformly continuous on H_1 for $\mathbf{U}$, $\{x: k(x) > 0,\ x \in H_1\}$ is an open set for $\mathbf{U}$, and hence

$$(A\mathbf{A})^\circ \supset \{x: k(x) > 0,\ x \in H_1\} \neq \emptyset.$$

Proof. Since $\mathbf{D} \supset \mathbf{U}$, every almost periodic function by $\mathbf{G}$ for $\mathbf{U}$ also is almost periodic by $\mathbf{G}$ for $\mathbf{D}$. Thus we have $\mathbf{U}_{\mathbf{A}} \subset \mathbf{D}_{\mathbf{G}}$ by definition for the almost periodic part $\mathbf{U}_{\mathbf{A}}$ of $\mathbf{U}$ by $\mathbf{G}$. We also have $\mathbf{U}_{\mathbf{A}} \subset \mathbf{U}$ by definition. For a uniformity $\mathbf{V}$ on S, if $\mathbf{V} \subset \mathbf{U}$ and $\mathbf{V} \subset \mathbf{D}_{\mathbf{G}}$, then every uniformly continuous function ϕ on S for $\mathbf{V}$ is uniformly continuous for $\mathbf{U}$ and for $\mathbf{D}_{\mathbf{G}}$, and hence ϕ is almost periodic by $\mathbf{G}$ for $\mathbf{U}$ by definition. Thus ϕ is uniformly continuous for $\mathbf{U}_{\mathbf{A}}$ by Theorem 66.2. Since $\mathbf{V} \subset \mathbf{D}_{\mathbf{G}}$ and $\mathbf{D}_{\mathbf{G}}$ is totally bounded, $\mathbf{V}$ also is totally bounded. Therefore we conclude by Theorem 20.5 that $\mathbf{V} \subset \mathbf{U}_{\mathbf{A}}$. Consequently we obtain $\mathbf{U}_{\mathbf{A}} = \mathbf{U} \wedge \mathbf{D}_{\mathbf{G}}$.

Theorem 66.5. $\mathbf{U}$ *is almost periodic by* $\mathbf{G}$ *if and only if* $\mathbf{U}^A = \mathbf{U}_{\mathbf{A}}{}^A$ *for any totally bounded set* A *for* $\mathbf{U}$.

Proof. If $\mathbf{U}$ is almost periodic by $\mathbf{G}$, then for any uniformly continuous function f on A for $\mathbf{U}$, there is an almost periodic function ϕ such that $f(x) = \phi(x)$ for $x \in A$. Therefore $\mathbf{U}^A \subset \mathbf{U}_{\mathbf{A}}{}^A$ by Theorem 20.5. It is obvious by definition that $\mathbf{U}^A \supset \mathbf{U}_{\mathbf{A}}{}^A$.

Conversely if $\mathbf{U}^A = \mathbf{U}_{\mathbf{A}}{}^A$, then for any uniformly continuous function f on A for $\mathbf{U}$ there is a uniformly continuous function ϕ on S for $\mathbf{U}_{\mathbf{A}}$ by Theorem 19.2 such that $f(x) = \phi(x)$ for $x \in A$, and ϕ is almost periodic by $\mathbf{G}$ for $\mathbf{U}$ by Theorem 66.2.

67. **Periodic Functions.** A function ϕ on a space S is said to be *invariant* by a transformation T on S, if $T\phi = \phi$, that is, if $\phi(xT) = \phi(x)$ for every $x \in S$. For a system of transformations $\mathbf{K}$ on S, ϕ is said to be *invariant* by $\mathbf{K}$, if ϕ is invariant by every $T \in \mathbf{K}$.

Let $\mathbf{G}$ be a transformation group on S. For a function ϕ on S, the system of transformations $X \in \mathbf{G}$

$$\{X\colon XT\phi = T\phi \text{ for every } T \in \mathbf{G}\}$$

is called the *fixer* of ϕ by $\mathbf{G}$ and denoted by $\mathbf{F}_{\phi}$.

Theorem 67.1. *The fixer* $\mathbf{F}_{\phi}$ *of* ϕ *by* $\mathbf{G}$ *is an invariant subgroup of* $\mathbf{G}$ *and* $\mathbf{F}_{X\phi} = \mathbf{F}_{\phi}$ *for every* $X \in \mathbf{G}$. *If* ϕ *is invariant by an invariant subgroup* $\mathbf{K} \subset \mathbf{G}$, *then* $\mathbf{K} \subset \mathbf{F}_{\phi}$.

Proof. If $XT\phi = T\phi$ and $YT\phi = T\phi$, then $(XY)T\phi = X(YT\phi) = XT\phi = T\phi$ and $X^{-1}T\phi = X^{-1}(XT\phi) = X^{-1}X(T\phi) = T\phi$. Thus the fixer **F** is a subgroup of **G**. If $XT\phi = T\phi$ for every $T \in \mathbf{G}$, then for any $T_1, T \in \mathbf{G}$ we have $(T_1XT_1^{-1})T\phi = T_1X(T_1^{-1}T\phi) = T_1T_1^{-1}T\phi = T\phi$. Therefore $X \in \mathbf{F}_\phi$ implies $TXT^{-1} \in \mathbf{F}_\phi$ for every $T \in \mathbf{G}$, that is, $\mathbf{F}_\phi$ is an invariant subgroup of **G**. It is obvious by definition that $\mathbf{F}_\phi = \mathbf{F}_{T\phi}$ for every $T \in \mathbf{G}$. If ϕ is invariant by an invariant subgroup **K** of **G**, then for any $X \in \mathbf{K}$ and $T \in \mathbf{G}$ we have $(T^{-1}XT)\phi = \phi$, and hence $XT\phi = T\phi$ for every $T \in \mathbf{G}$. Therefore $\mathbf{K} \subset \mathbf{F}_\phi$ by definition.

Let **K** be a system of transformations on S, containing the identity transformation E. For any connector U on S, setting

$$x(\mathbf{K}U) = (x\mathbf{K})U \quad \text{and} \quad x(U\mathbf{K}) = (xU)\mathbf{K} \quad \text{for } x \in S,$$

we obtain connectors $\mathbf{K}U$ and $U\mathbf{K}$ on S. It is obvious by definition that

$$U \leqq \mathbf{K}U \quad \text{and} \quad U \leqq U\mathbf{K}.$$

Lemma. *If* **H** *is an invariant subgroup of* **G**, *then for any invariant connector* U *on* S *by* **G**, *we have*

$$\mathbf{H}U = U\mathbf{H} = (U\mathbf{H})^{\mathbf{G}}, \quad U^{-1}\mathbf{H} = (U\mathbf{H})^{-1},$$
$$UV\mathbf{H} = U\mathbf{H}V\mathbf{H}, \text{ if } U \text{ and } V \text{ are invariant by } \mathbf{G}.$$

Proof. Since $XU = UX$ for every $X \in \mathbf{G}$, we have $\mathbf{H}U = U\mathbf{H}$, and $X(U\mathbf{H})X^{-1} = XUX^{-1}\mathbf{H} = U\mathbf{H}$ for every $X \in \mathbf{G}$, because $X\mathbf{H}X^{-1} = \mathbf{H}$ for every $X \in \mathbf{G}$. Thus $(U\mathbf{H})^{\mathbf{G}} = U\mathbf{H}$. If $x \in yU^{-1}\mathbf{H}$, then there is $H \in \mathbf{H}$ such that $xH \in yU^{-1}$, and hence $y \in xHU = xUH \subset xU\mathbf{H}$, that is, $x \in y(U\mathbf{H})^{-1}$. Conversely if $x \in y(U\mathbf{H})^{-1}$, then $y \in xU\mathbf{H}$, that is, there is $H \in \mathbf{H}$ such that $yH \in xU$, and hence $x \in yHU^{-1} = yU^{-1}H \subset yU^{-1}\mathbf{H}$. If V is invariant by **G**, then we have $UV\mathbf{H} = UV\mathbf{H}\mathbf{H} = U\mathbf{H}V\mathbf{H}$.

Let **U** be a uniformity on S, which is locally totally bounded and invariant by **G**. For an invariant subgroup **H** of **G**

$$\mathbf{U}^{\mathbf{G}}\mathbf{H} = \{U^{\mathbf{G}}\mathbf{H} : U \in \mathbf{U}\}$$

consists of invariant connectors by **G** and we can show easily by the Lemma that $\mathbf{U}^{\mathbf{G}}\mathbf{H}$ satisfies the basis conditions. Therefore there exists a uniformity on S of which $\mathbf{U}^{\mathbf{G}}\mathbf{H}$ is a basis. This uniformity is called the $\mathbf{H}$ *part* of $\mathbf{U}$ by $\mathbf{G}$ and denoted by $\mathbf{U}_{\mathbf{H}}$. It is obvious by definition that $\mathbf{U}_{\mathbf{H}} \subset \mathbf{U}$ and $\mathbf{U}_{\mathbf{H}}$ is invariant by $\mathbf{G}$.

Theorem 67.2. *A uniformly continuous function ϕ on S for $\mathbf{U}$ is invariant by an invariant subgroup $\mathbf{H}$ of $\mathbf{G}$ if and only if ϕ is uniformly continuous for the $\mathbf{H}$ part $\mathbf{U}_{\mathbf{H}}$ of $\mathbf{U}$.*

Proof. Since ϕ is uniformly continuous for $\mathbf{U}$ by assumption, for any $\mathcal{E} > 0$ we can find $U \in \mathbf{U}$ such that $x \in yU^{\mathbf{G}}$ implies $|\phi(x)-\phi(y)| < \mathcal{E}$. If ϕ is invariant by $\mathbf{H}$, then $\phi(x) = \phi(xX)$ for every $X \in \mathbf{H}$ and $x \in S$. Thus $x \in yU^{\mathbf{G}}\mathbf{H}$ implies $|\phi(x) - \phi(y)| < \mathcal{E}$. Therefore ϕ is uniformly continuous for $\mathbf{U}(\mathbf{H})$. Conversely if ϕ is uniformly continuous for $\mathbf{U}(\mathbf{H})$, then for any $\mathcal{E} > 0$ we can find $U \in \mathbf{U}$ such that $y \in xU^{\mathbf{G}}\mathbf{H}$ implies $|\phi(x) - \phi(y)| < \mathcal{E}$. Since $xX \in xU^{\mathbf{G}}\mathbf{H}$ for every $U \in \mathbf{U}$, $x \in S$ and $X \in \mathbf{H}$, we hence obtain

$$|\phi(x) - \phi(xX)| < \mathcal{E} \text{ for every } \mathcal{E} > 0,\ x \in S \text{ and } X \in \mathbf{H}.$$

Therefore $\phi(x) = \phi(xX)$ for every $x \in S$ and $X \in \mathbf{H}$, that is, $X\phi = \phi$ for every $X \in \mathbf{H}$.

A uniformly continuous function ϕ on S for $\mathbf{U}$ is said to be *periodic* by $\mathbf{G}$ for $\mathbf{U}$, if there is a totally bounded set A for $\mathbf{U}$ such that $A\mathbf{F}_{\phi} = S$ for the fixer $\mathbf{F}_{\phi}$ of ϕ by $\mathbf{G}$. With this definition we have by Theorem 67.1

Theorem 67.3. *If ϕ is periodic by $\mathbf{G}$ for $\mathbf{U}$, then $T\phi$ also is periodic by $\mathbf{G}$ for $\mathbf{U}$ for every $T \in \mathbf{G}$.*

Theorem 67.4. *Every periodic function on S by $\mathbf{G}$ for $\mathbf{U}$ is almost periodic by $\mathbf{G}$ for $\mathbf{U}$.*

Proof. If ϕ is periodic by $\mathbf{G}$ for $\mathbf{U}$, then there is a totally bounded set A by definition such that $A\mathbf{F}_{\phi} = S$. Since ϕ is invariant by $\mathbf{F}_{\phi}$, ϕ is uniformly continuous for the $\mathbf{F}_{\phi}$ part $\mathbf{U}_{\mathbf{F}_{\phi}}$ of $\mathbf{U}$ by Theorem 67.2. For any $U \in \mathbf{U}$ we can find a finite system $a_{\nu} \in A$ $(\nu = 1, 2, \ldots, n)$ such that $A \subset \bigcup_{\nu=1}^{n} a_{\nu}U^{\mathbf{G}}$, and hence

$$S = A\mathbf{F}_{\phi} \subset \bigcup_{\nu=1}^{n} a_{\nu}U^{\mathbf{G}}\mathbf{F}_{\phi}.$$

Thus $\mathbf{U}_{\mathbf{F}_\phi}$ is totally bounded, because $\mathbf{U}^{\mathbf{G}}\mathbf{F}_\phi$ is a basis of $\mathbf{U}_{\mathbf{F}_\phi}$. Since $\mathbf{U}_{\mathbf{F}_\phi}$ is invariant by $\mathbf{G}$, we see easily that $X\phi$ $(X \in \mathbf{G})$ is equi-continuous for $\mathbf{U}_{\mathbf{F}_\phi}$. Therefore the single equi-uniformity on S by $X\phi$ $(X \in \mathbf{G})$ is weaker than $\mathbf{U}_{\mathbf{F}_\phi}$ and hence totally bounded, that is, ϕ is almost periodic by $\mathbf{G}$ for $\mathbf{U}$ by definition.

Let $\mathbf{P}$ be the system of all periodic functions on S by $\mathbf{G}$ for $\mathbf{U}$. The multiple equi-uniformity on S by the double system $X\phi$ $(X \in \mathbf{G}, \phi \in \mathbf{P})$ is called the *periodic part* of $\mathbf{U}$ by $\mathbf{G}$. Let $\mathbf{U}_\mathbf{P}$ be the periodic part of $\mathbf{U}$ and let $\mathbf{U}_\mathbf{A}$ be the almost periodic part of $\mathbf{U}$ by $\mathbf{G}$. Then we obviously have $\mathbf{U}_\mathbf{A} \supset \mathbf{U}_\mathbf{P}$ by Theorem 67.4. Thus $\mathbf{U}_\mathbf{P}$ is totally bounded, since $\mathbf{U}_\mathbf{A}$ is totally bounded by Theorem 66.1. We also can prove that $\mathbf{U}_\mathbf{P}$ is invariant by $\mathbf{G}$ as we did for the almost periodic part in the proof of Theorem 66.1. Thus we have

Theorem 67.5. *The periodic part of* $\mathbf{U}$ *by* $\mathbf{G}$ *is totally bounded and invariant by* $\mathbf{G}$.

68. **Means.** A system of bounded functions $\mathbf{F}$ on a space S is called a *field* on S, if $1 \in \mathbf{F}$ and $\phi, \psi \in \mathbf{F}$ implies $\alpha\phi + \beta\psi \in \mathbf{F}$ for any real numbers α, β. Let $\mathbf{U}$ be a uniformity on S. If a field $\mathbf{F}$ on S consists of uniformly continuous functions on S for $\mathbf{U}$, then $\mathbf{F}$ is called a *field* on S *for* $\mathbf{U}$. For a transformation group $\mathbf{G}$ on S, a field $\mathbf{F}$ on S is said to be *invariant* by $\mathbf{G}$, if $\phi \in \mathbf{F}$ implies $T\phi \in \mathbf{F}$ for every $T \in \mathbf{G}$.

Let $\mathbf{F}$ be an invariant field on S for $\mathbf{U}$ by $\mathbf{G}$. A function $M(\phi)$ $(\phi \in \mathbf{F})$ on $\mathbf{F}$ is called a *mean* on $\mathbf{F}$ by $\mathbf{G}$, if

(1) $M(1) = 1$,

(2) $M(\alpha\phi + \beta\psi) = \alpha M(\phi) + \beta M(\psi)$ for $\phi, \psi \in \mathbf{F}$,

(3) $\phi \leqq \psi$ implies $M(\phi) \leqq M(\psi)$ for $\phi, \psi \in \mathbf{F}$,

(4) $M(T\phi) = M(\phi)$ for $\phi \in \mathbf{F}$ and $\mathbf{T} \in \mathbf{G}$.

Now we assume that $\mathbf{U}$ is locally totally bounded and invariant by $\mathbf{G}$. Let $\mathbf{A}$ be the system of all almost periodic functions on S for $\mathbf{U}$ by $\mathbf{G}$. $\mathbf{A}$ is obviously an invariant field on S for $\mathbf{U}$ by $\mathbf{G}$. Making use of the notation

$$\mathbf{A}^+ = \{\phi : 0 \leqq \phi \in \mathbf{A}\}$$

we see easily by Theorem 66.2 that $\mathbf{A}^+$ is the trunk of the almost periodic part $\mathbf{U}_{\mathbf{A}}$ of $\mathbf{U}$. Thus every mean M on $\mathbf{A}$ by $\mathbf{G}$ is considered an invariant measure $M(\phi)$ $(\phi \in \mathbf{A}^+)$ on S for $\mathbf{U}_{\mathbf{A}}$ by $\mathbf{G}$. The integral by this measure M is denoted by $M\text{-} \int \phi(x)dx$ for $\phi \in \mathbf{A}$. Then we can show easily by (1), (2), (3)

$$M\text{-} \int \phi(x)dx = M(\phi) \quad \text{for every } \phi \in \mathbf{A}.$$

Since $\mathbf{U}_{\mathbf{A}}$ is totally bounded and invariant by $\mathbf{G}$ by Theorem 66.1, the weak-uniformity $\mathbf{W}(\mathbf{U}_{\mathbf{A}})$ on $\mathbf{G}$ by the system of all point mappings also is totally bounded by Theorem 23.8 and invariant by the right transformation group by Theorem 42.6. Thus we see by Theorem of Existence in 55 and Theorem of Uniqueness in 56 that there exists uniquely a measure K on $\mathbf{G}$ for $\mathbf{W}(\mathbf{U}_{\mathbf{A}})$ which is invariant by the right transformation group on $\mathbf{G}$ and $K(1) = 1$. For this measure K on $\mathbf{G}$, setting

(5) $F(\phi, x) = K\text{-} \int \phi(xX)dX \quad (\phi \in \mathbf{A},\ x \in S),$

we obtain a binary function F on $(\mathbf{A}, S)$, and we obviously have

(6) $F(\alpha\phi + \beta\psi, x) = \alpha F(\phi, x) + \beta F(\psi, x)$ for $\phi, \psi \in \mathbf{A},\ x \in S,$

(7) $\phi \leqq \psi$ implies $F(\phi, x) \leqq F(\psi, x)$ for $\phi, \psi \in \mathbf{A},\ x \in S,$

(8) $F(1, x) = 1$ for $x \in S$.

Making use of the notation in 52, $F(\ ,x)$ is a mean on $\mathbf{A}$ by $\mathbf{G}$ for every $x \in S$. Because it is obvious by (6), (7), (8) that $F(\ ,x)$ satisfies (1), (2), (3) for every $x \in S$. For any $\phi \in \mathbf{A}$ and $T \in \mathbf{G}$ we have

$$F(T\phi, x) = K\text{-} \int T\phi(xX)dX = K\text{-} \int \phi(xXT)dX = K\text{-} \int \phi(xX)dX = F(\phi, x),$$

that is,

(9) $F(T\phi, x) = F(\phi, x)$ for $\phi \in \mathbf{A},\ x \in S,\ T \in \mathbf{G},$

and hence $F(\ ,x)$ satisfies (4) too.

$F(\phi,\ )$ is invariant by $\mathbf{G}$ for every $\phi \in \mathbf{A}$. Because $\mathbf{G}$ is steady by Theorem 58.6, and hence we have by Theorem 58.3

$$F(\phi, xT) = K\text{-} \int \phi(xTX)dX = K\text{-} \int \phi(xX)dX = F(\phi, x)$$

that is,

(10) $F(\phi, xT) = F(\phi, x)$ for $\phi \in \mathbf{A},\ x \in S,\ T \in \mathbf{G}.$

Furthermore $F(\phi, \ ) \in \mathbf{A}$ for every $\phi \in \mathbf{A}$. Because for any $\mathcal{E} > 0$ there is $U \in \mathbf{U}_{\mathbf{A}}$ by Theorem 66.2 such that $x \in yU^{\mathbf{G}}$ implies $|\phi(x) - \phi(y)| < \mathcal{E}$. Since $x \in yU^{\mathbf{G}}$ implies $xX \in yXU^{\mathbf{G}}$ for every $X \in \mathbf{G}$, we obtain

$$|\phi(xX) - \phi(yX)| < \mathcal{E} \ \text{ for } \ x \in yU^{\mathbf{G}} \text{ and } X \in \mathbf{G},$$

and hence $x \in yU^{\mathbf{G}}$ implies

$$|F(\phi, x) - F(\phi, y)| \leqq K\text{-} \int |\phi(xX) - \phi(yX)| dX \leqq \mathcal{E}.$$

Therefore $F(\phi, \ )$ is uniformly continuous for $\mathbf{U}_{\mathbf{A}}$. Thus $F(\phi, \ ) \in \mathbf{A}$ by Theorem 66.2. We can hence state

Theorem 68.1. *For the binary function $F(\phi, x)$ ($\phi \in \mathbf{A}$, $x \in S$) in* (5), *$F(\ , x)$ is a mean on* **A** *by* **G** *for every $x \in S$, $F(\phi, \ )$ is invariant by* **G**, *$F(\phi, \ ) \in \mathbf{A}$ for every $\phi \in \mathbf{A}$, and $F(\phi, \ ) = 0$, $\phi \geqq 0$, implies $\phi = 0$.*

Let **E** be the system of all functions on S which are bounded, uniformly continuous for **U** and invariant by **G**. We see easily by Theorem 65.1 that $\mathbf{E} \subset \mathbf{A}$. Thus **E** is a field on S for $\mathbf{U}_{\mathbf{A}}$, which is naturally invariant by **G**. Since $F(\phi, \ ) \in \mathbf{E}$ for every $\phi \in \mathbf{A}$, for any mean M_0 on **E**, setting $M(\phi) = M_0(F(\phi, \ ))$ for $\phi \in \mathbf{A}$, we obtain a mean M on **A** by **G** by (6), (7), (8), (9). Thus we can state

Theorem 68.2. *For any mean M_0 on* **E** *by* **G**, *setting*

$$M(\phi) = M_0(F(\phi, \ )) \ \text{ for } \ \phi \in \mathbf{A},$$

we obtain a mean M on **A** *by* **G**.

Conversely we have

Theorem 68.3. *For any mean M on* **A** *by* **G**, *we have*

$$M(F(\phi, \ )) = M(\phi) \ \text{ for every } \phi \in \mathbf{A}.$$

Proof. We have by Theorem 52.2

$$\begin{aligned} M(F(\phi, \ )) &= M\text{-} \int F(\phi, x)dx = M\text{-} \int (K\text{-} \int \phi(xX)dX)dx \\ &= K\text{-} \int (M\text{-} \int \phi(xX)dx)dX = K\text{-} \int (M\text{-} \int \phi(x)dx)dX = M(\phi). \end{aligned}$$

Theorem 68.4. *If $(a\mathbf{G})^{\mathbf{U}\text{-}} = S$ for some $a \in S$, then there exists uniquely a mean on* **A** *by* **G**.

Proof. If $(a\mathbf{G})^{\mathbf{U}\text{-}} = S$, then $F(\phi, \ )$ is constant on S for every $\phi \in \mathbf{A}$. Because it is obvious by (10) that $F(\phi, a) = F(\phi, x)$ for every $x \in a\mathbf{G}$. Since $F(\phi, \ )$ is uniformly continuous for **U** by Theorem 68.1, we hence obtain $F(\phi, a) = F(\phi, x)$ for every $x \in (a\mathbf{G})^{\mathbf{U}\text{-}} = S$. Thus for any mean M on $\mathbf{A}$ by $\mathbf{G}$ we have by Theorem 68.3 and (1)

$$M(\phi) = M(F(\phi, \ \ )) = M(F(\phi, a)) = F(\phi, a) \quad \text{for every } \phi \in \mathbf{A}.$$

69. Integration Theorems. Let $\mathbf{G}$ be a transformation group on a space S with a uniformity $\mathbf{U}$ which is locally totally bounded and invariant by $\mathbf{G}$. Let $\mathbf{A}$ be the system of all almost periodic functions on S for $\mathbf{U}$ by $\mathbf{G}$.

A measure L on S for $\mathbf{U}$ is said to be *equi-invariant* by $\mathbf{G}$, if L is invariant by $\mathbf{G}$ and for any finite system $T_\nu \in \mathbf{G}$ $(\nu = 1, 2, \ldots, n)$, for any totally bounded set $A \subset S$, and for any $\mathcal{E} > 0$, we can find a regular set G for L such that $G \supset A$, $L(G) > 0$ and

$$L(G \cap GT_\nu) > (1 - \mathcal{E})L(G) \quad \text{for every } \nu = 1, 2, \ldots, n.$$

As a generalization of the Bohr's mean value theorem about classical almost periodic functions we have

Theorem 69.1. *For an equi-invariant measure L on S for $\mathbf{U}$ by $\mathbf{G}$ we can find a directed system of regular sets G_δ $(\delta \in \Delta)$ for L such that for any totally bounded set $A \subset S$ there is $\delta_0 \in \Delta$ such that $A \subset G_\delta$ for $\delta_0 \geqq \delta \in \Delta$, the directed system $\frac{1}{L(G_\delta)} L\text{-}\int_{G_\delta} \phi(x)dx$ $(\delta \in \Delta)$ is convergent for every $\phi \in \mathbf{A}$, and setting*

$$M(\phi) = \lim_{\delta \in \Delta} \frac{1}{L(G_\delta)} L\text{-}\int_{G_\delta} \phi(x)dx \quad \text{for } \phi \in \mathbf{A},$$

we obtain a mean M on $\mathbf{A}$ by $\mathbf{G}$.

Proof. For a finite system $\phi_\nu \in \mathbf{A}$ $(\nu = 1, 2, \ldots, n)$, setting

$$xM_T = (\phi_1(xT), \ldots, \phi_n(xT)) \quad \text{for } T \in \mathbf{G} \text{ and } x \in S,$$

we obtain a system of mappings M_T $(T \in \mathbf{G})$ from S to the n power of the space of all real numbers. Since the almost periodic part $\mathbf{U}_\mathbf{A}$ of $\mathbf{U}$ is invariant by $\mathbf{G}$, $\mathbf{G}$ is equi-continuous for $\mathbf{U}_\mathbf{A}$ by Theorem 32.5. Thus M_T $(T \in \mathbf{G})$ is equi-continuous for $\mathbf{U}_\mathbf{A}$. Since $\mathbf{U}_\mathbf{A}$ is totally bounded and there is $\gamma > 0$ such that $|\phi_\nu(x)| \leqq \gamma$ for every $x \in S$ and $\nu = 1, 2, \ldots, n$, for any $\mathcal{E} > 0$ we can find a finite system $T_\mu \in \mathbf{G}$ $(\mu = 1, 2, \ldots, m)$ by Theorem 15.2 such that for any $T \in \mathbf{G}$ we can find μ such that

$$|T\phi_\nu(x) - T_\mu\phi_\nu(x)| < \frac{1}{2}\mathcal{E} \text{ for every } x \in S \text{ and } \nu = 1, 2, \ldots, n,$$

and hence for any regular set G for L we have

$$|L\text{-}\int_G T\phi_\nu(x)dx - L\text{-}\int_G T_\mu\phi_\nu(x)dx| \leqq \frac{1}{2}\mathcal{E}L(G) \text{ for every } \nu = 1, 2, \ldots, n.$$

Since L is equi-invariant by **G** by assumption, for any totally bounded set $A \subset S$ we can find a regular set G for L such that $G \supset A$, $L(G) > 0$ and

$$L(G \cap GT_\mu) > (1 - \frac{1}{4\gamma}\mathcal{E})L(G) \text{ for every } \mu = 1, 2, \ldots, m.$$

Then, setting $G_1 = G \cap (G \cap GT_\mu)^{\prime}$ and $G_2 = GT_\mu \cap (G \cap GT_\mu)^{\prime}$, we have by Theorem 51.4

$$|L\text{-}\int_G T_\mu\phi_\nu(x)dx - L\text{-}\int_G \phi_\nu(x)dx| = |L\text{-}\int_G \phi_\nu(xT_\mu)dx - L\text{-}\int_G \phi_\nu(x)dx|$$

$$= |L\text{-}\int_{GT_\mu} \phi_\nu(x)dx - L\text{-}\int_G \phi_\nu(x)dx| = |L\text{-}\int_{G_2} \phi_\nu(x)dx - L\text{-}\int_{G_1} \phi_\nu(x)dx|$$

$$\leqq \gamma L(G_2) + \gamma L(G_1) < \frac{1}{2}\mathcal{E}L(G),$$

because $L(G_1) = L(G_2) = L(G) - L(G \cap GT_\mu) < \frac{1}{4\gamma}\mathcal{E}L(G)$. Therefore we obtain

$$|L\text{-}\int_G T\phi_\nu(x)dx - L\text{-}\int_G \phi_\nu(x)dx| < \mathcal{E}L(G) \text{ for every } T \in \mathbf{G} \text{ and } \nu = 1, 2, \ldots, n.$$

For a system $(A, \mathcal{E}, \phi_1, \ldots, \phi_n)$ we obtain such a regular set G for L. We define $(A, \mathcal{E}, \phi_1, \ldots, \phi_n) \geqq (B, \delta, \psi_1, \ldots, \psi_m)$, if $A \subset B$, $\mathcal{E} \geqq \delta$ and $\{\phi_1, \ldots, \phi_n\} \subset \{\psi_1, \ldots, \psi_m\}$. Then the set of all $(A, \mathcal{E}, \phi_1, \ldots, \phi_n)$ constitutes a directed space Γ. According to Theorem 29.7, we can find a partial system of Γ:

$$(A_\delta, \mathcal{E}_\delta, \phi_{\delta,1}, \ldots, \phi_{\delta,n}) \in \Gamma \quad (\delta \in \Delta)$$

such that every bounded function on Γ is convergent for this partial system. We denote by G_δ a regular set for L obtained corresponding to $(A_\delta, \mathcal{E}_\delta, \phi_{\delta,1}, \ldots, \phi_{\delta,n})$ for every $\delta \in \Delta$. Then for any totally bounded set $A \subset S$, for any $\mathcal{E} > 0$ and for any $\phi \in \mathbf{A}$ we can find $\delta_0 \in \Delta$ such that $\delta_0 \geqq \delta \in \Delta$ implies $A \subset A_\delta$, $\mathcal{E} \geqq \mathcal{E}_\delta$ and ϕ is included in $\phi_{\delta,1}$, $\ldots, \phi_{\delta,n}$. Thus for $\delta_0 \geqq \delta \in \Delta$ we have $A \subset G_\delta$, $L(G_\delta) > 0$ and

$$|L\text{-}\int_{G_\delta} T\phi(x)dx - L\text{-}\int_{G_\delta} \phi(x)dx| \leqq \mathcal{E}_\delta L(G_\delta) \text{ for every } T \in \mathbf{G}.$$

Since $|\frac{1}{L(G_\delta)} L\text{-}\int_{G_\delta} \phi(x)dx| \leqq \frac{1}{L(G_\delta)} L\text{-}\int_{G_\delta} \gamma dx = \gamma$ for every $\delta \in \Delta$ and $\phi \in \mathbf{A}$, the directed system $\frac{1}{L(G_\delta)} L\text{-}\int_{G_\delta} \phi(x)dx$ $(\delta \in \Delta)$ is convergent for every $\phi \in \mathbf{A}$. Thus setting

$$M(\phi) = \lim_{\delta\in\Delta} \frac{1}{L(G_\delta)} L\text{-}\int_{G_\delta} \phi(x)dx \quad (\phi \in \mathbf{A}),$$

we obtain $M(T\phi) = M(\phi)$ for every $T \in \mathbf{G}$, because $\lim_{\delta\in\Delta} \mathcal{E}_\delta = 0$. Therefore, referring to Theorems 18.6, 51.2, 51.3, 51.6, we see easily that M is a mean on $\mathbf{A}$ by $\mathbf{G}$.

$\mathbf{G}$ is said to be *holomorphic* for $\mathbf{U}$, if $\mathbf{G}$ has a subgroup $\mathbf{H}$ such that $\mathbf{H}$ is transitive and there is an equi-invariant measure L on S for $\mathbf{U}$ by $\mathbf{H}$. If $\mathbf{G}$ is holomorphic for $\mathbf{U}$, then $\mathbf{G}$ is transitive by definition, and hence there exists uniquely a mean on $\mathbf{A}$ by $\mathbf{G}$ by Theorem 68.4.

Theorem 69.2. *If* $\mathbf{G}$ *is holomorphic for* $\mathbf{U}$ *and* $\mathbf{U}$ *is normal for* $\mathbf{G}$, *then for an invariant measure* $L \neq 0$ *on* S *for* $\mathbf{U}$ *by* $\mathbf{G}$ *we can find a directed system of regular sets* G_δ $(\delta \in \Delta)$ *for* L *such that for any totally bounded set* $A \subset S$ *there is* $\delta_0 \in \Delta$ *such that* $A \subset G_\delta$ *for* $\delta_0 \geqq \delta \in \Delta$, and

$$M(\phi) = \lim_{\delta\in\Delta} \frac{1}{L(G_\delta)} L\text{-}\int_{G_\delta} \phi(x)dx \quad \textit{for every } \phi \in \mathbf{A}$$

for the mean M *on* $\mathbf{A}$ *by* $\mathbf{G}$.

Proof. Let $\mathbf{H}$ be a subgroup of $\mathbf{G}$ such that $\mathbf{H}$ is transitive and there is an equi-invariant measure $L_{\mathbf{H}}$ on S for $\mathbf{U}$ by $\mathbf{H}$. Since $\mathbf{U}$ is normal for $\mathbf{G}$ by assumption, $\mathbf{U}$ also is normal for $\mathbf{H}$, because we have by (9) in 32

$$a(U^{\mathbf{G}})^{\mathbf{H}}(M_a^{-1})^{\mathbf{H}} M_x^{\mathbf{H}} \subset aU^{\mathbf{G}} M_a^{-1} M_x \quad \text{for } x, a \in S \text{ and } U \in \mathbf{U}.$$

L is obviously invariant by $\mathbf{H}$. Thus there is $\gamma > 0$ by Theorem of Uniqueness in 56 such that $L = \gamma L_{\mathbf{H}}$. Therefore we can find a directed system of regular sets G_δ $(\delta \in \Delta)$ for L by Theorem 69.1 such that for any totally bounded set $A \subset S$ there is $\delta_0 \in \Delta$ such that $A \subset G_\delta$ for $\delta_0 \geqq \delta \in \Delta$ and setting

$$M(\phi) = \lim_{\delta \epsilon \Delta} \frac{1}{L(G_\delta)} L\text{-} \int_{G_\delta} \phi(x)dx \quad \text{for } \phi \epsilon \mathbf{A}$$

we obtain a mean M on **A** by **H**, because **A** is included in the system of all almost periodic functions for **U** by **H**. Since there exists uniquely a mean on **A** by **G** and this mean also is a mean on **A** by **H**, M must be the mean on **A** by **G**.

70. **Additive Characters.** A function χ on S is called an *additive character* of a transformation group **G** on S for a uniformity **U** on S, if χ is uniformly continuous for **U** and there is a function τ_χ on **G** such that

(1) $\chi(xT) = \chi(x) + \tau_\chi(T)$ for every $x \epsilon S$ and $T \epsilon \mathbf{G}$.

This function τ_χ on **G** is called the *coefficient* of χ. Every constant on S is an additive character of **G** with coefficient 0.

About the coefficient τ_χ of an additive character χ we obviously have by definition (1)

(2) $\tau_\chi(XY) = \tau_\chi(X) + \tau_\chi(Y)$ for $X, Y \epsilon \mathbf{G}$,

(3) $\tau_\chi(X^{-1}) = -\tau_\chi(X)$ for $X \epsilon \mathbf{G}$,

(4) $\tau_\chi(X) = 0$ for $X \epsilon \bigcup_{x \epsilon S} \mathbf{F}_x$.

For any two additive characters χ_1, χ_2 of **G** for **U** and for any real numbers α, β, $\alpha\chi_1 + \beta\chi_2$ also is obviously an additive character of **G** for **U** and we have by (1)

(5) $\tau_{\alpha\chi_1 + \beta\chi_2} = \alpha\tau_{\chi_1} + \beta\tau_{\chi_2}$.

Theorem 70.1. *The coefficient* τ_χ *of an additive character* χ *of* **G** *for* **U** *is uniformly continuous on* **G** *for the weak-uniformity* **W(U)**.

Proof. We have by definition (1)

$$\tau_\chi(X) = \chi(xX) - \chi(x) \quad \text{for } X \epsilon \mathbf{G}$$

for any $x \epsilon S$. Since χ is uniformly continuous on S for **U**, τ_χ is uniformly continuous for **W(U)** by Theorem 14.3.

Theorem 70.2. *If* **G** *is transitive and* **U** *is invariant and regular for* **G**, *then for any function* τ *on* **G** *such that* τ *is uniformly continuous for the weak-uniformity* **W(U)**, $\tau(XY) = \tau(X) + \tau(Y)$ *for* $X, Y \epsilon \mathbf{G}$ *and* $\tau(X) = 0$

for $X \in \mathbf{F}_a$ *for the fixer* $\mathbf{F}_a$ *of* $\mathbf{G}$ *at* $a \in S$, *there is an additive character* χ *of* $\mathbf{G}$ *for* $\mathbf{U}$ *with the coefficient* τ.

Proof. Setting $\chi(aX) = \tau(X)$ for $X \in \mathbf{G}$, we obtain a function χ on S. Because $aX = aY$ implies $YX^{-1} \in \mathbf{F}_a$, and hence $\tau(YX^{-1}) = 0$ by assumption. On the other hand we have

$$\tau(YX^{-1}) = \tau(Y) + \tau(X^{-1}) \quad \text{and} \quad \tau(X) + \tau(X^{-1}) = \tau(E) = 0,$$

since $E \in \mathbf{F}_a$. Therefore $aX = aY$ implies $\tau(X) = \tau(Y)$. Since $\mathbf{G}$ is transitive by assumption, χ is defined on S.

For any $x \in S$ there is $T \in \mathbf{G}$ such that $x = aT$, and we have

$$\chi(xX) = \chi(aTX) = \tau(TX) = \tau(T) + \tau(X) = \chi(x) + \tau(X)$$

for every $X \in \mathbf{G}$. Since the point mapping M_a is uniformly open by Theorem 37.9, χ is uniformly continuous on S for $\mathbf{U}$ by Theorem 14.4. Therefore χ is an additive character of $\mathbf{G}$ for $\mathbf{U}$ with coefficient τ.

An additive character χ of $\mathbf{G}$ for $\mathbf{U}$ is said to be *normal,* if for any real number $\gamma \neq 0$ we can find a totally bounded set $A \subset S$ for $\mathbf{U}$ such that

$$A\{X: \tau_\chi(X) = n\gamma \text{ for some } n = 0, \pm 1, \pm 2, \dots\} = S$$

for the coefficient τ_χ of χ. With this definition we see easily that a constant on S is a normal additive character of $\mathbf{G}$ if and only if there is a totally bounded set $A \subset S$ for $\mathbf{U}$ such that $A\mathbf{G} = S$. Thus, if $\mathbf{G}$ is transitive, then every constant on S is a normal additive character of $\mathbf{G}$, because $a\mathbf{G} = S$ for any point $a \in S$.

A transformation $T \in \mathbf{G}$ is said to be *analytic* in $\mathbf{G}$ for $\mathbf{U}$, if there is a system $T^\xi \in \mathbf{G}$ $(-\infty < \xi < +\infty)$ such that

$$T^\xi T^\eta = T^{\xi+\eta} \quad \text{and} \quad T^1 = T$$

and T^ξ $(-\infty < \xi < +\infty)$ is uniformly continuous for the weak-uniformity $\mathbf{W}(\mathbf{U})$ on $\mathbf{G}$, that is, for any $W \in \mathbf{W}(\mathbf{U})$ we can find $\delta > 0$ such that $|\xi - \eta| < \delta$ implies $T^\xi \in T^\eta W$. If T is analytic, then T^η also is analytic for any real number η, because, setting $(T^\eta)^\xi = T^{\eta\xi}$ $(-\infty < \xi < +\infty)$, we can prove easily that $(T^\eta)^\xi$ satisfies the conditions about analytic transformations.

Theorem 70.3. *When* $\mathbf{G}$ *is transitive and* $\mathbf{U}$ *is locally totally bounded* *and invariant by* **G**, *an additive character* χ *of* **G** *for* **U** *with coefficient* τ_χ *is normal, if there is an analytic* $T \epsilon$ **G** *for* **U** *such that* $\tau_\chi(T) \neq 0$.

Proof. Since $\tau_\chi(T^{\xi+\eta}) = \tau_\chi(T^\xi) + \tau_\chi(T^\eta)$, we can show easily that $\tau_\chi(T^\xi) = \xi\tau_\chi(T)$ for any rational number ξ. Referring to Theorem 70.1, we see easily that the function $\tau_\chi(T^\xi)$ $(-\infty < \xi < +\infty)$ is uniformly continuous. Thus we obtain $\tau_\chi(T^\xi) = \xi\tau_\chi(T)$ for every real number ξ. Since $\tau_\chi(T) \neq 0$ by assumption, for any $\gamma \neq 0$ we can find $\alpha > 0$ such that $\alpha|\tau_\chi(T)| = |\gamma|$. For an invariant and totally bounded $U \epsilon$ **U** and for a point $a \epsilon S$ we can find $\delta > 0$ such that $|\xi - \eta| < \delta$ implies $T^\xi \epsilon$ $T^\eta M_a U M_a^{-1}$. For a finite system of positive numbers $0 = \xi_0 < \xi_1 < \dots$ $< \xi_n = \alpha$ such that $\xi_\nu - \xi_{\nu-1} < \delta$ $(\nu = 1, 2, \dots, n)$, we hence have

$$T^\xi \epsilon T^{\xi_\nu} M_a U M_a^{-1} \quad \text{for } \xi_\nu \leqq \xi \leqq \xi_{\nu+1} \quad (\nu = 0, 1, 2, \dots, n\text{-}1).$$

Thus we obtain by Theorem 11.2

$$T^\xi \epsilon E(M_a U M_a^{-1})^n = E M_a U^n M_a^{-1} \quad \text{for } 0 \leqq \xi \leqq \alpha.$$

For any $X \epsilon$ **G** we have by (2) and (3)

$$\tau_\chi(T^{-\xi}X) = \tau_\chi(X) - \tau_\chi(T^\xi) = \tau_\chi(X) - \xi\tau_\chi(T).$$

Thus we can find ξ such that $0 \leqq \xi \leqq \alpha$ and $\tau_\chi(T^{-\xi}X) = m\gamma$ for some $m = 0, \pm 1, \pm 2, \dots$. Setting $Y = T^{-\xi}X$, we hence obtain by (1) in 33

$$X = T^\xi Y \epsilon E M_a U^n M_a^{-1} Y = a U^n Y M_a^{-1}.$$

Therefore $aX \epsilon aU^n Y$ and $\tau_\chi(Y) = m\gamma$. Since **G** is transitive by assumption, we hence conclude

$$aU^n\{Y: \tau_\chi(Y) = m\gamma \text{ for some } m = 0, \pm 1, \pm 2, \dots\} = S.$$

Since aU^n is totally bounded for **U**, χ is normal by definition.

G is said to be *analytic* for **U**, if for any $T \epsilon$ **G** we can find a finite system $T_\nu \epsilon$ **G**($(\nu = 1, 2, \dots, n)$ such that every T_ν is analytic and $T = T_1 T_2 \dots T_n$.

Theorem 70.4. *If* **G** *is transitive and analytic for* **U**, *and if* **U** *is locally totally bounded and invariant by* **G**, *then every additive character is normal.*

Proof. For an additive character χ with coefficient τ_χ, if $\tau_\chi(T) \neq 0$ for some $T \in \mathbf{G}$, then there is a finite system of analytic $T_\nu \in \mathbf{G}$ ($\nu = 1, 2, \ldots, n$) such that $T = T_1 T_2 \ldots T_n$, and we have

$$\tau_\chi(T) = \sum_{\nu=1}^{n} \tau_\chi(T_\nu).$$

Since $\tau_\chi(T) \neq 0$ by assumption, we can find ν such that $\tau_\chi(T_\nu) \neq 0$. Thus χ is normal by Theorem 70.3.

71. Complex Valued Functions. For complex numbers ζ we will use the usual notations: $\mathbf{R}\zeta$ and $\mathbf{I}\zeta$ are the real and the imaginary part of ζ respectively, that is, $\zeta = \mathbf{R}\zeta + i\mathbf{I}\zeta$, $\overline{\zeta}$ is the conjugate complex number of ζ and $|\zeta|$ is the absolute value of ζ. Thus we have

$$\zeta + \overline{\zeta} = 2\mathbf{R}\zeta, \quad \zeta - \overline{\zeta} = i2\mathbf{I}\zeta, \quad \zeta\overline{\zeta} = |\zeta|^2.$$

Setting

(1) $\zeta U_\varepsilon = \{\xi : |\zeta - \xi| < \varepsilon\}$ for $\varepsilon > 0$,

we obtain a system of connectors U_ε ($\varepsilon > 0$) on the complex number space, and we can prove easily that U_ε ($\varepsilon > 0$) satisfies the basis conditions. The uniformity with basis U_ε ($\varepsilon > 0$) is called the *natural uniformity* on the complex number space.

The complex number space is considered the 2 power of the real number space, that is, $(\alpha, \beta) = \alpha + i\beta$ for two real numbers α, β. Then we can show easily that the natural uniformity on the complex number space is the 2 power of the natural uniformity on the real number space, since we have

(2) $\operatorname{Max}\{|\alpha|, |\beta|\} \leqq |\alpha + i\beta| \leqq 2\operatorname{Max}\{|\alpha|, |\beta|\}$

for two real numbers α, β.

A mapping from a space S to the complex number space is called a *complex valued function* on S. For a complex valued function f on S, $\mathbf{R}f$ and $\mathbf{I}f$ are called the real and the imaginary part of f. With this definition we can prove easily by (2)

Theorem 71.1. *For a uniformity* $\mathbf{U}$ *on* S *a complex valued function* f *on* S *is uniformly continuous if and only if both* $\mathbf{R}f$ *and* $\mathbf{I}f$ *are uniformly* *continuous for* **U**. *A system of complex valued functions* f_λ $(\lambda \in \Lambda)$ *is equi-continuous for* **U** *if and only if the system* $\mathbf{R}f_\lambda$, $\mathbf{I}f_\lambda$ $(\lambda \in \Lambda)$ *is equi-continuous for* **U**.

Let **G** be a transformation group on a space S and let **U** be a uniformity on S which is locally totally bounded and invariant by **G**. A complex valued function f on S is said to be *almost periodic* by **G** for **U**, if f is uniformly continuous for **U** and the single equi-uniformity on S by the system of functions Xf $(X \in \mathbf{G})$ is totally bounded. With this definition we have by Theorem 71.1

Theorem 71.2. *A complex valued function f on S is almost periodic by* **G** *for* **U**, *if and only if both* $\mathbf{R}f$ *and* $\mathbf{I}f$ *are almost periodic by* **G** *for* **U**.

Therefore we conclude by Theorem 66.2

Theorem 71.3. *A complex valued function f on S is almost periodic by* **G** *for* **U** *if and only if f is uniformly continuous for the almost periodic part of* **U** *by* **G**.

It is obvious by definition that a complex valued function f is invariant by a transformation T on S if and only if both $\mathbf{R}f$ and $\mathbf{I}f$ are invariant by T. We define the *fixer* of f by the same way as in 67:

$$\mathbf{F}_f = \{X\colon XTf = Tf \text{ for every } T \in \mathbf{G}\}.$$

Then we obviously have

$$(3)\quad \mathbf{F}_f = \mathbf{F}_{\mathbf{R}f} \cap \mathbf{F}_{\mathbf{I}f}.$$

Therefore the fixer $\mathbf{F}_f$ also is an invariant subgroup of **G**.

A complex valued function f on S is said to be *periodic* by **G** for **U**, if f is uniformly continuous for **U** and there is a totally bounded set $A \subset S$ such that $A\mathbf{F}_f = S$. If f is periodic by **G** for **U**, then $\mathbf{R}f$ and $\mathbf{I}f$ also are periodic by (3).

Theorem 71.4. *For a normal additive character χ of* **G** *for* **U**, $e^{i\chi}$ *is a periodic function on S by* **G** *for* **U**.

Proof. For the coefficient τ_χ of χ there is a totally bounded set $A \subset S$ such that

$$A\{X\colon \tau_\chi(X) = 2n\pi \text{ for some } n = 0, \pm 1, \pm 2, \dots\} = S,$$

and if $\tau_\chi(X) = 2n\pi$, then

$$Xe^{i\chi}(x) = e^{i\chi(xX)} = e^{i\chi(x)+2ni\pi} = e^{i\chi}(x)$$

for every $x \in S$, and hence X belongs to the fixer of $e^{i\chi}$. Therefore $e^{i\chi}$ is a periodic function on S by **G** for **U** by definition.

72. Normalized Systems. Let **G** be a transformation group on a space S with a uniformity **U**, which is locally totally bounded and invariant by **G**. Let **A** be the system of all almost periodic functions on S by **G** for **U**, and let M be a mean on **A** by **G**. M is considered an invariant measure on S by **G** for the almost periodic part $\mathbf{U_A}$ of **U** such that

$$M\text{-} \int dx = 1, \quad M\text{-} \int \phi(x)dx = M(\phi) \quad \text{for every } \phi \in \mathbf{A},$$

as shown in 68.

For a complex valued, almost periodic function f on S by **G** for **U** we define $M(f)$ by

$$M(f) = M(\mathbf{R}f) + iM(\mathbf{I}f),$$

since $\mathbf{R}f$ and $\mathbf{I}f$ are almost periodic by Theorem 71.2. Thus we have

$$M\text{-} \int f(x)dx = M\text{-} \int \mathbf{R}f(x)dx + iM\text{-} \int \mathbf{I}f(x)dx.$$

Theorem 72.1. *For a normal additive character* χ *of* **G** *for* **U** *we have*

$$M\text{-} \int e^{i\chi(x)}dx = 0$$

if χ *is not constant on* S.

Proof. If χ is not constant on S, then there is $T \in \mathbf{G}$ such that $\tau_\chi(T) = \pi$ for the coefficient τ_χ of χ, and

$$e^{i\chi(xT)} = e^{i\chi(x)+i\pi} = -e^{i\chi(x)}.$$

On the other hand, since M is invariant by **G**, we have

$$M\text{-} \int e^{i\chi(xT)}dx = M\text{-} \int e^{i\chi(x)}dx.$$

Thus we obtain $M\text{-} \int e^{i\chi(x)}dx = - M\text{-} \int e^{i\chi(x)}dx$, that is, $M\text{-} \int e^{i\chi(x)}dx = 0$.

A system of normal additive characters **C** is said to be *normalized* at $a \in S$, if $\chi(a) = 0$ for every $\chi \in \mathbf{C}$, $\chi \in \mathbf{C}$ implies $-\chi \in \mathbf{C}$, and χ_1, $\chi_2 \in \mathbf{C}$ implies $\chi_1 + \chi_2 \in \mathbf{C}$. With this definition we obtain by Theorem 72.1

Theorem 72.2. *For a normalized system* **C** *we have for* $\chi_1, \chi_2 \in \mathbf{C}$

$$M\text{-}\int e^{i\chi_1(x)}e^{-i\chi_2(x)}dx = \begin{cases} 0 & \text{for } \chi_1 \neq \chi_2 \\ 1 & \text{for } \chi_1 = \chi_2 \end{cases}.$$

Let **C** be a normalized system of normal additive characters of **G** at $a \in S$. Let f be a complex valued, almost periodic function on S by **G** for **U**. Then f is uniformly continuous on S for $\mathbf{U_A}$ by Theorem 66.2. We denote by **B** or $\mathbf{B}_\nu$ a finite subset of **C**. Then **B** ($\mathbf{B} \subset \mathbf{C}$) form a directed space, defining $\mathbf{B}_1 \geqq \mathbf{B}_2$ by $\mathbf{B}_1 \subset \mathbf{B}_2$.

Let **B** be an arbitrary finite subset of **C**. For any complex numbers ζ_χ ($\chi \in \mathbf{B}$) we have by Theorem 72.2

$$M\text{-}\int |f(x) - \sum_{\chi\in\mathbf{B}} \zeta_\chi e^{i\chi(x)}|^2 dx$$

$$= M\text{-}\int |f(x)|^2 dx - \sum_{\chi\in\mathbf{B}} (\overline{\zeta}_\chi M\text{-}\int f(x)e^{-i\chi(x)}dx - \zeta_\chi M\text{-}\int \overline{f(x)}e^{i\chi(x)}dx)$$

$$+ \sum_{\chi_1,\chi_2\in\mathbf{B}} \zeta_{\chi_1}\overline{\zeta}_{\chi_2} M\text{-}\int e^{i\chi_1(x)}e^{-i\chi_2(x)}dx$$

$$= M\text{-}\int |f(x)|^2 dx - \sum_{\chi\in\mathbf{B}} |M\text{-}\int f(x)e^{-i\chi(x)}dx|^2$$

$$+ \sum_{\chi\in\mathbf{B}} |M\text{-}\int f(x)e^{-i\chi(x)}dx - \zeta_\chi|^2.$$

Therefore, setting $\zeta_\chi = M\text{-}\int f(x)e^{-i\chi(x)}dx$ for $\chi \in \mathbf{B}$, we obtain

Theorem 72.3. *For any complex valued, almost periodic function* f *on* S *by* **G** *for* **U** *we have*

$$M\text{-}\int |f(x)|^2 dx \geqq \sum_{\chi\in\mathbf{C}} |M\text{-}\int f(x)e^{-i\chi(x)}dx|^2.$$

From this Theorem 72.3 we conclude immediately that for any complex valued, almost periodic function f we have

$$M\text{-}\int f(x)e^{-i\chi(x)}dx = 0$$

except for a countable subset of **C**.

Theorem 72.4. *For any system of complex numbers* ζ_χ ($\chi \in \mathbf{C}$) *such that* $\sum_{\chi\in\mathbf{C}} |\zeta_\chi| < +\infty$, *setting*

$$f(x) = \sum_{\chi \epsilon \mathbf{C}} \zeta_\chi e^{i\chi(x)} = \lim_{\mathbf{B} \subset \mathbf{C}} \sum_{\chi \epsilon \mathbf{B}} \zeta_\chi e^{-i\chi(x)} \quad \text{for } x \epsilon S,$$

we obtain an almost periodic function f on S by **G** *for* **U** *and*

$$\zeta_\chi = M\text{-} \int f(x) e^{-i\chi(x)} dx, \quad M\text{-} \int |f(x)|^2 dx = \sum_{\chi \epsilon \mathbf{C}} |\zeta_\chi|^2.$$

Proof. If $\sum_{\chi \epsilon \mathbf{C}} |\zeta_\chi| < +\infty$, then $\sum_{\chi \epsilon \mathbf{C}} \zeta_\chi e^{i\chi}$ is uniformly convergent on S, because $|e^{i\chi(x)}| = 1$ for every $\chi \epsilon \mathbf{C}$ and $x \epsilon S$. Thus f is almost periodic by Theorem 65.4, and for any $\mathcal{E} > 0$ we can find a finite subset $\mathbf{B}_0 \subset \mathbf{C}$ such that $\mathbf{B}_0 \subset \mathbf{B}_1 \subset \mathbf{C}$ implies

$$|f(x) - \sum_{\chi \epsilon \mathbf{B}_1} \zeta_\chi e^{i\chi(x)}| < \mathcal{E} \quad \text{for every } x \epsilon S.$$

Thus we obtain by Theorem 72.2

$$|M\text{-} \int f(x) e^{-i\chi(x)} dx - \zeta_\chi| \leqq \mathcal{E} \quad \text{for every } \chi \epsilon \mathbf{C}.$$

Since $\mathcal{E} > 0$ is arbitrary, we hence conclude

$$\zeta_\chi = M\text{-} \int f(x) e^{-i\chi(x)} dx \quad \text{for every } \chi \epsilon \mathbf{C}.$$

We also have

$$M\text{-} \int |f(x)|^2 dx - \sum_{\chi \epsilon \mathbf{C}} |\zeta_\chi|^2 \leqq M\text{-} \int |f(x) - \sum_{\chi \epsilon \mathbf{B}_1} \zeta_\chi e^{i\chi(x)}|^2 dx \leqq \mathcal{E}^2$$

for any $\mathcal{E} > 0$. Therefore we obtain by Theorem 72.3

$$M\text{-} \int |f(x)|^2 dx = \sum_{\chi \epsilon \mathbf{C}} |\zeta_\chi|^2.$$

73. Approximation Theorems. Let **U** be a totally bounded uniformity on a space S. We consider first real valued functions on S. Let **F** be a field on S for **U**.

Theorem 73.1. *If* $\phi, \psi \epsilon \mathbf{F}$ *implies* $\phi \vee \psi \epsilon \mathbf{F}$ *and for any* $U \epsilon \mathbf{U}$ *there is* $V \epsilon \mathbf{U}$ *such that* $V \leqq U$ *and for any* $x \epsilon S$ *we can find* $\phi_x \epsilon \mathbf{F}$ *such that* $\phi_x(y) \geqq 1$ *for* $y \bar{\epsilon} xU$ *and* $\phi_x(y) \leqq \frac{1}{2}$ *for* $y \epsilon xV$, *then for any uniformly continuous function f on S for* **U** *and for any* $\mathcal{E} > 0$ *there is* $\phi \epsilon \mathbf{F}$ *such that*

$$|f(x) - \phi(x)| \leqq \mathcal{E} \quad \textit{for every } x \epsilon S.$$

Proof. Since $\phi, \psi \in \mathbf{F}$ implies $\phi \vee \psi \in \mathbf{F}$ by assumption, $\phi, \psi \in \mathbf{F}$ implies $\phi \wedge \psi \in \mathbf{F}$, because $\phi \wedge \psi = -((-\phi) \vee (-\psi))$. Let $A \neq \emptyset$ be an arbitrary set of S. For any $U \in \mathbf{U}$ there is $V \in \mathbf{U}$ by assumption such that for any $x \in S$ there exists $\phi_x \in \mathbf{F}$ such that $\phi_x(y) \leqq \frac{1}{2}$ for $y \in xV$ and $\phi_x(y) \geqq 1$ for $y \bar{\in} xU$. Since A is totally bounded, we can find a finite system $a_\nu \in A$ $(\nu = 1, 2, \ldots, n)$ such that $A \subset \bigcup_{\nu=1}^{n} a_\nu V$. Setting $\phi = \bigwedge_{\nu=1}^{n} \phi_{a_\nu}$, we have $\phi(y) \leqq \frac{1}{2}$ for $y \in A$ and $\phi(y) \geqq 1$ for $y \bar{\in} AU$, because $y \bar{\in} AU$ implies $y \bar{\in} a_\nu U$ for every $\nu = 1, 2, \ldots, n$, and hence $\phi_{a_\nu}(y) \geqq 1$ for every $\nu = 1, 2, \ldots, n$. Thus, setting $\phi_A = 2((\phi \vee \frac{1}{2}) \wedge 1 - \frac{1}{2})$, we see easily that $\phi_A \in \mathbf{F}$, $0 \leqq \phi_A \leqq 1$, $\phi_A(x) = 0$ for $x \in A$ and $\phi_A(x) = 1$ for $x \bar{\in} AU$.

Let f be an arbitrary uniformly continuous function on S for $\mathbf{U}$. Since $\mathbf{U}$ is totally bounded by assumption, f is bounded on S. We set

$$\alpha = \sup_{x \in S} f(x) \quad \text{and} \quad \beta = \inf_{x \in S} f(x)$$

If $\alpha = \beta$, then f is a constant on S and $f \in \mathbf{F}$. Thus we assume $\alpha > \beta$. For any $n = 1, 2, \ldots$, we set $\mathcal{E} = \frac{1}{n}(\alpha - \beta)$, $A_0 = \emptyset$ and

$$A_\nu = \{x\colon f(x) \leqq \beta + \nu\mathcal{E}\} \quad (\nu = 1, 2, \ldots, n).$$

Then $\emptyset \neq A_1 \subset A_2 \subset \ldots \subset A_n = S$. Since f is uniformly continuous for $\mathbf{U}$ by assumption, there is $U \in \mathbf{U}$ such that $x \in yU$ implies $|f(x) - f(y)| < \mathcal{E}$. For such $U \in \mathbf{U}$ we have $A_\nu U \subset A_{\nu+1}$ for $\nu = 1, 2, \ldots, n\text{-}1$, because $y \in A_\nu$, $x \in yU$ implies

$$f(x) \leqq f(y) + \mathcal{E} \leqq \beta + \nu\mathcal{E} + \nu = \beta + (\nu + 1)\mathcal{E},$$

that is, $x \in A_{\nu+1}$.

As proved just above, we can find $\phi_\nu \in \mathbf{F}$ $(\nu = 1, 2, \ldots, n)$ such that $0 \leqq \phi_\nu \leqq 1$, $\phi_\nu(x) = 0$ for $x \in A_\nu$ and $\phi_\nu(x) = 1$ for $x \bar{\in} A_\nu U \subset A_{\nu+1}$. Setting

$$\phi = \beta + \mathcal{E} \sum_{\nu=0}^{n-1} \phi_\nu, \quad \phi_0 = 1,$$

we have $\phi \in \mathbf{F}$. For any $x \in S$ we can find $\mu = 0, 1, 2, \ldots, n\text{-}1$ such that $x \in A_{\mu+1}$ but $x \bar{\in} A_\mu$. For such μ we have

$$\beta + \mu\mathcal{E} < f(x) \leqq \beta + (\mu + 1)\mathcal{E},$$

$\phi(x) = \beta + \mathcal{E} \sum_{\nu=0}^{n-1} \phi_\nu(x) = \beta + \mu\mathcal{E} + \mathcal{E}\phi_\mu(x)$, and hence

$$\beta + \mu\mathcal{E} \leqq \phi(x) \leqq \beta + (\mu + 1)\mathcal{E}.$$

Therefore $|f(x) - \phi(x)| \leqq \mathcal{E}$ for every $x \in S$.

Lemma. *For* $a_0 = 1$, $a_\nu = \dfrac{2\nu - 1}{2\nu} a_{\nu-1}$ $(\nu = 1, 2, \ldots)$ *we have*

$$|\xi| = \sum_{\nu=0}^{\infty} a_\nu (1 - \xi^2)^\nu \xi^2 \quad for -1 \leqq \xi \leqq 1,$$

and this series is uniformly convergent for $-1 \leqq \xi \leqq 1$.

Proof. Since $a_\nu(1 - \xi^2)^\nu \xi^2 \geqq 0$ for $-1 \leqq \xi \leqq 1$, $\nu = 0, 1, 2, \ldots$, setting

$$\phi(\xi) = \sum_{\nu=0}^{\infty} a_\nu (1 - \xi^2)^\nu \xi^2 \qquad \text{for } -1 \leqq \xi \leqq 1,$$

we have $\phi(\xi)^2 = \sum_{\kappa=0}^{\infty} \Big(\sum_{\nu+\mu=\kappa} a_\nu a_\mu \Big)(1 - \xi^2)^\kappa \xi^4$ for $-1 \leqq \xi \leqq 1$. On the other hand, since $2\nu a_\nu = (2\nu - 1)a_{\nu-1}$ $(\nu = 1, 2, \ldots)$ by assumption, we have

$$2\kappa \sum_{\nu+\mu=\kappa} a_\nu a_\mu = \sum_{\nu+\mu=\kappa} 2\nu a_\nu a_\mu + \sum_{\nu+\mu=\kappa} 2\mu a_\nu a_\mu$$

$$= \sum_{\nu+\mu=\kappa,\ \nu \geqq 1} (2\nu - 1)a_{\nu-1} a_\mu + \sum_{\nu+\mu=\kappa,\ \nu \geqq 1} (2\mu - 1)a_\nu a_{\mu-1}$$

$$= \sum_{\nu+\mu=\kappa-1} (2\nu + 1)a_\nu a_\mu + \sum_{\nu+\mu=\kappa-1} (2\mu + 1)a_\nu a_\mu$$

$$= 2\kappa \sum_{\nu+\mu=\kappa-1} a_\nu a_\mu,$$

and hence $\sum_{\nu+\mu=\kappa} a_\nu a_\mu = a_0{}^2 = 1$. Therefore

$$\phi(\xi)^2 = \sum_{\kappa=0}^{\infty} (1 - \xi^2)^\kappa \xi^4 = \xi^2 \quad \text{for } -1 \leqq \xi \leqq 1,$$

and hence $\phi(\xi) = |\xi|$ for $-1 \leqq \xi \leqq 1$, because $\phi(\xi) \geqq 0$.

For $0 < \varepsilon < 1$ we can find ν_0 such that

$$\sum_{\nu \geqq \nu_0} a_\nu (1 - \varepsilon^2)^\nu \varepsilon^2 \leqq \varepsilon^3,$$

and then for $\varepsilon \leqq |\xi| \leqq 1$ we have

$$\sum_{\nu \geqq \nu_0} a_\nu (1 - \xi^2)^\nu \xi^2 \leqq \sum_{\nu \geqq \nu_0} a_\nu (1 - \varepsilon^2)^\nu \leqq \varepsilon,$$

and for $|\xi| \leqq \varepsilon$ we have

$$\sum_{\nu \geqq \nu_0} a_\nu (1 - \xi^2)^\nu \xi^2 \leqq \sum_{\nu=0}^{\infty} a_\nu (1 - \xi^2)^\nu \xi^2 = |\xi| \leqq \varepsilon.$$

Therefore $\sum_{\nu=0}^{\infty} a_\nu (1 - \xi^2)^\nu \xi^2$ is uniformly convergent for $-1 \leqq \xi \leqq 1$.

Theorem 73.2. *If $\phi, \psi \in \mathbf{F}$ implies $\phi\psi \in \mathbf{F}$ and if for any $U \in \mathbf{U}$ there is $V \in \mathbf{U}$ such that $V \leqq U$ and for any $x \in S$ we can find $\phi_x \in \mathbf{F}$ such that $\phi_x(y) \geqq 1$ for $y \bar{\in} xU$ and $\phi_x(y) \leqq \frac{1}{2}$ for $y \in xV$, then for any uniformly continuous function f on S for $\mathbf{U}$ and for any $\varepsilon > 0$ there is $\phi \in \mathbf{F}$ such that*

$$|f(x) - \phi(x)| \leqq \varepsilon \text{ for every } x \in S.$$

Proof. Let $\tilde{\mathbf{F}}$ be the system of all uniformly continuous functions f on S for $\mathbf{U}$ such that for any $\varepsilon > 0$ we can find $\phi \in \mathbf{F}$ such that

$$|f(x) - \phi(x)| \leqq \varepsilon \text{ for every } x \in S.$$

Then we see easily that $\tilde{\mathbf{F}}$ also satisfies the assumptions about $\mathbf{F}$. Furthermore we can prove easily that if a sequence $\tilde{\phi}_\nu \in \mathbf{F}$ ($\nu = 1, 2, \ldots$) is uniformly convergent to a function $\tilde{\phi}$ on S, then $\tilde{\phi} \in \tilde{\mathbf{F}}$. Thus for any $\tilde{\phi} \in \tilde{\mathbf{F}}$ we have $|\tilde{\phi}| \in \tilde{\mathbf{F}}$ by the Lemma. Since

$$\tilde{\phi} \vee \tilde{\psi} = \tilde{\psi} + \frac{1}{2}(|\tilde{\phi} - \tilde{\psi}| + \tilde{\phi} + \tilde{\psi}),$$

we hence conclude that $\tilde{\phi}, \tilde{\psi} \in \tilde{\mathbf{F}}$ implies $\tilde{\phi} \vee \tilde{\psi} \in \tilde{\mathbf{F}}$. Therefore for any uniformly continuous function f on S for $\mathbf{U}$ and for any $\varepsilon > 0$ there is $\tilde{\phi} \in \tilde{\mathbf{F}}$ by Theorem 73.1 such that $|f(x) - \tilde{\phi}(x)| \leqq \frac{1}{2}\varepsilon$ for every $x \in S$. For such $\tilde{\phi} \in \tilde{\mathbf{F}}$ we can find $\phi \in \mathbf{F}$ by assumption such that $|\tilde{\phi}(x) - \phi(x)| \leqq \frac{1}{2}\varepsilon$ for every $x \in S$, and hence $|f(x) - \phi(x)| \leqq \varepsilon$ for every $x \in S$.

As another generalization of the Weierstrass' approximation theorem about polynomials we have

Theorem 73.3. *Let* $\mathbf{W}_{\mathbf{F}}$ *be the weak-uniformity on S by a field* $\mathbf{F}$ *on S. If* $\mathbf{F}$ *satisfies one of the conditions*

(l) $\phi, \psi \in \mathbf{F}$ *implies* $\phi \vee \psi \in \mathbf{F}$,

(r) $\phi, \psi \in \mathbf{F}$ *implies* $\phi\psi \in \mathbf{F}$,

then for any uniformly continuous function f on S for $\mathbf{W}_{\mathbf{F}}$ *and for any* $\mathcal{E} > 0$ *there is* $\phi \in \mathbf{F}$ *such that*

$$|f(x) - \phi(x)| \leqq \mathcal{E} \text{ for every } x \in S.$$

Proof. For any $U \in \mathbf{W}_{\mathbf{F}}$ we can find $\delta > 0$ and a finite system $\phi_\nu \in \mathbf{F}$ ($\nu = 1, 2, \ldots, n$) by Theorem 23.6 such that

$$xU \supset \{y: |\phi_\nu(y) - \phi_\nu(x)| < \delta \text{ for every } \nu = 1, 2, \ldots, n\}.$$

If $\mathbf{F}$ satisfies *(1)*, then setting

$$\phi_x(y) = \frac{1}{\delta} \sum_{\nu=1}^{n} |\phi_\nu(y) - \phi_\nu(x)| \text{ for } y \in S,$$

$$xV = \{y: |\phi_\nu(y) - \phi_\nu(x)| < \frac{1}{2n}\delta \text{ for every } \nu = 1, 2, \ldots, n\},$$

we have $\phi_x \in \mathbf{F}$ and $V \in \mathbf{W}_{\mathbf{F}}$ such that $\phi_x(y) \leqq \frac{1}{2}$ for $y \in xV$ and $\phi_x(y) \geqq 1$ for $y \,\overline{\in}\, xU$. If $\mathbf{F}$ satisfies *(r)*, then setting

$$\phi_x(y) = \frac{1}{\delta^2} \sum_{\nu=1}^{n} (\phi_\nu(y) - \phi_\nu(x))^2 \text{ for } y \in S,$$

$$xV = \{y: |\phi_\nu(y) - \phi_\nu(x)| < \frac{1}{\sqrt{2n}}\delta \text{ for every } \nu = 1, 2, \ldots, n\}$$

we obtain $\phi_x \in \mathbf{F}$ and $V \in \mathbf{W}_{\mathbf{F}}$ such that $\phi_x(y) \leqq \frac{1}{2}$ for $y \in xV$ and $\phi_x(y) \geqq 1$ for $y \,\overline{\in}\, xU$. Therefore, in either case, for any uniformly continuous function f on S for $\mathbf{W}_{\mathbf{F}}$ and for any $\mathcal{E} > 0$ we can find $\phi \in \mathbf{F}$ by Theorem 73.1 or 73.2 such that $|f(x) - \phi(x)| \leqq \mathcal{E}$ for every $x \in S$.

We consider now complex valued functions on S.

Theorem 73.4. *Let* $\mathbf{F}$ *be a system of bounded complex valued functions on S such that* 1) $1 \in \mathbf{F}$, 2) $\phi \in \mathbf{F}$ *implies* $a\phi \in \mathbf{F}$ *for any complex number* a *and* $\overline{\phi} \in \mathbf{F}$ *for the conjugate complex* $\overline{\phi}$ *of* ϕ, 3) $\phi, \psi \in \mathbf{F}$ *im-*

plies $\phi + \psi \in \mathbf{F}$ *and* $\phi\psi \in \mathbf{F}$. *Let* $\mathbf{W_F}$ *be the weak-uniformity on* S *by* $\mathbf{F}$. *Then for any uniformly continuous, complex valued function* f *on* S *for* $\mathbf{W_F}$ *and for any* $\mathcal{E} > 0$ *we can find* $\phi \in \mathbf{F}$ *such that*

$$|f(x) - \phi(x)| \leqq \mathcal{E} \text{ for every } x \in S.$$

Proof. Setting $\mathbf{F}_0 = \{\mathbf{R}\phi: \phi \in \mathbf{F}\}$, we see easily that $\mathbf{F}_0$ is a field of real valued functions on S satisfying *(r)* and $\mathbf{F}_0 \subset \mathbf{F}$, because $\mathbf{R}\phi = \frac{1}{2}(\phi + \overline{\phi})$. Furthermore $\phi \in \mathbf{F}$ implies $\mathbf{I}\phi \in \mathbf{F}_0$, because $\mathbf{I}\phi = \mathbf{R}\frac{1}{i}\phi$. Therefore $\mathbf{W_F} = \mathbf{W_{F_0}}$ by Theorem 71.1.

For any uniformly continuous, complex valued function f on S for $\mathbf{W_F}$, both $\mathbf{R}f$ and $\mathbf{I}f$ are uniformly continuous for $\mathbf{W_F}$ by Theorem 71.1, and hence for any $\mathcal{E} > 0$ we can find $\phi, \psi \in \mathbf{F}_0$ by Theorem 73.3 such that

$$|\mathbf{R}f(x) - \phi(x)| \leqq \frac{1}{\sqrt{2}}\mathcal{E}, \ |\mathbf{I}f(x) - \psi(x)| \leqq \frac{1}{\sqrt{2}}\mathcal{E} \text{ for every } x \in S.$$

Then we have $\phi + i\psi \in \mathbf{F}$ and

$$|f(x) - (\phi(x) + i\psi(x))| \leqq \mathcal{E} \text{ for every } x \in S.$$

74. **Character Parts.** Let $\mathbf{U}$ be a uniformity on a space S such that $\mathbf{U}$ is locally totally bounded and invariant by a transformation group $\mathbf{G}$ on S. Let $\mathbf{C}$ be a normalized system of normal additive characters of $\mathbf{G}$ for $\mathbf{U}$. The weak-uniformity on S by the system of functions $e^{i\chi}$ $(\chi \in \mathbf{C})$ is called the *character part* of $\mathbf{U}$ by $\mathbf{C}$ and denoted by $\mathbf{U_C}$. Since $e^{i\chi}$ is a periodic function on S by $\mathbf{G}$ for $\mathbf{U}$ by Theorem 71.4, $\mathbf{U_C}$ is weaker than the periodic part $\mathbf{U_P}$ of $\mathbf{U}$, and totally bounded. Since for the coefficient τ_χ of $\chi \in \mathbf{C}$ we have

$$Te^{i\chi}(x) = e^{i\chi(xT)} = e^{i\chi(x)}e^{i\tau_\chi(T)}$$

and $|e^{i\tau_\chi(T)}| = 1$ for every $T \in \mathbf{G}$, we have

$$|e^{i\chi}(xT) - e^{i\chi}(yT)| = |e^{i\chi}(x) - e^{i\chi}(y)|$$

for any $x, y \in S$ and $T \in \mathbf{G}$. Therefore, if we set

$$xU = \{y: |e^{i\chi_\nu}(y) - e^{i\chi_\nu}(x)| < \mathcal{E} \text{ for every } \nu = 1, 2, \ldots, n\}$$

for a finite system $\chi_\nu \in \mathbf{C}$ $(\nu = 1, 2, \ldots, n)$, then we have

$$xTUT^{-1} = \{yT^{-1}: |e^{i\chi_\nu(y)} - e^{i\chi_\nu(xT)}| < \varepsilon \text{ for every } \nu = 1, 2, \ldots, n\}$$
$$= \{z: |e^{i\chi_\nu(zT)} - e^{i\chi_\nu(xT)}| < \varepsilon \text{ for every } \nu = 1, 2, \ldots, n\}$$
$$= \{y: |e^{i\chi_\nu(y)} - e^{i\chi_\nu(x)}| < \varepsilon \text{ for every } \nu = 1, 2, \ldots, n\} = xU$$

for every $x \in S$ and $T \in \mathbf{G}$. Since all such connectors U form a basis of $\mathbf{U}_\mathbf{C}$ by Theorem 23.6, we hence conclude that $\mathbf{U}_\mathbf{C}$ is invariant by $\mathbf{G}$. Thus we can state

Theorem 74.1. *The character part* $\mathbf{U}_\mathbf{C}$ *of* $\mathbf{U}$ *by a normalized system* $\mathbf{C}$ *is totally bounded and invariant by* $\mathbf{G}$.

Theorem 74.2. *If a complex valued function* f *on* S *is uniformly continuous for the character part* $\mathbf{U}_\mathbf{C}$, *then for any* $\varepsilon > 0$ *we can find a finite system* $\chi_\nu \in \mathbf{C}$ $(\nu = 1, 2, \ldots, n)$ *and complex numbers* a_ν $(\nu = 1, 2, \ldots, n)$ *such that*

$$|f(x) - \sum_{\nu=1}^{n} a_\nu e^{i\chi_\nu(x)}| \leqq \varepsilon \text{ for every } x \in S.$$

Proof. Let $\mathbf{F}$ be the system of all linear combinations $\sum_{\nu=1}^{n} a_\nu e^{i\chi_\nu}$ for a finite system $\chi_\nu \in \mathbf{C}$ $(\nu = 1, 2, \ldots, n)$, $n = 1, 2, \ldots$. Then every function $f \in \mathbf{F}$ is obviously uniformly continuous for $\mathbf{U}_\mathbf{C}$. Therefore the weak-uniformity on S by $\mathbf{F}$ coincides with $\mathbf{U}_\mathbf{C}$. Furthermore we see easily that $\mathbf{F}$ satisfies 1), 2) and 3) in Theorem 73.4. Consequently, if f is uniformly continuous for $\mathbf{U}_\mathbf{C}$, then for any $\varepsilon > 0$ there is $\phi \in \mathbf{F}$ such that

$$|f(x) - \phi(x)| \leqq \varepsilon \text{ for every } x \in S.$$

Let $\mathbf{A}$ be the system of all almost periodic functions on S by $\mathbf{G}$ for $\mathbf{U}$, and let M be a mean on $\mathbf{A}$ by $\mathbf{G}$. Since $\mathbf{U}_\mathbf{C} \subset \mathbf{U}_\mathbf{A}$ by Theorems 66.3 and 74.1, every uniformly continuous function on S for $\mathbf{U}_\mathbf{C}$ is an almost periodic function by $\mathbf{G}$.

Theorem 74.3. *If a complex valued function* f *on* S *is uniformly continuous for* $\mathbf{U}_\mathbf{C}$, *then we have*

$$M\text{-}\int |f(x)|^2 dx = \sum_{\chi \in \mathbf{C}} |M\text{-}\int f(x) e^{-i\chi(x)} dx|^2.$$

Proof. For any $\varepsilon > 0$ we can find a finite system $\chi_\nu \in \mathbf{C}$ and complex numbers a_ν $(\nu = 1, 2, \ldots, n)$ by Theorem 74.2 such that

$$|f(x) - \sum_{\nu=1}^{n} a_\nu e^{i\ {}_\nu(x)}| \leqq \mathcal{E} \text{ for every } x \in S.$$

Thus we have

$$\begin{aligned}
\mathcal{E}^2 &\geqq M\text{-} \int |f(x) - \sum_{\nu=1}^{n} a_\nu e^{i\chi_\nu(x)}|^2 dx \\
&\geqq M\text{-} \int |f(x)|^2 dx - \sum_{\nu=1}^{n} |M\text{-} \int f(x) e^{-i\chi_\nu(x)} dx|^2 \\
&\geqq M\text{-} \int |f(x)|^2 dx - \sum_{\chi \in \mathbf{C}} |M\text{-} \int f(x) e^{-i\chi(x)} dx|^2.
\end{aligned}$$

Therefore we obtain by Theorem 72.3

$$M\text{-} \int |f(x)|^2 dx = \sum_{\chi \in \mathbf{C}} |M\text{-} \int f(x) e^{-i\chi(x)} dx|^2.$$

INDEX

absolute 13
adding point 84
additive character 236
adjoint uniformity 104
adjusted 134, 135
almost periodic 223, 225, 206
——— ——— part 225
almost uniformly continuous 206
analytic 237, 238
approximation 206
atom 4

basis 4, 119
——— condition 4, 119
binary function 171
——— mapping 43
bounded 12, 14, 49, 52

Cauchy system 16, 47
character 107
——— part 248
characteristic function 159
closed 5, 45
closure 5, 46
coefficient 177, 236
——— function 188
commutative 111
compact 19, 22
comparable xiv
complement xiii
complete 17, 18
completion 84, 161
——— closure 147
——— condition 84
complex valued function 239
component 24, 25, 136
composition 38
connected 23, 24, 25
connector 1
continuous 29, 30, 52
convergent 15, 45, 54

directed system 14
——— space 14
discrete 3, 5
double system 79

element ix
empty set x
equi-continuous 39, 41, 42, 95
equi-invariant 233
equivalence unimorphism 155
equivalent 155

field 230
finite character 107
fix 92
——— hull 93
fixed set 92
fixer 92, 240
full xii, 37
function 49

generated 92
group 115

holomorphic 235
homeomorphism 9

identical connector 1

identity 57
image xi, 27
induced isomorphism 156
--- neighbourhood 134, 135
--- topology 7
--- transformation 155
--- uniformity 118, 134
inner transformation 196
integrable 213
integral 168, 209
interior 5, 8
intersection xi, xiii
interval connector 51
invariant 94, 108, 177, 179, 190, 227, 230
inverse 2, 116
--- image 27, 29
--- transformation xii
inversion 131
isomorphism 156

left-invariant 188
left totally bounded 124, 125
--- transformation 120
--- --- group 120
local unimorphism 177
locally compact 88
--- equi-continuous 95
--- semi-uniformly adjusted 140
--- semi-unimorphic 64
--- sharp 105
--- totally bounded 14
--- unimorphic 64
locally uniformly adjusted 139
--- --- continuous 34
--- --- regular 112, 121

mapping xi
mean 230
measurable 211
measure 159, 160
--- character 198
multiple equi-uniformity 79

natural uniformity 51, 239
neighbourhood 117
--- condition 117
normal 104, 237
--- connector 104
normalized 241

one-to-one xii
open 5, 8, 38

part 228
partial system 15
partition 167, 201
--- mapping 200
--- space 36, 200
--- uniformity 201
periodic 229, 240
--- part 230
point xi
point mapping 97
positive 159
power 72, 127
--- mapping 131
primitive 65
product 2, 49, 69, 70, 72, 127, 130, 174
--- space 43
projection 69
proper 107
pure 5, 37, 159
purification 36, 37
purifying mapping 36

radius 51
reflexive 136
regular 112, 119, 162, 165
--- partition 167
regularly adjusted 138
regulation xi
relative connector 9
--- function 161
--- mapping 29
--- neighbourhood 195
--- set 10
--- uniformity 10
right-invariant 188
right totally bounded 124, 125
--- transformation group 116

semi-invariant 177, 179
semi-regular 140
semi-transitive 109

semi-uniformly adjusted 139
sequential 5
set xii
sharp 105
single equi-uniformity 77
space xi
steady 193
strong-power 73
strongly adjusted 137
stronger 57, 59, 118
strongest weaker uniformity 63
subgroup 92, 193
subset xii
subspace xii
symmetric 2, 4, 117
system xi

topological 35
--- property 16
topology 5
--- condition 5
totally bounded 12, 14, 125, 159
transformation xii
transformation closure 147
--- group 91
transitive 111
trivial connector 62
--- uniformity 62
trunk 159

uniformity 3
--- condition 3
uniform Cauchy system 47
--- closure 46
--- space 5
uniformly adjusted 139
--- closed 46
--- continuous 31, 32, 43, 52, 95, 171
--- convergent 46
--- open 38
--- regular 112, 120
unimorphic 37, 85
unimorphism 37, 85
union xii
unit 115

value 49

weaker 57, 59, 118
weakest stronger neighbourhood 118
--- --- uniformity 60
weak-power 72
weak-uniformity 65, 66
whole set xii

As the author of this book states in his preface, the concept of uniform spaces became familiar to mathematicians nearly 30 years ago. Elaboration and explanation of it, following other works on the subject, appear in this work.

Although, as the author further points out, the specifics of this book, *Uniform Spaces and Transformation Groups*, may be controversial among mathematicians, as attested by the fact that some of them have opposed publication of this work, the author believes that it will prove to be helpful to many mathematics scholars.

Hidegoro Nakano was educated in Japan where he received his doctorate in science in 1934. He has been professor of mathematics at the University of Tokyo and Hokkaido University, and visiting professor at Queen's University, of Kingston, Ontario. He is now professor of mathematics at Wayne State University.

The manuscript was prepared for publication by Ralph Busick. The book was designed by Richard Kinney. The book is set in Varitype Baskerville with Varitype Sans Serif for chapter headings and Univers for other display.

The book is printed on S.D. Warren's Old Style paper and bound in Columbia Mills' Fictionette Cloth over boards. Manufactured in the United States of America.